Substance Abuse Treatment in Recovery

Pascal Scoles, DSW, LC

The Substance Abuse and Mental Health Services Administration publications referenced below are in the public domain and parts of the documents were reproduced with minor editorial changes by the author. In no instance did the editorial changes alter the intent of the material.

Center for Substance Abuse Treatment (1999). **Cultural Issues in Substance Abuse Treatment.** SAMHSA. DHHS Pub. No. (SMA) 99-3278. Washington, DC: US Government Printing Office. Chapter 2.

Center for Substance Abuse Treatment (1999). **Substance Abuse Treatment for Persons with HIV/AIDS.** SAMHSA. Treatment Improvement Protocol (TIP). No. 37. DHHS Publication No. (SMA) 00-3410. Washington, DC: US Government Printing Office. Chapter 1.

Center for Substance Abuse Treatment. (1998). **Comprehensive Case Management For Substance Abuse Treatment.** (TIP). No. 27. DHHS Publication 98-3222. Washington, D.C.: U.S. Government Printing Office. 1-7.

Center for Substance Abuse Treatment (2005). **Substance Abuse Treatment for Persons with Co-Occurring Disorders.** SAMHSA. Treatment Improvement Protocol (TIP). No. 42. DHHS Publication No. (SMA) 05-3992. Rockville, MD: Substance Abuse and Mental Health Services Admin. 7-8, 31, 38-40, 67, 224.

Center for Substance Abuse Treatment (2009). **What are Peer Recovery Support Services?** HHS Publication No. (SMA) 09-4454. Rockville, MD: Substance Abuse and Mental Health Services Administration, U.S. Department of Health and Human Services.

Center for Substance Abuse Treatment. (2005). **Medication-Assisted Treatment for Opioid Addiction in Opioid Treatment Programs.** Treatment Improvement Protocol (TIP) Series 43.HHS Publication No. (SMA) 12-4214.Rockville, MD: Substance Abuse and Mental Health Services Administration.

Center for Substance Abuse Treatment. (2006). **Addiction Counseling Competencies: The Knowledge, Skills, and Attitudes of Professional Practice**. Technical Assistance Publication (TAP) Series 21. HHS Publication No. (SMA) 08-4171. Rockville, MD: Substance Abuse and Mental Health Services Administration.

Center for Substance Abuse Treatment. **Screening, Assessment, and Treatment Planning for Persons with Co-Occurring Disorders**. COCE Overview Paper 2. (2006). DHHS Publication No. (SMA) 06-4164 Rockville, MD: Substance Abuse and Mental Health Services Administration, and Center for Mental Health Services.

Center for Substance Abuse Treatment. (2009). **Substance Abuse Treatment: Addressing the Specific Needs of Women.** Treatment Improvement Protocol (TIP) Series, No. 51. HHS Publication No. (SMA) 15-4426. Rockville, MD: Center for Substance Abuse Treatment. Executive Summary

Free to Choose: Transforming Behavioral Health Care to Self-Direction. (2005). DHHS Publication No. SMA-05-3982. Rockville, MD: Center for Mental Health Services, SAMHSA.

Seeding a System's Response to Trauma: Philadelphia's Integrated Network of Trauma-informed and Trauma-focused Behavioral Health Care (2013). Philadelphia Department of Behavioral Health and Intellectual disAbility Services

Substance Abuse and Mental Health Services Administration. **Addressing the Specific Behavioral Health Needs of Men.** (2013). Treatment Improvement Protocol (TIP) Series 56. HHS Publication No.(SMA) 13-4736. Rockville, MD: Substance Abuse and Mental Health Services Administration

Substance Abuse and Mental Health Services Administration. (2014). SAMHSA's **Concept of Trauma and Guidance for a Trauma-Informed Approach.** HHS Publication No. (SMA). Rockville, MD: Substance Abuse and Mental Health Services Administration.

Substance Abuse and Mental Health Services Administration. (2015). **Behavioral Health Barometer: Pennsylvania, 2015.** HHS Publication No. SMA–16–Rockville, MD: Substance Abuse and Mental Health Services Administration.

Substance Abuse and Mental Health Services Administration. (2015). **Screening and Assessment of Co-occurring Disorders in the Justice System.** HHS Publication No. (SMA)-15-4930. Rockville, MD: Substance Abuse and Mental Health Services Administration

Substance Abuse and Mental Health Services Administration. (2017). NSDUH 2017 Report- Rockville, MD.

Disclaimer

I believe that addiction and its consequences are the most serious health problems now facing our society. Cardiovascular disease, respiratory illnesses, such as emphysema, many forms of cancer, and AIDS are just a few of the conditions that derive, directly or indirectly, from addiction.

Deepak Chopra, M.D.
Overcoming Addiction

Preface

Substance Abuse Treatment in Recovery was written to introduce clinical social workers, psychologists and addiction counselors to the importance of assessment, and service planning in recovery-oriented systems of care.

The book is addressed to three types of learners: (1) under-graduates majoring in human services, such as addiction counseling, social work, psychology, etc. There is an expectation that undergraduate students will have completed an introductory course in Addictions and/or an introductory course in Psychology prior to reading this textbook: (2) graduate students in social work or counseling psychology who are interested in assessment and treatment planning of chemically dependent individuals and (3) continuing education for certified peer specialists and professionals already working in the behavioral health field who have an interest in a basis review of the medical and social models of service and treatment planning and how it relates to clinical evaluation.

The book is divided into two main sections the medical model and the social model of assessment and planning. The text begins with a discussion of human development, helping relationship, drugs and brain function, and screening and assessment. Chapter 5 begins with the cognitive and behavioral aspects of a mental status evaluation, which culminates with the differential diagnosis. The book than discusses substance use disorders and the various levels of care. It proceeds through disorders associated with substance use such as, mood, anxiety, and personality disorders. Under medical conditions it provides information on HIV/AIDS and Hepatitis C is provided as well as all of the psychosocial and environmental problems in the DSM. Chapter 7 discusses case management in the substance abuse field. Particular attention is given to Levels of Care, Patient Placement Criteria and social action initiatives.

The second part of the text (Social Model) is an introduction to community empowerment models of recovery, person first assessment and planning issues that supports recovery. The text ends with the self-help movement and its impact on effective service planning and self-empowerment in recovery.

Pascal Scoles

Pascal Scoles, D.S.W., LCSW

Pascal Scoles is Professor, Behavioral Health/Human Services, Department of Psychology, Education and Human Services, and Director, Office of Collegiate Recovery, Student Life, Community College of Philadelphia. 1700 Spring Garden Street. Philadelphia, PA 19130.

Dr. Scoles is a Licensed Clinical Social Worker. He received his doctorate in Addictions and Health from the University of Pennsylvania, School of Social Policy & Practice, his M.S.W. from Rutgers University and his bachelors' degree from LaSalle College, Philadelphia, PA. For more than forty years he has been an educator, therapist, teacher and consultant to treatment facilities, city and state governments, the criminal justice system, as well as a psychotherapist to chemically dependent individuals and their families. From 1979 to 1985, Dr. Scoles served as Chairman and Vice Chairman of the Mayor's Drug and Alcohol Executive Commission, City of Philadelphia. In 2011 Dr. Scoles was reappointed for a fifth time to the Mayor's Commission on Addiction & Recovery. In 2007 he was appointed to the Addictions Advisory Board, City of Philadelphia, Department of Behavioral Health and Intellectual disAblities. In 2012 he was appointed to the Faith and Spiritual Affairs Advisory Board, City of Philadelphia, Department of Behavioral Health and Intellectual disAblities.

He was a member of the Governor's Alcohol and Highway Safety Task Force, State of New York and from 1974 to 1986 served as the Senior Consultant to the Pennsylvania Department of Transportation, Alcohol–Highway Safety Program. The statewide Court Reporting Network (CRN) Evaluation system as well as the statewide DUI safe driving schools were developed and implemented by Dr. Scoles under contract with the Commonwealth of Pennsylvania and the National Highway Traffic Safety Administration, Department of Transportation.

In 1986 he received the Meritorious Service Award, from Commonwealth of Pennsylvania *"in recognition of commendable service to the Citizens of Pennsylvania"*. In 2006 he received the Presidential Faculty Award, Community College of Philadelphia and in 2007 he was the recipient of the Lifetime Achievement Award, Veteran's Services Department (Impact Corp.). In 2015 he received the Recognition Award for ten years of dedicated service from the Faith and Spiritual Affairs Advisory Board, City of Philadelphia, Department of Behavioral Health and Intellectual disAblities.

Current interest focusses on professional development and facilitating various community-based organizations and governmental bodies to partner with each other and the College to modify policies, procedures and/or practices that adversely affect consumer groups.

Table of Contents

Chapter 11: Self-Help Movement & the Healing Process 273

References 300

Chapter One
Human Development, Supportive Community Networks and Substance Abuse Treatment

Study after study appears to conclude with the same research findings that substance use begins in one's early teens and concludes with a group of individuals changing their pattern of substance use or abuse in their mid to late 30's. (Heyman, 2009; Dawson, 1996). A Harvard Medical School report indicates that the clear majority of people who successfully quit drinking for a year or more do it alone, without any treatment program or *"support group"*. The Harvard report, also notes that some heroin addicts break their addictive habit in an average of eleven years and that at least 50% of alcoholics eventually become drug free, although only 10% are ever treated for substance abuse. (Harvard Mental Health Letter, 1995).

The National Institute on Alcohol Abuse and Alcoholism (NIAAA) National Epidemiologic Survey of 43,000 individuals with alcohol and related conditions concluded that:

> *About 75 percent of persons who recover from alcohol dependence do so without seeking any kind of help, including specialty alcohol (rehab) programs and AA. Only 13 percent of people with alcohol dependence ever receive specialty alcohol treatment (NIAAA)*

Cahalan (1970) in a national drinking practices study noted that drinking problems decrease in men after age 50 and the amount of alcohol consumed also decreases. Cahalan, Cisin, and Crossley (1974) in another national survey of drinking practices found that about one-third more individuals had problem drinking in a period before their three-year study period than during the study period itself, suggesting a tendency toward spontaneous remission of drinking problems. Goodwin, Crane, and Guze (1971) found that on an eight-year follow-up with individuals who received no treatment about 18 percent of the alcoholic felons had been abstinent for at least two years. Lemere (1953) reported long-term abstinence in eleven percent of untreated alcoholics over an unspecified interval. Kendall and Staton (1966) reported 15 percent abstinence in untreated alcoholics after a seven-year follow-up. Kissin, Platz, and Su (1970) reported a 4 percent one-year improvement rate in untreated lower-class alcoholics. Imber et al. (1976) described a follow-up of 58 alcoholics who received no treatment for their alcohol dependency. It was noted that the rate of abstinence was 15 percent at one year and 11 percent after three years. In 2012, an estimated 23.9 million Americans aged twelve or older were current (past month) illicit drug users, meaning they had used an illicit drug during the month prior to the survey interview. This estimate represents 9.2 percent of the population aged 12 or older. Illicit drugs included marijuana/hashish, cocaine (including crack), heroin, hallucinogens, inhalants, or prescription-type psychotherapeutics (pain relievers, tranquilizers, stimulants, and sedatives) used non-medically (SAMHA, 2012).

Most of the studies mentioned above suggest that a spontaneous recovery rate for alcohol and other drugs, of at least one-year duration, is about 4-18 percent. Spontaneous recovery is a phenomenon of learning and memory which was first seen in classical (Pavlovian) conditioning and refers to the re-emergence of a previously extinguished conditioned response after a delay. Spontaneous recovery is associated with the learning process called classical conditioning, in which an organism learns to associate two stimuli, such that one stimulus comes to produce a response that originally was produced by the other stimulus. Although principles of classical conditioning had been noted by many Western scholars throughout the late nineteenth and early twentieth centuries, the discovery of classical conditioning is usually attributed to Ivan Pavlov, a nineteenth-century physiologist who came across classical conditioning while conducting research on canine digestion (Benjamin, 2007).

Although there may be differences in the ways in which spontaneous or natural recovery occurs the phenomena has persisted from the original studies in the 1960's and 70's into the 21st century. This phenomena is characterized throughout the whole spectrum of alcohol and other drugs: alcohol (Cunningham et al. 2006; Bischof et al. 2000; Weisneret al. 2003; Matzger et al. 2005; Bischof et al., 2003), marijuana (Copersinoet al., 2006), heroin (Waldorf and Biernacki, 1979), binge eating, smoking, sex and gambling (Hanninen et al., 1999; Nathan, 2003).

The process of *"maturing out"* appears to be an active process of renewal and growth leading to transformative growth that involves the body, mind and spiritual dimensions -it is not a passive activity. Maturing into adulthood takes time, motivation, and a supportive environment imbedded in an understanding community. The process of recovering from years of behavioral health challenges can take decades. Peele (1999), indicates that the advantages of the *"maturing out"* approach, is that people come to see that *"recovery"* is a natural process that is more likely than not to occur as long as they make realistic progress in key areas of their lives. Key areas of life tend to involve work, school, friendship, recreational and physical activities, citizenship, including volunteering, engaging in the political process, and other aspects of civic life, and participating in spiritual and religious activities (Salzer, 2006). Peele (1992) believes that the addiction is not lifelong and all-powerful; rather, it is something with which ordinary people with a proper support network can manage. It appears that a supportive community network can help many people find additional strength, hope and motivation to pursue a path of health and growth that will put their behavioral health challenges into a more manageable life process resulting in less stress and anxiety.

So if spontaneous or maturing out recovery accounts for about 4 to18% of the alcohol and other drug (AOD) challenges to the field of behavioral health treatment how does one effectively partner with the other 82% who have alcohol and other drug issues? To answer this question, we must ask a few more questions. What developmental factors influence growth? What is a supportive community network? and what constitutes evidence-based practice?

If a mental health and substance abuse challenges begin in the early teens and for some matures out at about the mid-thirties what developmental challenges need to be addressed by practitioners? Historically, many of our developmental approach to these challenges has been fueled by ones' training which in the Western culture is based on Freud, Piaget, Maslow, Erickson, etc. (Scoles, 2001). Historically, the battle between the Western ego and the Eastern psyche was a struggle that initially united but eventually destroyed the relationship between Sigmund Freud, Alfred Adler, and Carl Jung. Carl Gustav Jung, a Swiss psychiatrist, was Sigmund Freud's junior by 19 years. Their close personal relationship lasted from 1906 to 1913 (Gary, 1988). Though Sigmund Freud (1856-1939) distinguished himself as an intellectual, it was Alfred Adler (1870 -1937), and Carl Jung (1875-1961) who moved the emerging mental health field toward a reevaluation of the meaning of life. Adler's view of human nature-that we shape our own destiny rather than merely being determined by our childhood experiences-was historically considered heretical by Freud. It was Adler who felt that what we believe happened in our life is our reality. Adler's social interest concept and striving for superiority introduced psychology to the development of the *"life force"* or spiritual dimension in therapy (Adler, 1979). Adler, who died almost two years before Freud, and parted with his mentor and teacher in 1911, had a significant influence on what we know today as the Cognitive Therapy of Aaron Beck (Beck, 1976) and the Rational Emotive Therapy of Albert Ellis. (Ellis,1973).

Following his separation from Freud, Adler took the position that his major difference with Freud centered on his belief that *"the journey in front of us was far more important than the path behind us and that we are more than our past. We are creators of our future".* (Ansbacher 1974, p. 32) Carl Jung, who also disagreed with Freud on many substantive issues, supported this perspective (Storr, 1983). Adler's early influence on the development of a positive psychology gained momentum after the death of Jung in 1961, with the publication of Jung's **Collected Works** in English during the 1960's and early 70's. Bruno Bettelheim (1982), partly reacting to Jung's **Collective Works,** published an article in the **New Yorker** entitled, *"Reflections of Freud and the Soul".* Much of the article was in defense of Freud since some

3

mental health professionals believed that Freud did not have a substantive grasp of many of the spiritual issues of psychotherapy. Bettelheim, a psychoanalyst by training, felt that Americans misunderstood Freud partly due to the poor translation of his work into English, even though Freud and his daughter, Anna Freud, reviewed and approved all the translations into the English language. Bettelheim felt that Freud was very involved in spirituality and the structure of the soul. According to Bettelheim, Freud wanted to make clear, that,

> ... *psychoanalysis was concerned not just with man's body and his intellect, as his medical colleagues were, but most of all with the dark world of the unconscious which forms such a large part of the soul of living man.* (p.86)

Apparently, nowhere in his writings does Freud give a precise definition of the term soul or spirit. Even Bettelheim, in his attempt to find the soul, as defined by Freud stated that,

> *I should point out, that when Freud speaks of the soul, he's speaking not about religious phenomena, but a psychological concept. It too is a metaphor. Freud's atheism is well known. He went out of his way to assess it. There is nothing supernatural about his idea of the soul and it has nothing to do with immortality. If anything endures after us, it is another people's memory of us and what we create. By soul or psyche, Freud means that which is most valuable in man while he is alive (p.87) (underlined by author)*

The above statement about soul/spirit activity is not the understanding one gets from a Jungian perspective. The spirit/soul of psychoanalysis appears to live and die with the body and does not have any transcendent function. Freud's view omitted any serious references to spirituality. He believed that instincts in the unconscious were collected in the id, which generated one's drive, the libido. The libido, in turn, channeled energy into an acceptable societal expression called sublimation. In sharp contrast to this view the soul or spirit in Jungian psychology, no more depends on the body it inhabits than the body depends on the clothes it wears. According to Freud, if the human soul is something, it must be of unimaginable complexity and diversity so that it cannot possibly be approached through a mere psychology of instincts, (Bettelheim, p.89) Jung, unlike Freud, de-emphasized the nature of man as a biological instinctive drive, and introduced the idea of a cultural and collective unconscious, which contains information from the history of humanity with both spiritual and religious needs (Jung, 1968. pp.3-53). According to Jung, our middle-aged experiences are more important than our early childhood. Our *"psychic birth"* does not occur until adolescence, which is marked by dramatic physical and emotional development, such as hormonal changes, completing our education, finding a career, getting married, etc. (Storr, 1993, pp. 191-228).

4

During the first half of life the ego dominates our existence: we establish our position, we live among the struggles of our mundane life. In the second half of life, different issues appear to emerge. The first half of life we struggled towards achievement and the second half of life we move towards integration. Ultimately, one's movement toward wholeness or individuation ends with the defeat of the ego, with the final victory being "egolessness" or Selfhood. On the path of life, many symbols appear in the unconscious that need to be introduced to consciousness and made a part of the struggle for individuation and wholeness. (Singer 1994, p. 190)

The Eastern developmental emphasis on self-awareness and self-analysis (self-help) balanced well with the outward ego consciousness of the West. Jung felt that emphasizing this inner-outer struggle would allow the psyche to integrate and move toward selfhood (Buddha nature) or wholeness. The road to wholeness was through the path of individuation. The outer world was relegated to a subordinate position, when one views the totality of life. This relegation is the only way individuals can find serenity and peace in an alcohol and drug world. In the process of life, the Self (inner world) becomes central to unifying and regulating the various opposing tendencies. Although Jung embraced the Eastern concept (Indian) of a Path of Liberation he believed that one could never reach ultimate perfection as in the Buddhist concept of *"Nirvana"*. The Western psyche struggles with the Eastern concept that the way to overcome pain, anxiety, and depression etc. is to live through the process of life (Clark, 1994). In the West we *"soften"* our suffering with drugs and alcohol and forget that the journey is more important than the destination.

Jung believed that the West had an overly developed fascination with, interest in, and dependence on, the Ego state. Jung's influence on the development of Transpersonal Psychology, Gestalt Psychotherapy and the introduction of Yoga into Western therapeutic approaches contributed to expanding our understanding of spirituality in therapy (Bolen, 1979).

Human growth theory not only helps a person develop a better sense of his/her conscious identity, but it also has an obligation to explore the deeper meaning of one's existence. The more one feels his/her beliefs, values and thoughts are generated outside of oneself, and the more one gives those directed activities the power to control his /her life. The objective in life is to create a balance between personal mythology (inner self) and ego complexes (outer self) so that the psyche (soul/spirit) can take command of one's life rather than having the spirit constantly be a stepchild to science.

Since much of one's training is related to developmental deficits as a primary cause of adult behavioral health problems one needs to ask if we add a spiritual path that embraces a faith/spiritual perspective will it change the way practitioners treat behavioral health challenges?

Human Growth and Development

Just as there are discernible stages in human physical and psychological growth, so there are stages in human spiritual development. There does appear to be a pattern of progression through identifiable stages in human spiritual life. Knowing that individuals are unique and do not always fit neatly into the average psychological or spiritual development the stages below are guidelines to helping us understand our journey.

We know that there are many paths to one's human growth and development. Most Western science seems content with Maslow's hierarchy of needs, Erickson's psychosocial development, etc. to explain adolescent and adult behavioral health challenges (White, Hayes, & Livesey, 2005). Over the year's behavioral theorists have been engaged in the development of a few paths less traveled by traditional scientific inquiry. Fowler's Stages of Faith Development (1981) and Ken Wilber's Integral Spirituality (2006) are just a few less traveled paths that allow the introduction of a developmental perspective of spirituality that can complement the bio-psycho-social perspective.

Maslow's Hierarchy of Needs

Maslow's hierarchy of needs begins with the most basic of physical human needs and ends with an individual movement toward self-actualization. Maslow believed that our needs exist in a hierarchy; therefore, one cannot address self-esteem or self-actualization unless the basic physiological and social needs are first met and to some extent satisfied. He articulated a structure that takes into consideration basic physiological needs without ignoring a person's capability to succeed beyond his/her instinctive beginnings. Maslow gained support for his theory from Jung who believed that our instinctive beginnings are like "innate templates" in the brain that let some perceptions enter while screening out others.

> *We must never forget that the world is, in the first place, a subjective phenomenon. The impressions we receive from these accidental happenings are also our own doing. It is not true that the impressions are forced on us unconditionally; our own predispositions condition the impression.* (Jung, CW 4, para. 400)

Through the process of *"selective inattention"* we effectively ignore certain phenomena. At birth we enter consciousness with our ancient cultural traditions (collective unconscious), which have a tendency to influence our perception of reality. Assuming we enter consciousness with a cultural and collective unconsciousness, Maslow (1970) proposed a ladder of motivations based on five (5) innate needs. The basic assumptions underlying the hierarchy are that the lower the need the greater its strength;

the higher the need the weaker its priority. Higher needs are less necessary for survival. The satisfaction of higher needs, such as self-esteem, self-actualization, etc. depend on greater opportunity and freedom of expression than pursuing physiological or safety needs.

Maslow described the needs as:

Physiological Needs - Food, clothing and shelter are so fundamental to survival that if any of these needs are not satisfied, basic survival can become a way of everyday life. For most working and middle class individuals, physiological needs play a minimal role in their daily lives. For the poor and near poor, the inability to satisfy physical needs is one high risk factor that can contribute to drug use and hinder a sense of belonging. In the substance abuse field these basic needs for food, clothing and shelter are addressed by an elaborate system of community-based housing. This sheltered housing environment provides food, clothing and basic amenities while encouraging mutual self-help through a solid program of recovery.

Safety Needs - Security, order and stability are important to satisfactory growth and development of infants and young children. The concept of structure and routine, and the idea that the world is predictable and orderly, leads to less anxiety and more security in adult life. If one grows up in a dysfunctional family characterized by alcohol or drug abuse, it is not uncommon that children of these alcoholic/drug dependent parents show the kinds of insecurity and pervasive anxiety lifestyles so typical of traumatized survivors of stress. Safety needs of adult children of alcoholics reflect many of the developmental problems of inadequate security of young children. (Ackerman, 1978).

- A fear of losing control.

- All or none black or white thinking.

- Fear of experiencing feelings.

- Overdeveloped sense of responsibility or irresponsibility.

- Difficulty with intimacy and with asking for what is wanted or needed.

- Flashbacks of childhood, yet many memory gaps.

- Feeling little, or like a child, when under stress.

- Unreasonable loyalty.

- Addiction to excitement.

- Difficulty in relaxing.

- Feelings of guilt, abandonment, and/or depression.

- Tendency to confuse love with self - pity.

- A backlog of shock and grief.

- Compulsive behaviors.

- Living in a world of denial.

- Guessing at what is normal.

- A tendency toward physical symptoms, (e.g., headaches, gastrointestinal problems, etc.)

3. **Belongingness and Love Needs** - These needs are best expressed after reasonable satisfaction of the physiological and safety needs. The development of close relationships love for other human beings or caring for individuals and our neighbors who share similar values, beliefs, etc. is difficult to satisfy when one lives in neighborhoods with no neighbors or have friends that aren't friendly. Toward the end of his life, Jung feared that humankind might destroy itself through its ecological neglect. According to Jungian practitioners, the neglect of the natural world by destroying our streets, our homes, our neighbor's property, etc. is harming a part of our larger selves. (Harris, 1999) The failure to satisfy the need for love and belongingness is a mitigating factor in the increase in alcohol and drug use patterns in our communities. Alcohol and drug dependency can give one the illusion of normality and a false sense of belonging. Whenever belongingness and love needs are deficient, one lacks a balance in work and play, has difficulty relaxing, has difficulty developing interests, hobbies, positive non-drug altered states of consciousness and has inappropriate feelings of anger and rage.

4. Esteem Needs - When children believe that there is little warmth, security, or sensitivity for their feeling or their situation, how can they feel good about themselves? The development of self-esteem always emanates from the self. If one grows up with negative and rejecting statements and mixed messages, why wouldn't one feel helpless, hopeless, discouraged and inferior? Many chemically dependent individuals in recovery have difficulty resolving conflict, expressing feelings of concern, being creative, dealing effectively with criticism and making effective choices partly because they lack self-esteem.

5. Self-Actualization - The fulfillment of one's capabilities and potentialities is the final stage in development. One must believe that self-actualization is a goal of life sought after but rarely achieved in an individual's life. Maslow felt that about 1% of the population shares the following self-actualization characteristics:

- Reality is perceived as unbiased and not influenced by prior judgment or preconceived concepts.

- Commitment to focus one's energy on some dedicated cause or vocation in life

- A need for privacy and solitude is more important than the need to engage with others.

- A need to perceive the world with freshness and wonder. The mundane events and trivial activity can be appreciated with delight (Mindfulness of Life).

- Interpersonal relationships are few but intense and profound.

- Sympathy/Empathy dominates their social interest.

- A resistance to social and cultural pressures to think and behave in a certain way.

- A sense of inventiveness and originality in their work; flexible, spontaneous and willing to make mistakes.

- A commitment to tolerance and acceptance of no negative display of racial, religious or social prejudice.

- An acceptance of strengths and weaknesses without trying to destroy or falsify their self-image.

- An emotional life, which tends to be open, direct and natural. They rarely hide their feelings except when it would substantially injure other individuals.

- At times experience intense feelings of ecstasy, like a religious or mystical experience, during which the self transcends its reality.

This hierarchy-based model has relevance to the alcohol and drug treatment community. One is often struck by the reality that many chemically dependent individuals are caught in a cesspool of addiction. Partly due to their own circumstances, but also due to a circle of poverty, racism and neglect it becomes easy for chemically dependent people to find *"cheap grace"* or become *"self-actualized"* for a few days or a few hours by taking mind-altering substances. Drugs allow the addictive person to forget their physiological needs, their economic insecurity, or their lifelong lack of any meaningful love and affection. Many clinicians feel that a lack of good parenting skills, economic opportunity, and reasonable health care, if not the most influential variables in one's addiction, are surely significant contributors to the high relapse rates of alcoholics and drug addicts. One could be the most skilled therapist yet still have difficult convincing chemically dependent individuals to step outside of their environment and view life differently. The best some sober/drug free individuals can achieve will always appear to be an illusion of recovery in which one struggles to live sober in a world devoid of meaning and saturated with anger, fear, anxiety and despair.? That search is, *"A transcendent experience always sought but never reached"*. (Zoya. 1989) This positive searching psychology is in fundamental disagreement with many of the psychological tenants of western psychology.

Erickson's Psychosocial Development

Erik Erikson (1902-1994) an ego-psychologist refined and expanded Freud's theory of personality development. Erikson believed that society and culture influence the way in which an individual grows into a mature adult. He felt that personalities unfold in eight developmental tasks that are psychosocial in nature and are guided by an epigenetic principle (predetermined unfolding of events). According to Erikson, if one manages a developmental stage well he/she will carry a certain virtue or balance which will help the individual master the rest of his/her developmental stages. Erikson's concept of balance is similar to Jung's concept of compensation. Maladaptation's, malignancies and generally dysfunctional behaviors are partly a result of our inability to satisfactorily manage a given task. Poor management of any stage could endanger all of one's future development. Although Erikson theorized eight stages, it seems appropriate today to view development in terms of phases or transitions in the life cycle. Like all conceptual models of behavior, they provide the reader with a framework that allows one to process events in the context of a given culture. Much of Erikson's stages describe individual development with little attention given to the person in relationship to others. The only developmental exception is Erikson's stage six-Intimacy vs. Isolation. The idea of development through relationship has gained increasing attention since Erikson's publication of *Childhood and Society* in 1963. Jane Loevinger's (1976) thesis of moral development and recognition of one's emotional interdependence were later reflected in Carol Gilligan's (1982) feminist moral approach to development. Many feminist writers believe that developmental approaches have a distinct male context and ignore what is uniquely feminine. According to Gilligan, this feminine trait recognizes one's emotional interdependence, cooperativeness and cyclic

10

growth. As in most debates the balance is more a compensatory function where characteristics are not exclusively the domain of any gender, but differences are used to sensitize divergent views with the expectation of finding the *"middle way"*.

The Epigenetic Principle:

Stage 1-Trust vs. Mistrust

Oral-sensory stage-birth to approximately one year or eighteen months. During this first phase the individual develops a sense of trust while maintaining the capacity for mistrust. It is important that parents give the child a sense of continuity, consistency and familiarity. If this occurs the individual will feel that the world is a safe place to live in and people are reliable and caring. If the opposite occurs (unreliability, etc.), the child could feel rejected and mistrust is likely to develop. Mistrust will make the child suspicious and apprehensive around other people. In its extreme form the child could develop a tendency to be withdrawn as a young adult. He/she could develop into an adult characterized by paranoia or depression.

If the proper balance (compensatory function) exists between trust and mistrust the infant will develop the virtue of hope. In later life hope is helpful in coping with disappointments in love, changes in one's careers and many other life transitions.

Stage Two - Autonomy vs Shame or Doubt

This is the anal-muscular stage from about eighteen (18) months to approximately four (4) years of age.

During this phase the individual develops a degree of autonomy with minimal shame or doubt. The toddler explores and manipulates his or her environment and begins to feel a sense of his/her independence. This independence is the beginning of self-control and the early stages of self-esteem. This is a time of freedom with control and responsibility. No control will lead to some shame or doubt, which according to Erickson, leads to impulsiveness. Impulsiveness in later childhood or adulthood is reflected in an individual who does things without much consideration given to his/her abilities. The opposite concept, too much shame and doubt, could lead to compulsiveness. This is an individual who must follow rules precisely without any mistakes. The proper balance (compensatory function) of autonomy with some doubt will develop the virtue of will power, the strong ability to exercise self-control.

Stage Three- Initiative vs Guilt

This is the genital-locomotor stage from about four (4) to six (6) years of age. During this phase, the child learns new skills, feels purposeful, takes on challenges and begins to exercise responsibility. Imagination and future thoughts become a part of their current reality.

If a child has too much initiative and too little guilt, there is a tendency to develop a sense of ruthlessness about life. These are children and later adults, who don't care how they achieve their goals; getting to the objective is of paramount importance. In the extreme form, ruthlessness is the adult antisocial personality disorder. If the person has too much guilt Erikson felt the individual would develop a variety of inhibitions. This is a state of doing nothing in life therefore there isn't any need to feel guilty. Inhibited adults may be impotent or frigid or lack a zest for life.

A good balance (compensatory function) leads to a life with purpose. This is an adult with imagination, initiative and responsibility. The person's initiative is tempered with a clear understanding of an individual's limitation and past failings.

Stage Four- Industry vs Inferiority

This is the latency stage from about six (6) to twelve (12) years of age. During this phase the child learns how to control his imagination.

The idea is to develop a sense of productive work activity and avoid feelings of inferiority. Teachers, friends and other community members now join the family. Children must learn not only to conceive a plan but also how to carry the plan into action and/or completion. It is the child's first serious learning of a successful identity. If the child does not experience success during this period, feelings of inferiority or incompetence could develop. Racism, sexism and other forms of discrimination are acknowledged during this developmental time and become factors in the child's evolving feelings of inferiority.

Too much industry leads to the maladaptive tendency called narrow virtuosity. This is usually reflected in children who grow up too fast such as child actors, child prodigies, etc. This could lead to feelings of emptiness or despair in adulthood. Feelings of inferiority could lead to inertia, which are commonly referred to in adult life as "inferiority complexes". These inferiorities inhibit people from developing social skills and usually restrict social interactions. A good balance (compensatory function) between industry and inferiority is called the virtue of competency, having suitable or sufficient skills, knowledge and expertise to accomplish some purpose in life.

Stage Five- Identity vs. Role Confusion

This is adolescence, which begins with puberty and ends around eighteen (18) or twenty (20) years of age.

This stage of development was considered by Jung to be one of the critical transitions in life, referred to as "psychic birth". *The developing adolescent must either break away to become their own person or remain trapped in a false Persona adaptation to parental demands* (Harris, 1996, p. 93). It is the second symbolic touching of the triangle to the circle (birth being the first). It is the first time the individual must attempt to identify and know how he/she fits into the larger society. It is the critical rite of passage stage into adult life from childhood. During this transition uncertainty about one's place in society and the world can create an identity crisis. Too much ego-identity can lead to fanaticism; a belief in the idea that one's way is the only way. Adolescence is a time of idealism, a tendency to see all things in black and white. This "all or nothing thinking" could lead to a fanatical idealist in adult life who will gather others around them to promote their beliefs and life style at the expense of other's rights. If one develops a lack of identity (identity diffusion) it can lead to repudiation. Repudiation drives individuals into such destructive activity as drug and alcohol abuse, psychotic fantasies, and religious cults, hate groups, etc.

A successful developmental integration (compensatory function), according to Erikson, would lead to fidelity. Fidelity is a sense of loyalty to society standards despite its imperfections, prejudices and inconsistencies

Stage Six- Intimacy vs. Isolation

This is a stage of young adulthood, which lasts from about eighteen (18) to around thirty (30) years of age.

This is usually a time to develop close relationships with others. It is a time of commitment and career development. Due to the impersonal nature of today's society it is very difficult to find intimacy. Erikson felt that an unsuccessful adaptation to intimacy is a form of promiscuity. In a broad sense this refers to a tendency to develop superficial relationships with not just a loved one but also with friends, neighbors and community. If one successfully negotiates this phase of development, one should find the virtue of love. Love is not meant in the erotic sense but being able to put aside differences and antagonisms through mutual respect for each other.

Stage Seven –Generatively vs. Stagnation

This is a stage of middle adulthood which begins around thirty (30) and ends somewhere in the fifties (50's).

It is a period when the individual makes the unselfish commitment of contributing to the welfare of future generations with little or no reciprocity. Jung felt that this developmental midlife quest is the beginning of a critical transition to spirituality. The nonproductive path would be to move toward a rejection of one's aging process and panic about getting old by trying to recapture one's youth. This individual can become self-absorbed and care for no one but his or her own needs. If one successfully negotiates this transition, he/she will have the capacity for caring, and a sense of a spiritual path that will serve him/her well for the rest of his/her life. It was during this stage of development, after six years of struggle, that the Buddha attained enlightenment. (Epstein, 1995, p.43). Symbolically, this stage is the third point of the triangle that touches the circle. It reflects the spiritual influence of the life process

Stage Eight- Ego Integration vs. Despair

This last stage, referred to late adulthood or maturity, begins in the mid - fifties to around sixty (60) years of age.

It is a time to develop ego integration or as Jung stated, Selfhood. Although Erikson didn't reflect much on this stage it appears to be a time of spiritual awakenings and a period of reflection and contribution. Some of Erikson's ideas of this stage, as being a period of biological uselessness, etc. are changing since productive work continues and retirement is being deferred until the 70's since individuals are living well into their 80's and 90's. It is a period when an individual comes to terms with the end of his/her life. It should be a time of spiritual development and growth. If an individual fails to accept the aging process, he/she could develop disdain for life. This is usually interpreted as contempt for living. A feeling of contempt for anything is regarded as being unworthy. The main objective during this phase of life is to accept some concept of transpersonal Self-related reality (Harris, 1996, p. 136). Baker and Wheelwright (1982), Jungian analysts, believed that during this time the individual must:

1. Accept death as a part of life.
2. Review, reflect upon, and sum up life.
3. Accept limits to what one could accomplish.
4. Let go of the dominance of the ego.
5. Encourage and honor the Self.
6. Articulate one's own reason for being.
7. Engage unused potentials: "die with life" (pp. 266-270).

If the individual successfully navigates this stage, Erikson believes the individual will have wisdom - the quality of having or showing good judgment to themselves and others.

Fowler's stages of faith development

James W. Fowler (1981) developed a series of stages of faith across the life span. His work builds on Jean Piaget, Erik Erikson, and Lawrence Kohlberg regarding aspects of psychological development in children and adults. Fowler defines faith as a set of assumptions of how one is related to others and the world one lives in throughout their life span. The assumptions are based on one's ability to trust, commit, and relate to the world.

1. Primal or Undifferentiated faith (birth to 2 years), is characterized by an early learning of the safety of their environment. If the individual experiences consistent nurturing the individual will develop a sense of safety and trust about the universe and the divine.

2. Intuitive-Projective faith (ages of three to seven), begins the psyche's unprotected exposure to the Unconscious, and the evolution thought patterns. The beginning of religion and generally a beginning sense of spirituality is learned mainly through family and friends storytelling experiences, and cultural images, of people who share the individual's environment.

3. Mythic-Literal faith (mostly in school children), during this stage an individual begins to have a strong belief in the justice and reciprocity of the universe, deities are almost always anthropomorphic. During this time metaphors and symbolic language are often misunderstood and are taken literally.

4. Synthetic-Conventional faith (arising in adolescence; ages 12 to about mid-twenties) characterized by conformity to a faith in religious authority and the development of a personal identity. Conflicts with one's beliefs are ignored at this stage due to the fear of threat from inconsistencies.

5. Reflective faith (usually mid-twenties to late thirties) a stage of confusion and struggle. The individual takes personal responsibility for his or her beliefs and feelings. Reflection on one's own developmental faith beliefs, can lead to openness to a new complexity of faith, which can lead to conflicts in one's belief.

15

6. Conjunctive faith (mid-life crisis) during this stage conflicts in need of resolution from previous stages are significant due partly based on a complex understanding of a multidimensional, interdependent *"truth"* that cannot be explained by any particular statement of faith.

7. Universalizing faith or what some might call *"enlightenment."* The individual would treat any person with compassion as he or she views people as from a universal community and should be treated with universal principles of love and justice.

Ken Wilber's Integral Spirituality

Ken Wilber's books on Integral Spirituality (2005) stages of spiritual development reflect a perspective that embraces spirituality, culture and consciousness. Wilber correlates his stages with Fowler's and thus presents an integrated model of spiritual development. Ken Wilber begins with a very primitive mind which evolves into the third level of development in which the individual is egocentric and self-protective. Wilber believes this is the same as Fowler's Mythic-Literal Stage (pre- adolescence).

Following the pre-adolescent stage Ken Wilber's spiritual development evolves to a conventional/conformist stage. In this stage the person has expanded his/her level of concern beyond their individual subjective self and now includes his/her ethnic and cultural group. This stage leads to an ethnocentric view of the world. During this stage it appears that one's faith is individualistic with a fundamentalist thought that his/her God is right no matter what others may believe and practice. The individual is extremely patriotic and ethnocentric. This mindset is essentially equivalent to Fowler's Synthetic-Conventional level (ages12 to about mid-twenties). This is usually not a time when pluralistic faith emerges. If one does not move past this developmental stage it is difficult for the individual to engage in what his holiness the Dali Lama refers to as pluralistic faith which allows one to be more ecumenical (Dali Lama, 2010).

In the mid to late twenties a person realizes that faith and to some extent truth is something that needs to be discovered and not delivered to the individual. The concept of blind faith is a serious debate with the evolving Self. It is during this developmental stage that the individual begins to move away from a person's primary identification and expands to a worldview and becomes more of a citizen of the world. The individual becomes *"world centric."* It is obvious however that some people never reach this level at all. Wilber's developmental level corresponds roughly to Fowler's Individual-Reflective stage and our rational level (usually mid-twenties to late thirties).

During the early 40's a person begins to bring concepts together and look for common ground as opposed to difference (ecumenically or pluralistic faith).

15

This is a time when the individual should realize that there are many paths to seeing ones' reality. This worldview helps change the individual to have more compassion for others and may become heavily involved in social causes. This can be a time for more idealistic thinking. According to Wilber a person can include in their worldview mystical or cosmic experiences.

In many of his other works, Wilber elaborates and tries to explain the existence of various developmental lines, of which spiritual development is only one. Other lines include the cognitive, the ethical, the logical, the mathematical, the musical, the spatial, etc. Because people can develop at a different rate along each line, one can easily note the existence of some people who are very highly sophisticated, say scientifically, while still existing at a much less sophisticated spiritual level (Wilber, 1977, 1996, 1999, 2000, 2001).

What is significant about all development (psychological and spiritual) is that no matter how far one evolves, we retain in ourselves the ancient vestiges of our previous stages. Like the process of recovery and life in general one need to confront their Shadow and continually work to humanize it. Through the humanizing of the Shadow we gain resilience and begin the conversion of transformation. The humanizing of the Shadow is fostered not just by an all-inclusive appreciation of our human growth and development (body, mind and spirit) but also gains support and encouragement from a supportive community process that fosters resilience and demands evidence-based treatment that compliments ones culture.

Supportive Community Networks

The fact that support groups like AA and NA typically portray testimonials as validity for their approach to recovery should not be confused with evidence-based treatment. Self-help groups are a fellowship of likeminded individuals who share their lives as a way of giving hope and encouragement to a process those values sharing life experiences as a way of bringing balance to the body mind and spirit. For many, self-help meetings reinforce positive life style changes and help build resilience that reflect the best of the theory and practice of cognitive-behavioral therapy and the general field of positive psychology. Central to all stories of recovery is the theme of personal empowerment and transformation. All self-help programs are based on a voluntary commitment to change. Some believe that the greatest weakness of the 12 Step Program-its dogmatism-is possibly also its greatest strength. The 12 Step Program gives people who are highly vulnerable and clutching for support something concrete, and something more faith based and less scientific. One is hard put to fault the kind of personal support that so many recovering alcoholics and other drug addicts have derived from what is commonly referred to as the Fellowship. One of the great tragedies of modern life is the loss of supportive communities that

16

encourage a more resilient perspective on life events. Over the past 60 years many different community self-help groups have evolved to give encouragement, support and understanding to individuals who face lifelong adversities from various traumas. Many support groups have borrowed heavily from the Twelve Steps of Alcoholics Anonymous. Many support groups outline a way of living that is not just related to issues of chemical use and abuse but provide a spiritual path to a more positive life worth living (Scoles, 2011; Ash, 1993). As stated in the original tenants of the Oxford movement the flow to a successful positive life is centered on one's ability to: (1) make an examination of conscience, (2) review one's personal defects, (3) make restitution to people we hurt, (4) resolve to help others in need, and (5) find a spiritual space to practice our new found wisdom. The above five tenants were originally developed from a Christian perspective, but they are positive principles reflected in all faith-based organizations (Scoles, 2019).

Delgado and Delgado (1982) reflecting on culture and the healing process reported four significant resources that constitute a natural community-based support network that embraces

> 1. The use of extended family, which will enhance the social and emotional support network.

> 2. The use of folk healers, who utilize culturally specific methods, to facilitate the healing of emotional, spiritual, and physical ailments.

> 3. The use of faith/religious institutions, which offer additional social and psychological support services, emergency assistance in crisis, and spiritual advice.

> 4. The use of merchants and social/civic clubs, which traditionally are neighborhood based and could provide a wide variety of social activity and support.

As noted by White and Ali (2010), distinguishing *"recovery,"* which is a personal, individual process, from *"wellness,"* which involves families and the whole community involves a process of trust and understanding from the 12 Step community and those individuals promoting practice guidelines that emphasize the person/family/community paradigm. The future of substance abuse treatment and recovery in the United States appears to be more of a struggle between a personal individual process (recovery) and wellness which evolves a comprehensive support network perspective. Both of these movements need to be integrated into one unified process of related activities. The first movement is treatment renewal. Led by front line service providers to reconnect treatment to the process of long-term recovery and rebuild relationships between treatment organizations, local communities and local recovery support groups. The second movement, the recovery advocacy movement, rose in reaction to the re-stigmatization, de-medicalization and re-criminalization/penalization of AOD problems in the 1980s and 1990s. The goals of this second movement include reaffirming the reality of long-term addiction recovery, celebrating the legitimacy of multiple pathways of recovery, enhancing the variety, availability and quality of local/regional treatment and recovery support services, and transforming existing treatment into "recovery-oriented systems of care" (White, 2000; White & Kurtz, 2006).

In an attempt to bring the above two movements together The Substance Abuse and Mental Health Services (SAMHSA) provides a working collaborative definition of the guiding principles of recovery and treatment renewal that attempts to deal with these complex behavioral health challenges. The guiding principles assume that no single factor can predict whether or not a person will become addicted to drugs. Risk for addiction is influenced by a person's biology, social environment, and age or stage of development. The more risk factors an individual has, the greater the chance that taking drugs can lead to addiction. For example:

Biology. The genes that people are born with—in combination with environmental influences—account for about half (50%) of their addiction vulnerability. Additionally, gender, ethnicity, and the presence of other mental disorders may influence risk for drug abuse and addiction.

Environment. A person's environment includes many different influences––from family and friends to socioeconomic status and quality of life in general. Factors such as peer pressure, physical and sexual abuse, stress, and parental involvement can greatly influence the course of drug abuse and addiction in a person's life.

Development. Genetic and environmental factors interact with critical developmental stages in a person's life to affect addiction vulnerability, and adolescents experience a double challenge. Although taking drugs at any age can lead to substance dependents, the earlier that drug use begins, the more likely it is to progress to more serious abuse. And because adolescents' brains are still developing in the areas that govern decision making, judgment, and self-control, they are especially prone to risk-taking behaviors, including the experimentation with drugs of abuse. (www.samsha.gov-Recovery Support Strategic Initiative).

The Nine Guiding Principles of Recovery

There are nine guiding principles that support the above assumptions and give credibility to the development of a comprehensive support network perspective that can impact on the 82% of individual's negative environment and exposure to drugs of abuse which will create an atmosphere for change that impacts positively on the individual their family and the community's quality of life.

1. Recovery should be person-driven

Self-determination and self-direction are the foundations for recovery as individuals define their own life goals and design their unique path(s) towards those goals. Individuals optimize their autonomy and independence to the greatest extent possible by leading, controlling, and exercising choice over the services and supports that assist their recovery and resilience. In so doing, they are empowered and provided the resources to make informed decisions, initiate recovery, build on their strengths, and gain or control over their lives.

2. Recovery occurs via many pathways

Individuals are unique with distinct needs, strengths, preferences, goals, culture, and backgrounds — including trauma experience that affect and determine their pathway(s) to recovery. Recovery is built on the multiple capacities, strengths, talents, coping abilities, resources, and inherent value of each individual. Recovery pathways are highly personalized. They may include professional clinical treatment; use of medications; support from families and in schools; faith-based approaches; peer support; and other approaches. Recovery is non-linear, characterized by continual growth and improved functioning that may involve setbacks. Because setbacks are a natural, though not inevitable, part of the recovery process, it is essential to foster resilience for all individuals and families. Abstinence from the use of alcohol, illicit drugs, and non-prescribed medications is the goal for those with addictions. Use of tobacco and non- prescribed or illicit drugs is not safe for anyone. In some cases, recovery pathways can be enabled by creating a supportive environment. This is especially true for children, who may not have the legal or developmental capacity to set their own course.

3. Recovery is holistic

Recovery encompasses an individual's whole life, including mind, body, spirit, and community. This includes addressing: self-care practices, family, housing, employment, transportation, education, clinical treatment for mental disorders and substance use disorders, services and supports, primary healthcare, dental care, complementary and alternative services, faith, spirituality, creativity, social networks, and community participation. The array of services and supports available should be integrated and coordinated.

4. Recovery must be supported by peers and allies'

Mutual support and mutual aid groups, including the sharing of experiential knowledge and skills, as well as social learning, play an invaluable role in recovery. Peers encourage and engage other peers and provide each other with a vital sense of belonging, supportive relationships, valued roles, and community. Through helping others and giving back to the community, one helps one's self. Peer- operated supports and services provide important resources to assist people along their journeys of recovery and wellness. Professionals can also play an important role in the recovery process by providing clinical treatment and other services that support individuals in their chosen recovery paths. While peers and allies play an important role for many in recovery, their role for children and youth may be slightly different. Peer supports for families are very important for children with behavioral health problems and can also play a supportive role for youth in recovery.

5. Recovery must be supported through relationship and social networks.

An important factor in the recovery process is the presence and involvement of people who believe in the person's ability to recover; who offer hope, support, and encouragement; and who also suggest strategies and resources for change. Family members, peers, providers, faith groups, community members, and other allies form vital support networks. Through these relationships, people leave unhealthy and/or unfulfilling life roles behind and engage in new roles (e.g., partner, caregiver, friend, student, and employee) that lead to a greater sense of belonging, personhood, empowerment, autonomy, social inclusion, and community participation.

6. Recovery must be culturally-based and influenced

Culture and cultural background in all of its diverse representations—including values, traditions, and beliefs—are keys in determining a person's journey and unique pathway to recovery. Services should be culturally grounded, attuned, sensitive, congruent, and competent, as well as personalized to meet everyone's unique needs.

7. Recovery must be supported by addressing trauma

The experience of trauma (such as physical or sexual abuse, domestic violence, war, disaster, and others) is often a precursor to or associated with alcohol and drug use, mental health problems, and related issues. Services and supports should be trauma-informed to foster safety (physical and emotional) and trust, as well as promote choice, empowerment, and collaboration.

20

8. Recovery involves individual, family, and community strengths and responsibility

Individuals, families, and communities have strengths and resources that serve as a foundation for recovery. In addition, individuals have a personal responsibility for their own self-care and journeys of recovery. Individuals should be supported in speaking for themselves. Families and significant others have responsibilities to support their loved ones, especially for children and youth in recovery. Communities have responsibilities to provide opportunities and resources to address discrimination and to foster social inclusion and recovery. Individuals in recovery also have a social responsibility and should have the ability to join with peers to speak collectively about their strengths, needs, wants, desires, and aspirations.

9. Recovery must be based on respect

Community, systems, and societal acceptance and appreciation for people affected by mental health and substance use problems— including protecting their rights and eliminating discrimination—are crucial in achieving recovery. There is a need to acknowledge that taking steps towards recovery may require great courage. Self- acceptance, developing a positive and meaningful sense of identity, and regaining belief in one's self are particularly important (www.samsha.gov-Recovery Support Strategic Initiatives).

The challenge facing a comprehensive community support network is a need for ones community to embrace a paradigm shift that will facilitate change toward a holistic model of recovery and resilience that embraces the spiritual dimension, not just as a part of the self-help movement but as a part of an integrated model of psychological and spiritual health that complements the biological and genetic foundation of people in need.

Evidence-Based Substance Abuse Treatment

Besides the inclusion of spirituality into the mainstream of human development and the focus on a caring community support network substance abuse treatment must clearly demonstrate that behavioral health challenges listed as improved exceeds the 4 to 18% of individuals who would recover without any intervention. Without evidence-based protocols one cannot legitimately claim to be successful just because they have matched the *"maturing out"* or *"spontaneous remission"* phenomena associated with recovery. As practitioners we should all be concerned about *"evidence"* that consists merely of testimonials, self-published pamphlets or books, or items from popular media shows. Generally, complex behavioral health challenges require complex solutions.

A transformed healthcare system must embrace the concept that the health of individuals is affected by the health of the overall community. *"pathology of the individual"* cannot be separated from the *"pathology of the community"* they coexist and commingle. Provider agencies exist within the community. They are members of the community and therefore have a responsibility to participate in and assist in improving the overall health of the community. A counselor cannot just live in his/her office and be an effective change agent. He or she must embrace therapeutic strategies that support and empower the community. Evidence based behavioral health interventions, such as, Cognitive-Behavioral Therapy (CBT), Dialectical Behavior Therapy (DBT) and trauma informed initiates like the Sanctuary Model as well as many other strategies are compatible with an approach to healing that supports community concerns by helping individuals and their families develop strategies for coping with cravings and avoiding high-risk situations, exploring the positive and negative consequences of continued drug use, recognizing cravings early and identify situations that might put one at risk for use. In Cognitive-Behavioral Therapy (CBT) strategies are based on the theory that learning processes play a significant role in the development of maladaptive behavioral patterns like substance abuse. By applying a range of different skills, one learns to stop drug abuse and address a range of other problems that often co-occur with the substance abuse. A central element of CBT is helping individuals to identify related problems and help the individual develop self-control through effective coping strategies. In Dialectical Behavior Therapy (DBT) people learn skills from one of four different modules: interpersonal effectiveness, distress tolerance/reality acceptance skills, emotion regulation, and mindfulness skills. The Sanctuary Model helps children who have experienced the damaging effects of interpersonal violence, abuse, and trauma. Trauma includes substance abuse, eating disorders, depression, and anxiety. The model is intended for use by residential treatment settings for children, public schools, domestic violence shelters, homeless shelters, group homes, outpatient and community-based settings, juvenile justice programs, substance abuse programs, parenting support programs, and other programs aimed at assisting children (SAMHSA, 2007).

Effective treatment services, like the above strategies embrace a holistic approach that integrates well into a comprehensive social support network perspective geared toward: (1) the elimination of stress in the overall community; (2) being attentive toward environmental factors such as, divorce, death and illness; and (3) supporting and providing opportunities for better housing, increased employment opportunities and positive family activities. Without attention to these communal interventions one will continue to live in a static environment or a neighborhood in decline which becomes a toxic wasteland for individuals, their families and their community.

The key to how individuals, families and communities work together and change has more to do with a collaborative and healing environment that embraces and integrates a variety of therapeutic catalysts into the life of individuals, their families and communities. Therapeutic catalysts were originally applied by Prochaska, and DiClemente, to individual therapy. The therapeutic catalysts applied to community processes are:

1. **Consciousness Raising** - a community that provides increased information about life challenges and how their community can combat unhealthy neighborhood processes.

2. **Environmental Reevaluation** - a community that assesses how one's challenges affect the personal and physical environment of their neighborhood.

3. **Emotional arousal and dramatic relief** - a community that engages different community partners to work on behavioral health challenges through provision of services that lead to healthy solutions.

4. **Self-Reevaluation**. A treatment setting that reflects the needs of their community with respect to clarifying values and challenging beliefs or expectations of the community in which they work.

5. **Self-Liberation** - Choosing and committing to action plans or believing in the ability to act and have a positive impact in their community.

6. **Counter Conditioning**. Encouraging and supporting community alternatives for anxiety caused by disruptive community members.

7. **Helping Relationships** - Focusing on being open and trusting about challenges with people who care about their community. Interventions should include pastoral or other spiritual counseling, self-help groups, social support, etc.

8. **Stimulus Control** - a community that avoids or counters stimuli that elicit destructive behaviors. Interventions could include avoiding high-risk cues and avoiding situations that may be stressful and traumatic.

9. **Reinforcement Management** - Rewarding one or being rewarded by others for making positive changes to one's community (Prochaska, and DiClemente, 1984, 1986; TIP, 1999).

The need to view *"pathology"* from a broader wellness transformative function is particularly relevant to behavioral health challenges and to the development of resilience and protective factors in children and adolescents because it helps people recognize the larger worldview that one must create and make a part of their new reality. This new worldview system brings a different perspective to an otherwise myopic life during mental health or alcohol and other drug challenges. Singer (1991) states that Jung saw the transpersonal perspective as,

> *a view of people and their relations to the larger world that is compatible with the new worldview that sees the universe and everything in it, including human beings, as a series of interconnecting, interacting, and mutually influencing systems. Transpersonal psychology approaches human beings in the context of the wider world, including the invisible world of spirit…. In the transpersonal view, the only way the spiritual world can manifest is through ordinary people in the visible world (Singer, 142-143)*

Jung's study of Christianity, Hinduism, Buddhism, and other traditions led him to believe that his journey of transformation, which he called individuation, is the foundation of all religions and to some extent spirituality. He believed it is a journey to meet the Self and at the same time to meet the Divine. Unlike Freud's objectivist worldview, Jung's belief that the universe (or nature as the totality of everything) is identical with divinity, led him to believe that spiritual experiences were essential to ones well-being, and that health identifies individual human life with the universe as a whole (Crowley, 2000; Jung, 1968).

The evolving field of behavioral health requires not only an individual who possesses a comprehensive therapeutic worldview but also, as White and Kurtz (2006) indicate, a constellation of knowledge and skills that counselors, lay helpers and recovery coaches (as well as community leaders) need to perform related to integrated community-based services. Those critical skills include:

- developing and sustaining a supportive, non-exploitive, recovery/resilience-focused relationship with each individual and family seeking service,

- assessing each person, family and community's recovery capital and recovery resource needs,

- remaining aware of all national and local recovery/resilience support resources,

- empowering each individual and/or family to make choices related to his/her own pathway/style,

- maintaining relationships with key individuals/groups within local communities of recovery,

■ matching the needs and preferences of people to recovery/resilience support resources,

■ Linking (guiding into relationship with) each person to an identified person/group designed to promote recovery and the development of resilience and protective factors,

■ Monitoring each person's response to a chosen pathway/style of recovery and their need for amplified clinical or peer-based recovery/resilience support resources,

■ Offering feedback and support related to recovery/resilience pathway/style choices,

■ providing, when needed, early re-intervention and recovery re-initiation services,

■ facilitating the development of needed recovery support resources.

The influence of Newtonian physics and Pre-Darwinian biology on the biomedical movement of modern medicine had an inordinate impact on the development of twentieth century behavioral health field. The biomedical perspective (as opposed to the psychosocial and/or spiritual) of psychoanalytic theory helped the emerging mental health professions join the mainstream of *"medical science"*. To be recognized by the 19th century medical community the science of mental health had to develop a system in which complex psychic phenomena (emotional problems in living) were explained in terms of simpler, component behavior with physically measurable data that followed scientific laws and were reasonably predictable. The socioeconomic issues such as, housing, employment, maintaining a job, access and money to buy health foods, etc. were never addressed by the emerging profession of psychiatry. The World Health Organization (WHO, 2003) states

> *No group is immune to mental disorders, but the risk is high among the poor, homeless, unemployed, persons with low education, victims of violence, migrants and refugees, indigenous populations, children and adolescents, abused women, and the neglected elderly (p.74)*

When one only looks at the biological reasons for behavioral health challenges the assumption is that getting well and overcoming deficiencies is a function of the individual (Perry, 1996) rather than the system of care. This kind of narrow perspective has contributed to a behavioral health delivery system that continually struggles to provide an integrated care model.

25

Freud's break with Jung was more about the materialistic effort to separate mental illness from religion and spirituality, in order to join the mainstream scientific medical community. The need for a diagnostic nomenclature, which attempts to explain life in a singular dimension, primarily physical and mechanical, with little or no consideration to one's spirituality, was a necessity if the emerging profession of psychiatry was to become established as a part of medicine. Although psychiatry has tried to merge biomedical and psychosocial perspectives in the diagnosis of mental disorders, the language does not sufficiently disguise its biomedical bias. Surely psychiatric labels do help us converse with our professional colleagues and comply with managed care requirements (reimbursement agents), but the person, in front of the therapist is more than a label and greater than modern science (Scoles, 2019, 1-24).

Finally, the helping professions can make a difference not only by broadening their perspective to include a better balance between biology, environment, social conditions and spirituality but to incorporate their perspective on health to also include knowledge about governmental policies and legislation which affect our ability to work with behavioral health challenges. The helping professions must include advocacy at the political level as a part of the healing process. Behavioral health challenges must be viewed in terms of civil and political rights.

Chapter Two
Human Relationships and Culture in Counseling
The Fundamentals of Helping Relationships

All therapeutic relationships have behavioral cues or characteristics that help the client/recovering person perceive the helper (therapist/sponsor) as competent and capable of helping them with their behavioral health challenges. The most frequently reported relationship enhancers are:

> ➢ *Competence/expertness*
> ➢ *Attractiveness*
> ➢ *Trustworthiness.*

If one can meet the above three enhancers there is a good likelihood that the helping relationship will become a positive therapeutic experience. Many of these therapeutic enhancers are descriptive and behavioral in nature. One can possess all of them and not be an effective helper but without them it is difficult to believe that any significant behavioral changes could occur in recovery. (Zamostny, Corrigan and Eggert, 1981)

Competence and expertness is developed by the helper from such things as: (1) years in recovery, (2) relevant education, (3) specialized training, (4) the acquisition of clinical licenses, and (5) the type of setting in which the therapist practices. A difficult concept for beginning helpers to understand is the thought that their language and clothing attire has a lasting impression on the client's initial feelings of their competence. The communication of legitimate power is not only vested in physical attire, but also in the agency in which one works. The helper's reputation and that of the healthcare facility should be of concern to counselors. Much of their professional influence on an individual is related to a person's perception of the agency's collective history of success in resolving behavioral health challenges. Finally, a counselor's office should reflect his professional lifestyle and communicate a sense of living with feelings and emotions.

The perception of expertness does not appear to automatically translate to experience. Individuals seeking behavioral health services do not necessarily view counselors with many years of therapeutic work, or for that matter, years of recovery, as more competent or knowledgeable.

A recovering client reflecting on a non-addictive counselor indicated,

> *My self-esteem was low; I was suicidal I could not help my family and my children had no food or winter clothing. This provided excuses for me to drink. Being forced into therapy, many times, I finally met a therapist who had never experienced any of the things*

27

that I had, but her emotional expression and concern for me and her understanding and sensitivity to my culture helped me cope with my feelings. She knew of similar abusers who had been through the same things and asked me if it would be okay if I told them about me. This process helped me because she understood and seemed concerned about some of the anger I held in me about American society's perception of African American men. Finding a counselor who was culturally sensitive and understood the problems of African American men helped me open to her on other issues such as my alcoholism. To this day, two years into my recovery, I am shocked at how she cared for me.

Non-verbal and verbal behaviors interacting together contribute to a person's perception of competence. Direct eye contact, body orientation, facing the helpee with a forward stance, leaning and attentive posture, effective head and facial movements with occasional affirmative head nods, appropriate smiling and effective vocal quality with a moderate rate of speech and natural conversational style with precise and fluid language identify effective communicators. This coupled with moderate levels of self-disclosure, verbal attentiveness, directness and confidence in one's presentation and interpretations allow the initial stages of helping to crystallize to a point where an effective healing relationship could develop beyond the initial Stage I model of helping. (Egan, 2002, pp. 137-240)

Many of these descriptive and behavioral cues of Stage I help a individual tell his or her story and establish working alliances that connect the helper to the helpee and establish Stage II activities; helping individuals create a better future. If the healing process is successful in Stage II, Stage III activities can focus on helping individuals implement their goals. As individual processes the three stages of helping he/she must demonstrate greater skills and technical competency. (Egan, 2002, pp.21-39)

Besides competence, the helper must also demonstrate **attractiveness** and **trustworthiness** before the therapeutic relationship can challenge individuals to set goals make plans and find solutions to their problems. **Attractiveness** is related to a helper's friendliness, likeability and compatibility with the person seeking help. When helper and helpee have mutual interpersonal attractiveness, it allows individuals to feel more relaxed and receptive to self-disclose. The mutual self-disclosure of concerns previously experienced by the helper, which are similar to the helpee's challenges, enhances competence and attractiveness of the helper. The third interrelated relationship enhancer, **trustworthiness**, is the perception by the helpee that the helper will not mislead or hurt the client. The helpee must perceive the helper's honesty, lack of ulterior motive, and sincerity as being beyond reproach. Trustfulness is communicated to the helpee through appropriate acceptance of helpee self-disclosure, nonjudgmental attitudes, and consistency of verbal accurate feedback, accurate and reliable information giving and non-defensive reflection on the helpee's interpretation of helper statements.

The above relationship enhancers are necessary to begin the therapeutic encounter but, alone, they will not sustain a helpee through the various stages of a problem-solving approach to psychotherapy. The core skills needed to help people develop better coping behaviors focus on:

1. Empathy (accurate understanding)
2. Genuineness (congruence)
3. Respect (positive regard)

Empathy is sharing with another person and understanding their frame of reference. This ability moves away from sympathy in that it does not think or feel for a given person. Empathic healers/helpers build rapport and gather information that connects to a helpee's sensory systems. People in need must feel that helpers are trying to understand their problems by reflecting on the implicit meaning of their messages. Through the helper's questions and statements, the helpee feels that the helper senses his/her issues and gives them the same importance. An empathetic person not only appreciates the outer world of the person in need but also can comprehend an individual's inner thoughts, fears and beliefs. (Egan, 2002, pp. 48-53)

The helpee usually sees genuineness when a helper is oneself, without playing a role or being phony. Both individuals do not appear to be emotionally distant from each other. The helper is perceived as a person not much different from them except that he/she has acquired skills and expertise to work others. When helpers do not focus on their authority or create, through language and posture, excessive and unnecessary emotional distance in the relationship, helpee's feel the helper is honest and helpful.

Genuineness is seen through the consistent words, actions and feeling tone of the helper, who appears aware of his/her feelings and understands his/her inconsistencies or discrepancies. Finally, the need to be spontaneous and open to self-disclosure is a quality that, when used discretely, can help people in need motivate themselves to new goals and actions. Self-disclosure is the providing of information by the helper to helpee about themselves with the intention of increasing the disclosure level of behavioral health challenged individuals. When used properly it facilitates sensitivity and warmth and helps the person build confidence in the therapeutic relationship. When used inappropriately, it can communicate to the helpee the idea that the helper is needier than the client is or that the helpee could feel overburdened and overwhelmed by the helper's problems. In general, self-disclosure is appropriate when it meets the helpee's needs and shows benefit by the helpee's exploration of his/her problems.

Respect for an individual, also called positive regard, is a way of treating other human beings with a sense of dignity and worth. In many ways effective healers have an interest in the person in need, accept the individual's struggles, and feel a willingness to work with him/her. The feeling that the helper understands their problems and demonstrates concern for the individual's seriousness communicates a sense of respect. The use of paraphrasing and reframing a helpee's messages shows the individual you are listening and trying to understand his/her concerns. The helper's ability to maintain confidentiality is on time for appointments, set aside time for the helpee's undivided attention and being concerned about the privacy of their sessions, are all ways the helper is showing positive regard and commitment to the therapeutic relationship. The ability to suspend judgment of a person's actions or motives until all the facts are understood and described by the individual communicates a non-judgmental attitude that helps the person in need clarify his/her thoughts, feelings and actions.

Understanding that relapses occur in recovery does not mean that the helper supports or condones the behavior. It means that the helper is trying to understand the circumstances and help the individual take corrective action in the future. The communication of respect is always associated with warmth in the encounter. Non-verbal behaviors such as a soft soothing voice, a smiling interested face, looking directly into the other person's eyes and a relaxed posture communicate a caring for the individual that is difficult to express on a purely verbal plain. Such verbal statements as, "You're doing well avoiding people who get you into trouble", or "You are to be complimented on your ability to keep focused on your sobriety," help build respect for the individual and communicate a sense of caring. Being able to comment in the "here and now" about an idea or event brings immediacy to therapeutic relationship and reinforces warmth. Immediacy goes to the heart of self-reevaluation in that it allows the individual to take corrective emotional control of an experience and clarify one's behavior. (Egan, 2002, pp. 93-116).

In conclusion, if one can demonstrate competence, attractiveness and trustworthiness, there is a high probability that the individual will return for a second and possibly third session. All these interpersonal influences must be encapsulated in the core conditions of effective helpers for the helper to be a legitimate influence on the recovering person. Empathy, genuineness and positive regard usually must commingle, creating the foundation for change.

Ethical Conduct

Good ethical practice incorporates a sense of hope, a belief in virtue, self-introspection, a compassion and love for life and finally a belief in meaning and transcendence in life (Faiver, 2001, pp.56-59).

- *Hope* gets expressed as a sense of faith in life that allows one to endure experiences of suffering; usually a loss of hope implies a loss of faith in one's existence. Many hopeless people believe that things will never get better.

- *Virtue* is a quality of being in touch with one's individual power. Real virtue involves the ability to make judgments and honor one's commitments (in developing resilience it implies, acting responsibly). Making judgments requires taking authority, which implies a commitment to change. Much of one's "shadow life" has to do with individuals who appear to not be committed to the positive aspects of power.

- *Self-introspection* involves a willingness to experience a conscious examination of our shortcomings. This self-reflective process acknowledges and accepts the nature of wrongs and explores the meaning of life. If an individual is to reevaluate his/her life there must be a sense that their space is unique and special. The exploration of one's shadow side, as well as discovering or uncovering one's personal mythology cannot exist outside of a special space.

- *Compassion and Love* - It is difficult to imagine someone working in the fields of behavioral health that does not recognize the sufferings and struggles of behavioral health challenges. Love is a willingness to extend oneself for the spiritual growth of oneself or another and render oneself vulnerable to the humanity of each person in need of our help.

- *Meaning and Transcendence* - The thought that life is worth living, that there is a purpose to life and not just an individual having an experience. We are truly spiritual beings having a human experience, not human beings having a spiritual experience.

The above commitments to the pursuit of ethical truth acknowledge a helpers' responsibility to ethical practice. Much of a person's commitment to ethical practice is interpreted in a code of ethical conduct.

Cultural Competence

Cultural competency (or cultural pluralism) means more than speaking the language and recognizing the cultural icons of a people. It means changing any pre-judgments or biases one may have of a people's cultural beliefs and customs. It is rooted in respect, validation, and openness towards someone with different social and cultural perceptions and expectations than one's own. Culturally competent care is provided with an understanding of and respect for the cultural values and beliefs. This is accomplished through the efforts of a staff trained to understand and respect the attitudes, beliefs, and behaviors of culturally, ethnically and racially different individuals. Thus, cultural competency should improve the efficacy of treatment by offering services anchored in a culturally appropriate context.

During clinical supervision an African American student reflected on his experience with other Africans,

> *In therapy, cultural competency is essential to being an effective counselor. Being African American I should be able to appreciate the cultures of not only people of different genders, races, etc. but also of different Africans who have recently came to America and are not descendants of slaves. Their skin is as dark as mine, and their lips are as wide as mine, yet we are different culturally. They come from tribes and may have scars across their faces and expanded lower lips, which might by many in America be savagery. Being culturally sensitive has taught me to respect their tribal heritage and appreciate our cultural differences. It has also given me a better appreciation for the African American experience in America.*

Culture permeates all life domains. Jungian analysts believe that when you treat the individual you treat the culture (Samuels, 1991). The saliency of culture is heightened in the lives of those living in a sociocultural setting other than the one they come from. For those who have not experienced socio-cultural change, cultural issues might come to the fore in interactions with individuals who do not share the same culture of origin. These encounters prompt the realization that different cultures view the world in different ways. One way to bridge those differences is through the acquisition of knowledge about other cultures. Cultural knowledge not only enhances the understanding of different worldviews, but also provides insight into the optimum approach to problem solution strategies (Mokuau, 1997). Cultural competence is a set of academic and interpersonal skills that allow individuals to increase their understanding and appreciation of cultural differences and similarities within, among, and between groups (Woll, 1996). According to the Center for Substance Abuse Prevention (1994), a culturally competent program is one that demonstrates sensitivity and understanding of cultural differences in treatment and program design, implementation, and evaluation. Within the treatment setting, cultural competence is a fundamental ingredient that helps to develop trust, as well as an understanding of the way members of different cultural groups define health, illness, and health care (Gordon, 1994). A culturally competent model of treatment acknowledges the client's cultural strengths, values, and experiences while encouraging behavioral and attitudinal change. Treatment services that are culturally responsive are characterized by:

- Staff knowledge of the native language of the client.

- Staff sensitivity to the cultural nuances of the client population.

- Staff backgrounds representative of those of the client population.

- Treatment modalities that reflect the cultural values and treatment needs of the client population.

- Representation of the client population in decision-making and policy implementation.

These features, each by itself, do not constitute cultural competence, nor do they automatically create a culturally competent system. Culturally competent systems include professional behavioral norms for both treatment staff and the organization, norms that are built into the organization's mission, structure, management, personnel, program design, and treatment protocols. In other words, culturally competent systems need to implement cultural competence at various levels: attitude, practice, policy, and structure (Mason, 1995).

Some researchers have described cultural competence as a continuum on which the clinician increases his or her understanding and effectiveness with different groups (Castro, et. al. 1999; Cross 1988; Kim et. al. 1992). The continuum moves through four phases:

- **Cultural destructiveness**, in which an individual regards other cultures as inferior to their dominant culture, to more positive attitudes and greater levels of skills described below

- **Cultural sensitivity** is being *"open to working with issues of culture and diversity"* (Castro et al. 1999, p.505). Viewed as a beginning point on the continuum, however, a culturally sensitive individual has limited cultural knowledge, and may still think in terms of stereotypes.

- **Cultural competence**, when viewed as the next stage on this continuum, includes an ability to *"examine and understand nuances"* and exercises *"the full cultural empathy."* This enables the counselor to *"understand the client from the client's own cultural perspective"* (Castro et al. 1999, p.505).

- **Cultural proficiency** is the highest level of cultural capacity. In addition to understanding nuances of culture in even greater depth, the culturally proficient counselor also is working to advance the field through leadership, research, and outreach (Castro et al. 1999, p.505).

Effective helpers who are culturally relevant should at least meet the criteria for cultural competence and move toward cultural proficiency.

It is important to remember about clients, not counselors, define what is culturally relevant to them. It is possible to damage the relationship with a client by making assumptions, however well intentioned, about the client's cultural identity. For example, a client of Hispanic origin may be a third-generation United States citizen, fully acculturated, who feels little or no connection with his/her Hispanic heritage. A counselor who assumes this client shares, the beliefs and values of many Hispanic cultures would be making an erroneous generalization. Similar it is helpful to remember that all of us represent multiple cultures. Clients are not simply, African-American, white, or Asian. A client who is a 20-year-old to the African-American from the rural south may identify, to some extent, with youth, rural south, or African-American cultural elements-or may, instead, identify more strongly with another cultural element, such as faith, that is not clear. Counselors are advised to open a respectful dialogue with clients around the cultural elements that have significance to them.

Approaches to Cultural Competence

Much of the literature on treating racial/ethnic minority clients advocates the use of culturally responsive treatments. Recommendations have been made to modify treatment modalities offered by mainstream programs by including racial/ethnic specific features, as well as to develop new forms of culturally responsive treatment. Some have recommended increased use of ethnic paraprofessionals (Sue, 1976; Wu and Windle, 1980). Although Sue's recommendations focus primarily on Asians and Pacific Islanders, others report similar findings for Hispanic Americans (Barrera, 1978; Padilla, Ruiz, and Alvarez, 1975), African Americans (Vail, 1978; Sue, 1977), and American Indians (Colorado, 1986).

Research on the relationship between *"racial or ethnic matching"* of clients and counselors in a treatment context reveals complex dynamics on how the therapeutic alliance might affect treatment outcomes. It appears that although some individuals prefer counselors from their same racial/ethnic/cultural background, this is not always sufficient to ensure client engagement and retention (Beutler et al., 1997). Similarities in sociodemographic variables and level of acculturation also appear to affect the nature of the therapeutic relationship. Flaskerud (1986) recommends that in addition to matching a client's and counselor's racial and ethnic backgrounds and language, careful and close attention should be paid to site accessibility regarding location and hours, and the provision of

34

comprehensive adjunct services, including medical, legal, social, educational and economic/vocational services.

Cultural competence requires the willingness of treatment counselors and the treatment system under which they operate to conduct self-appraisals to develop an understanding of how they may differ from the community or clients they serve. Cultural competence also entails acknowledgment of existing inherent cultural biases and influences on one's attitudes and behaviors (Henderson and Primeaux, 1981). A counselor's comfort in relating to persons who are different is communicated in many nonverbal and unconscious ways. Common factors that influence comfort include ethnic and racial characteristics, socioeconomic background, religious affiliation, and physical or mental handicaps (Axelson, 1985). However, cultural competence also requires effective communication that goes beyond mere language proficiency to focus on meanings and interpretations (Garcia, 1995). Within a culturally competent framework, knowledge of cultural beliefs, expectations and morals is crucial to effective communication (Moffic and Kinzie, 1996).

A significant part of cultural competence is training that examines not only personal beliefs but also prior interactions with the targeted client population. The analysis of personal bias and worldview will allow staff to assess their strengths and weaknesses in order to build training priorities. According to Leong and Kim (1991), three areas of competency are required in this self- assessment and training process: beliefs/attitudes, knowledge, and skills.

Training can only begin to be meaningful when staff and management understand and accept the need for training and self-assessment. The most difficult element is gaining total program cooperation. All members must "buy in" to a process of reviewing and expanding their own worldview, including learning about the specific cultures of their clients. Training must be an ongoing process with "booster" sessions as well as retreats to discuss the policy and programmatic implications of any significant modality shifts. Using outside consultants is a more favorable and recommended alternative than relying upon agency ethnic staff to supply such training. By using consultants, all staff is given fair opportunity to participate and share in the learning process.

Once training begins, and new programmatic objectives and goals are established for the targeted client population, ongoing support is required for the program objectives. However, program development and adaptation require an ongoing and long-term commitment in planning and development of time, consultation, and supervision.

Members of some minority groups have limited access to health care and are often at increased risk of substance abuse and its associated problems. This is so for several reasons, among them, the migration experience, poverty, unemployment, and cultural differences between members of minority groups and the large society. Within the United States socioeconomic context, some members of minority groups have sought economic and personal self-empowerment through the drug economy. Unfortunately, illusions of material wealth often end tragically in addiction, imprisonment, or death, and further the deterioration of a community's most valuable resource, its human potential.

Barriers to Treatment Affecting Substance Abusers from Racial/Ethnic Groups

Regardless of the treatment model in use, racism on an institutional or individual level can be a barrier to treatment effectiveness. Institutional racism within a treatment system is evident when the program or treatment design is oblivious to the racial, cultural, or ethnic backgrounds, values, and mores of its client population. Latent prejudice on the part of treatment staff as well as language and cultural differences undermine efforts to help patients achieve recovery from substance abuse.

A community in social and economic distress may resent and mistrust treatment providers who are "outsiders." Negative experiences with service providers who may have lacked regard, awareness, or concern for cultural differences often reinforce unfavorable attitudes and distrust. Substance abuse treatments program may be rendered ineffective if the community has not been involved in their planning and implementation.

Many treatment professionals and community leaders believe that treatment staffs that come from the same community are better suited to providing culturally responsive treatment since they are often knowledgeable about community networks and are able to design programs that address the belief systems, cultural values, attitudes, and behaviors of community members.

Lesbian, Gay, Bisexual, Transgender (LGBT) Experiences

Persons who identify as LGB or T constitute special populations within racial/ethnic groupings. In modern usage, the term LGBT is intended to emphasize a diversity of sexuality and gender identity-based cultures and is sometimes used to refer to anyone who is non-heterosexual instead of exclusively to people who are homosexual, bisexual, or transgender (Shankle, 2006) To recognize this inclusion, a popular variant adds the letters "QI" for Queer Identified or for those questioning their sexual identity, just the "Q" (e.g., "LGBTQI" or "LGBTQ"). Research, however, has tended to focus on either sexual orientation or ethnicity; thus, few studies address the interaction between them. There is a paucity of research on the relationship between sexual orientation and effectiveness of specific modalities that support recovery and resilience; on the interaction of sexual orientation and ethnicity in managing recovery and on how particular ethnic communities regard and treat their gay and lesbian members who may be experiencing behavioral health challenges. Therefore, systems of care for ethnic homosexual and bisexual people addicted to substances or experiencing other behavioral health challenges may be seriously flawed in most human service systems. Programs that treat these challenges must make special efforts to find out as much as possible about the attitudes held toward people who identify as gay and lesbian by the specific racial/ethnic group(s) to whom they provide services.

Practitioners write much of the current literature on behavioral health treatment issues affecting people who identify as gay, lesbian, or bisexual based on their clinical observations. Their findings identify the need for special services for gay people who are abusing substances or who have other behavioral health challenges and address the clinical issues specific to them that must be understood by treatment professionals working with this population.

Factors that are central to the onset of behavioral health issues for gay/lesbian individuals include: difficulties with self-esteem, relationships with others, isolation, alienation, and low self-efficacy (Holmes and Hodge, 1997). Clearly, these are some of the same causal factors that contribute to the prevalence of behavioral health issues in the general population. However, being homosexual or bisexual, a woman, or a member of an ethnic minority group compounds the problems this seriously underserved population faces.

In Senreich's study (2009) of gay/lesbian/bisexual individuals' perceptions of their substance abuse treatment experience, the following was revealed:

❖ Overall, gay/bi men and lesbian/bi women felt less connected therapeutically supported and less satisfied with treatment as compared to their hetero counterparts.

❖ Because of the above, gay/bi men and lesbian/bi women had less completion and higher rates of leaving treatment as well.

❖ 57% of gay/bi respondents indicated that their orientation negatively affected them in treatment.

❖   Lastly, counselors in treatment settings need to be trained more effectively to help LGB persons cope with *"internalized homophobia"* (negative feelings one has toward themselves because of being homosexual and the stigma in society about homosexuality) which was cited as a key factor leading to abuse of substances.

Additionally, treatment providers should be aware of local community resources (e.g., gay A.A. groups, faith communities that are affirming to members of those communities, etc.). Awareness of local gay groups and resources helps providers to ensure improved opportunities of retaining people receiving services through the provision of culturally competent referrals appropriate to the needs of the person. In addition, because poor coping skills are considered to be a major cause of return to the use of alcohol or other drugs, providers who work with people who identify as gay/lesbian just as in any other responsible therapeutic interaction, should address issues such as: spirituality, healthy relationships, citizenship, and issues related to emotional and physical health and wellness including HIV infection and AIDS. The issues of sexual orientation or gender identity/expression should not be ignored, and treatment providers should be aware of the roles they can play in defining attitudes and assumptions about recovery, health and wellness.

Overall, many people in the LGBT communities who enter recovery for behavioral health challenges are dealing with shame and fear of being rejected. This fear stems from a history of oppression, marginalization and scorn, not only directed toward their behavioral health challenges, but also toward their sexual orientation. Many gay men report a history of non-acceptance, prejudice, and a lack of understanding in their encounters with practitioners (Holmes and Hodge, 1997). Lesbians face reactions to their sexuality, as well as issues specific to women seeking care. A counselor, therapist, physician is an authority figure whose approval or disapproval typically carries a great deal of weight. Therefore, practitioners should consider carefully their own attitudes and beliefs about gay and lesbian people. Their values and biases may influence the process of recovery and inhibit the development of resilience.

Universal Cultural Themes in the Development of Culturally Competent Treatment Programs

Although every racial/ethnic minority group is characterized by unique cultural, migratory, social, economic, and political experiences, two themes relevant to cultural competence run across the groups: (1) family structure and (2) cultural healing and spiritual beliefs. They both should play prominent roles in the development of effective culturally competent substance abuse treatment services.

Family Structure

Kinship and family ties are extremely important to all racial/ethnic groups, since they form a network of mutual support that can provide material, emotional, and social resources to members in distress. However, a tight family structure can also serve to hide and prolong substance abuse problems. Family notions of propriety develop over generations and do not disappear when the family is transplanted to a new geographical location. Young people who attempt to abandon family standards often find in later life that they carry the values they had challenged earlier. Treatment providers must consider family attitudes and behaviors in the context of race, ethnicity, and culture. This will enable staff to include cultural characteristics in their efforts to restore or maintain family health.

Cultural Healing and Spiritual Beliefs

Folk beliefs strongly influence the behavior of many minority groups seeking health care and substance abuse treatment. Some Asians and Pacific Islanders consult traditional healers such as acupuncturists and herbalists, or use traditional remedies such as self-restraint and meditation to supplement Western medical interventions. Personal health is viewed as an individual's responsibility and requires balance between body and spirit. However, the extent of use and efficacy of traditional medicine among these cultures has not been adequately documented. Tribal healers and spiritual leaders play powerful roles in the health practices of American Indians. Coordination of health care, substance abuse treatment, and social programs with tribal healers and spiritual leaders is important since treatment outcomes are often strongly influenced by the Indian client's spiritual beliefs and practices.

Hispanic Americans traditionally perceive illness as an imbalance of physical or mystical forces; illness is often attributed to God's will, magical powers, evil spirits, powerful human forces, or emotional upsets (Randall-David, 1989). There is little or no conceptual difference between physical and emotional illnesses. Spiritual healers and priests play an important role in managing crises and planning therapeutic interventions. Spiritual healing (e.g., *santeria, espiritismo)* is practiced in different Hispanic communities.

Spirituality also plays a major role in the African American community. Voodoism, a type of spiritual healing, is a mixture of indigenous and Catholic beliefs. Hope and perseverance is maintained through Voodoism, and serves as a unifying force for many Haitians in Haiti and in the United States.

39

Chapter Three
Neurotransmitters, Drugs and the Brain

The adult human brain weighs about three to four pounds. Anatomically, the front and uppermost portion of the brain is the Cerebral Cortex. The Cortex has a left and right half referred to as "hemispheres". Each half is connected by a band of fibers called the *corpus callosum,* which serves as an information highway between the two hemispheres. The Cerebral Cortex performs a number of functions, such as cognitive, sensory and motor.

The communication of information in the brain about changes in ones internal and external environments is filtered through the neurons and nuclei that release biochemical substances called neurotransmitters. These neuro-chemicals are manufactured and stored within the neuron and released as a consequence of action. To date, we are aware of about forty (40) neurotransmitters. The most common neurotransmitters and their general functions are in Table I below

Table 1:Neurotransmitters and Identified Functions

Neurotransmitter	Identified Function
Dopamine	motor systems, pleasure/reward, mental illness, craving
Norepinephrine	arousal, stress, mental illness, learning, sleep
Epinephrine Serotonin	sympathetic arousal sleep, dreaming, mental illness, craving, eating
Gamma-amino butyric acid (GABA) Glutamate	relaxation/anxiety, alcohol intoxication
Aspartate	alcohol effects
Substance P	pain responses
Acetylcholine	motor systems, learning
Opioid Peptides	pain responses, learning, eating

Source: Brick, J. and C. Erickson, (1999).

Once released, neurotransmitters enter the small space (synapse) between the axon terminal of one neuron and the dendrite of another neuron. The neurotransmitter then comes into contact with binding sites (receptors located in the next neuron).

Depending on the type of receptor it will increase or decrease the action of the neuron. After a fraction of a second, the neurotransmitter drifts back into the synapse (small space). There are over thirty (30) types of neurotransmitter receptors, some on the presynaptic others on the post-synaptic neurons. Once the neurotransmitters drift off the receptor it floats in the synapse where it may be:

(1) deactivated (metabolized) by enzymes,
(2) contact other receptors, or
(3) it might be taken back into the neuron through a process called reuptake

A simplified version of the synaptic gap and its biochemical activity is presented in Figure 1.

Figure 1 Schematic Representation of Neuron and Synaptic Transmission

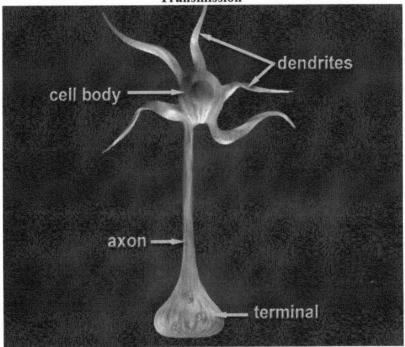

Source: NIDA: Teaching Packet IV for Health Professionals, Teachers and Neuroscientists

All drugs of abuse (psychoactive drugs) have an effect on how a given neurotransmitter functions. A drug, once it crosses the blood-brain barrier, appears to increase functional activity by:

(1) Directly activating the receptor site

(2) Increase the release of a neurotransmitter.

(3) Inhibits the reuptake of the transmitter into the neuron, allowing it to stay in the synapse (gap) where it is free to interact with receptors again.

(4) Inhibits enzymes from breaking down the neurotransmitter

> Within the Axon of the neuron are neurotransmitters held in storage and released when the neuron is stimulated.

> The small space between the synaptic knob and the dendrite is called the synapse. A nerve impulse stimulates the release of neurotransmitters across the synapse.

> The neurotransmitters bind to the receptor sites on the dendrite of the next neuron causing a change.

> Once in the neuron, enzymes could break it down or repackage it for future release or storage. Many drugs of abuse like cocaine, alcohol, etc. can alter the metabolizing enzyme or the reuptake process.

In general, drugs like Methadone that increase functional activity of neurons are called *Agonists*. Drugs that decrease functional activities, such as Naltrexone, block receptors, decrease neurotransmission action or manufacture, or increase reuptake or enzymatic breakdown are called *Antagonists*. For example, the Benzodiazepines interact with receptors on neurons that use the neurotransmitter GABA to change the way your brain cells function. Since GABA has an inhibitory action the neuro-chemicals change (IPSP production) is associated with relaxation *and* a decrease in anxiety, hence the name tranquilizer drug. GABA is one of the brains endogenous (made within the body) sedating chemicals. GABA can be taken to calm the body in much the same way as Valium, Librium and other tranquilizers without the fear of addiction. About 750mgs of this amino acid will produce a sedative effect. The opposite is true for chemicals that are expected to increase anxiety. Caffeine, nicotine and chocolate (Xanthenes) block the benzodiazepine receptors and prevents its natural calming effect. Lithium, used to treat bipolar disorders can increase the uptake of both tyrosine and tryptophan; both of these amino acid precursors impact on serotonin and norepinephrine levels. The Selective Serotonin Reuptake Inhibitors (SSRI's) such as, Prozac, Luvox, Zoloft, Paxil, etc. rather than increasing the functional activity of brain serotonin they selectively inhibit serotonin reuptake, thereby keeping the neurotransmitter in the synapse where it is free to interact with other receptors again.

Tryptophan is the precursor to the important neurotransmitter serotonin, which regulates several vital processes in the body, including sleep, emotional stability, pain sensitivity and addictive cravings. When levels of serotonin drop too low, a vast array of symptoms, ranging from anxiety and insomnia to obsessive/compulsive behavior and suicidal depression, can occur.

Tryptophan helps control hyperactivity in children, alleviates stress, is good for the heart, aids in weight control and enhances the release of hormones necessary to produce vitamin B6 (pyridoxine).

The body is able to manufacture serotonin from the amino acid tryptophan, which is found in certain foods. Many people who reach for ice cream, sweets and pastries when they feel stressed or depressed are instinctively attempting to increase their uptake of tryptophan to elevate their serotonin levels and improve their mood. Unfortunately, it takes great quantities of these "comfort foods" (with their unhelpful fat, sugar and calories) to significantly affect serotonin levels.

Tyrosine is important in the treatment of anxiety, depression, allergies, and headaches. It aids in the production of melanin (pigment of the skin and hair) and in the functions of the adrenal, thyroid, and pituitary glands. Low plasma levels of tyrosine have been associated with hypothyroidism; a disorder that mimics many of the symptoms of clinical depression. Tyrosine acts as a mood elevator, suppresses the appetite, and reduces body fat. It is involved in the initial breakdown of phenylalanine in the liver. A lack of tyrosine triggers a deficiency of the hormone norepinephrine at a specific brain location, which results in depression and mood disorders. In addition to being a precursor for norepinephrine, tyrosine is also used to synthesize epinephrine and dopamine. It has been used for withdrawal from drugs.

Some neurotransmitter activity has to do with symptoms of psychosis, like Schizophrenia, which appears to result from a biochemical imbalance within the brains dopamine system. Although we don't know precisely how it works, some scientists have theorized that schizophrenic reactions produce an unusual amount of dopamine agonist known as Phenylethylamine, an amphetamine like agonist.

Other researchers theorize that schizophrenia may be a disease related to abnormal metabolism of dopamine due to the destruction of norepinephrine containing neurons. Schizophrenic clients appear to have lower DBH activity (dopamine-beta-hydroxylase enzyme) leading to increased accumulation of dopamine.

Finally, there have been some studies that suggest schizophrenia is related to levels of serotonin. Since most hallucinogenic drugs have chemical structures like serotonin, which can enhance hallucinations, and since we know that if one increases the amino acid tryptophan to a given group of individuals it will exacerbate schizophrenic like symptoms. (In non-psychotic individuals tryptophan overload has a sedative-like effect).

The problem with dopamine blockers to treat psychotic symptoms, like Haldol, is that they are prolactin-inhibitors, causing side effects, such as, breast enlargement in men, impaired ejaculation in men with loss of orgasm and abnormal menstrual cycles or infertility in women. In addition to the above, endocrine side effects, the dopamine blockers have a profound effect on the extra pyramidal system causing pseudo- Parkinsonism (drooling, shuffling, tremors, rigidity, etc.) Akathisias (restlessness and continuous motor activity) and acute dystonic reactors (facial grimacing, muscle spasms of the tongue, face, neck and back).

Many anticholinergic drugs, like Cogentin are successful in treating the above symptom complex. The use of medication to treat coexisting disorders, such as, cocaine dependency and depression has been a continuing concern of both the addiction treatment community and the psychiatric field. Over the years many chemically dependent individuals have been over-medicated or inappropriately medicated by ill-informed psychiatrists and other physicians. Partly based on that experience and the recovery communities' misinterpretation of psychiatric medication usage, a healthy suspicion developed regarding the appropriateness of pharmacotherapy in the treatment and management of dual disorders. Over the past ten years there has been slow acceptance of medication to treat many coexisting disorders, by both the substance abuse treatment community and the mental health establishment. Recent advances in neurophysiology and the development of medications with little or no serious side effects and low addictive potential have gone far to bridge the medication gap.

Mental Health Medications & Non-Narcotic Analgesics

Many chemically dependent clients are fearful of taking psychiatric medication. Some view any medication as a concrete reminder of their addiction, while others are undermining the therapeutic process by suggesting to clients that they should be drug free. Despite all this controversy, with adequate education, most clients accept the treatment centers recommendations and make an honest attempt to follow their treatment plan.

The addiction counselor can be quite helpful to the prescribing physician and better manage the case if he/she is able to monitor the client's response to medication. Counselors should be aware of side effects, reoccurrence of psychiatric symptoms, inadequate or minimal response to medication, etc.

44

When discrepancies are noted the counselor should initiate a reevaluation (case consultation) with the prescribing physician. (Brick and Erickson, 1999 and Julien, R. 1995).

Comprehensive Drug Abuse Prevention and Control Act of 1970 drugs are identified for legal prosecution. This classification system is based not on the drug properties of a compound but on its perceived abuse potential (McPherson, Yudko, et al., 2009):

Drug Schedule

-**Schedule I compounds**- no recognized medical use. Examples: marijuana, LSD, Heroin, MDMA
-**Schedule II compounds**- recognized medical use, but with a very high abuse potential. Examples: morphine, and the amphetamines.
-**Schedule III compounds**-- recognized medical use, but with a moderate abuse potential. Examples: codeine, katamine.
-**Schedule IV compounds**- recognized medical use, but with a mild abuse potential. Examples: benzodiazepine and phenobarbital.
-**Schedule V compounds**- recognized medical use, but with a low abuse potential. Example: buprenorphine

The medication discussion, which follows, has very little to do with the above drug schedule. The information below is a beginning understanding of certain psychiatric drugs and non-narcotic analgesics used in the management of the dually diagnosed patient. When in doubt the counselor's best source of information is the prescribing physician.

Mental Health Medications*

Medications can play a role in treating several behavioral health challenges (mental disorders). Treatment may also include counselling and psychotherapy. In some cases, psychotherapy and or counselling alone may be the best treatment option.

Choosing the right treatment plan should be based on a person's individual needs and medical situation, and under a mental health professional's care.

The author does not endorse or recommend any particular drug, herb, or supplement. Results from National Institutes on Mental Health (NIMH)-

*Retrieved in December 2019 NIMH » Mental Health Medications.pdf and WWW.nimh.nih.gov.

This health topic is intended to provide basic information about mental health medications. It is not a complete source for all medications available and should not be used as a guide for making medical decisions.

Information about medications changes frequently. Check the U.S. Food and Drug Administration (FDA) website for the latest warnings, patient medication guides, or newly approved medications. Brand names are not referenced on this report, but you can search by brand name on MedlinePlus Drugs, Herbs and Supplements Drugs website. The MedlinePlus website also provides additional information about each medication, including side effects and FDA warnings.

Understanding Medications

When completing the Assessment part of the evaluation make sure that all medications and vitamin supplements are recorded for the physician's review. If the client reports any problems with their medicine or if an individual is worried that it might be doing more harm than good set up an appointment with the medical director of the treatment facility. Upon medical review the physician (in many programs a Psychiatrist) may be able to adjust the dose or change the prescription to a different medication that may work better for the client.

Below is a list to provide basic information about mental health medications.

Antidepressants

What are antidepressants?

Antidepressants are medications commonly used to treat depression. Antidepressants are also used for other health conditions, such as anxiety, pain and insomnia. Although antidepressants are not FDA approved specifically, to treat ADHD, antidepressants are sometimes used to treat ADHD in adults.

The most popular types of antidepressants are called selective serotonin reuptake inhibitors (SSRIs). Examples of SSRIs include:

Fluoxetine
Citalopram
Sertraline
Paroxetine
Escitalopram

Other types of antidepressants are serotonin and norepinephrine reuptake inhibitors (SNRIs). SNRIs are similar to SSRIs and include venlafaxine and duloxetine.

Another antidepressant that is commonly used is bupropion. Bupropion is a third type of antidepressant which works differently than either SSRIs or SNRIs. Bupropion is also used to treat seasonal affective disorder and to help people stop smoking.

SSRIs, SNRIs, and bupropion are popular because they do not cause as many side effects as older classes of antidepressants and seem to help a broader group of depressive and anxiety disorders. Older antidepressant medications include tricyclics, tetracyclics, and monoamine oxidase inhibitors (MAOIs). For some people, tricyclics, tetracyclics, or MAOIs may be the best medications.

How do people respond to antidepressants?

According to a research review by the Agency for Healthcare Research and Quality, all antidepressant medications work about as well as each other to improve symptoms of depression and to keep depression symptoms from returning. For reasons not yet well understood, some people respond better to some antidepressant medications than to others.

Therefore, it is important to know that some people may not feel better with the first medicine they try and may need to try several medicines to find the one that works for them. Others may find that a medicine helped for a while, but their symptoms came back. It is important to carefully follow a physician's directions for taking medicine at an adequate dose and over an extended period of time (often 4 to 6 weeks). It usually takes that long for the medicine to work. Once a person begins taking antidepressants, it is important to not stop taking them without the help of a doctor. Sometimes people taking antidepressants feel better and stop taking the medication too soon, and the depression may return. When it is time to stop the medication, the doctor will help the person slowly and safely decrease the dose. It's important to give the body time to adjust to the change. People don't get addicted (or "hooked") on these medications, but stopping them abruptly may also cause some withdrawal symptoms

What are the possible side effects of antidepressants?

Some antidepressants may cause more side effects than others. The most common side effects listed by the FDA include:

Nausea and Nausea and vomiting
Weight gain

47

Diarrhea
Sleepiness
Sexual problems

The counselor and/or the client should call the doctor right away if you have any of the following symptoms, especially if they are new, worsening, or worry you (U.S. Food and Drug Administration, 2011):

Thoughts about suicide or dying
Attempts to commit suicide
New or worsening depression
New or worsening anxiety
Feeling very agitated or restless
Panic attacks
Trouble sleeping (insomnia)
New or worsening irritability
Acting aggressively, being angry, or violent
Acting on dangerous impulses
An extreme increase in activity and talking (mania)
Other unusual changes in behavior or mood

Combining the newer SSRI or SNRI antidepressants with one of the commonly-used "triptan" medications used to treat migraine headaches could cause a life-threatening illness called *"serotonin syndrome."* A person with serotonin syndrome may be agitated, have hallucinations (see or hear things that are not real), have a high temperature, or have unusual blood pressure changes. Serotonin syndrome is usually associated with the older antidepressants called MAOIs, but it can happen with the newer antidepressants as well, if they are mixed with the wrong medications

Anti-Anxiety Medications

What are anti-anxiety medications?

Anti-anxiety medications help reduce the symptoms of anxiety, such as panic attacks, or extreme fear and worry. The most common antianxiety medications are called benzodiazepines. Benzodiazepines can treat generalized anxiety disorder. In the case of panic disorder or social phobia (social anxiety disorder), benzodiazepines are usually second-line treatments, behind SSRIs or other antidepressants. Benzodiazepines used to treat anxiety disorders include:

Clonazepam
Alprazolam
Lorazepam

48

Short half-life (or short-acting) benzodiazepines (such as Lorazepam) and beta-blockers are used to treat the short-term symptoms of anxiety. Beta-blockers help manage physical symptoms of anxiety, such as trembling, rapid heartbeat, and sweating that people with phobias (an overwhelming and unreasonable fear of an object or situation, such as public speaking) experience in difficult situations. Taking these medications for a short period of time can help the person keep physical symptoms under control and can be used *"as needed"* to reduce acute anxiety.

Buspirone (which is unrelated to the benzodiazepines) is sometimes used for the long-term treatment of chronic anxiety. In contrast to the benzodiazepines, buspirone must be taken every day for a few weeks to reach its full effect. It is not useful on an *"as-needed"* basis.

How do people respond to anti-anxiety medications?

Anti-anxiety medications such as benzodiazepines are effective in relieving anxiety and take effect more quickly than the antidepressant medications (or buspirone) often prescribed for anxiety. However, people can build up a tolerance to benzodiazepines if they are taken over a long period of time and may need higher and higher doses to get the same effect. Some people may even become dependent on them. To avoid these problems, doctors usually prescribe benzodiazepines for short periods, a practice that is especially helpful for older adults, people who have substance abuse problems and people who become dependent on medication easily. If people suddenly stop taking benzodiazepines, they may have withdrawal symptoms or their anxiety may return. Therefore, benzodiazepines should be tapered off slowly.

What are the possible side effects of anti-anxiety medications?

Like other medications, anti-anxiety medications may cause side effects. Some of these side effects and risks are serious. The most common side effects for benzodiazepines are drowsiness and dizziness. Other possible side effects include:

Nausea
Blurred vision
Headache
Confusion
Tiredness
Nightmares

Tell your doctor if any of these symptoms are severe or do not go away:

Drowsiness
Dizziness
Unsteadiness
Problems with coordination
Difficulty thinking or remembering
Increased saliva
Muscle or joint pain
Frequent urination
Blurred vision
Changes in sex drive or ability
(The American Society of Health-System Pharmacists, Inc, 2010).

If you experience any of the symptoms below, call your doctor immediately:

Rash
Hives
Swelling of the eyes, face, lips, tongue, or throat
Difficulty breathing or swallowing
Hoarseness
Seizures
Yellowing of the skin or eyes
Depression
Difficulty speaking
Yellowing of the skin or eyes
Thoughts of suicide or harming yourself
Difficulty breathing
Common side effects of beta-blockers include:
Fatigue
Cold hands
Dizziness or light-headedness
Weakness

Beta-blockers generally are not recommended for people with asthma or diabetes because they may worsen symptoms related to both. Possible side effects from buspirone include:

Dizziness
Headaches
Nausea
Nervousness
Lightheadedness
Excitement
Trouble sleeping

Anti-anxiety medications may cause other side effects that are not included in the lists above.

Stimulants

What are Stimulants?

As the name suggests, stimulants increase alertness, attention, and energy, as well as elevate blood pressure, heart rate, and respiration (National Institute on Drug Abuse, 2014). Stimulant medications are often prescribed to treat children, adolescents, or adults diagnosed with ADHD. Stimulants used to treat ADHD include:

Methylphenidate
Amphetamine
Dextroamphetamine
Lisdexamfetamine Dimesylate

Note: In 2002, the FDA approved the non-stimulant medication atomoxetine for use as a treatment for ADHD. Two other nonstimulant antihypertensive medications, clonidine and guanfacine, are also approved for treatment of ADHD in children and adolescents. One of these non-stimulant medications is often tried first in a young person with ADHD, and if response is insufficient, then a stimulant is prescribed.

Stimulants are also prescribed to treat other health conditions, including narcolepsy, and occasionally depression (especially in older or chronically medically ill people and in those who have not responded to other treatments).

How do people respond to stimulants?

Prescription stimulants can have a calming and *"focusing"* effect on individuals with ADHD. Stimulant medications are safe when given under a doctor's supervision. Some children taking them may feel slightly different or *"funny."*

Some parents worry that stimulant medications may lead to drug abuse or dependence, but there is little evidence of this when they are used properly as prescribed. Additionally, research shows that teens with ADHD who took stimulant medications were less likely to abuse drugs than those who did not take stimulant medications.

What are the possible side effects of stimulants?

Stimulants may cause side effects. Most side effects are minor and disappear when dosage levels are lowered. The most common side effects include:

Difficulty falling asleep or staying asleep
Loss of appetite
Stomach pain
Headache
Less common side effects include:
Motor tics or verbal tics (sudden, repetitive movements or sounds)
Personality changes, such as appearing *"flat"* or without emotion

Call your doctor right away if you have any of these symptoms, especially if they are new, become worse, or worry you.

Stimulants may cause other side effects that are not included in the list above.

Antipsychotics

What are antipsychotics?

Antipsychotic medicines are primarily used to manage psychosis. The word *"psychosis"* is used to describe conditions that affect the mind, and in which there has been some loss of contact with reality, often including delusions (false, fixed beliefs) or hallucinations (hearing or seeing things that are not really there). It can be a symptom of a physical condition such as drug abuse or a mental disorder such as schizophrenia, bipolar disorder, or very severe depression (also known as *"psychotic depression"*).

Antipsychotic medications are often used in combination with other medications to treat delirium, dementia, and mental health conditions, including:

Attention-Deficit Hyperactivity Disorder (ADHD)
Severe Depression
Eating Disorders
Post-traumatic Stress Disorder (PTSD)
Obsessive Compulsive Disorder (OCD)
Generalized Anxiety Disorder

Antipsychotic medicines do not cure these conditions. They are used to help relieve symptoms and improve quality of life. Older or first-generation antipsychotic medications are also called conventional "typical" antipsychotics or "neuroleptics".

Some of the common typical antipsychotics include:

Chlorpromazine
Haloperidol
Perphenazine
Fluphenazine

Newer or second-generation medications are also called "atypical" antipsychotics. Some of the common atypical antipsychotics include:

Risperidone
Olanzapine
Quetiapine
Ziprasidone
Aripiprazole
Paliperidone
Lurasidone

According to a 2013 research review by the Agency for Healthcare Research and Quality, typical and atypical antipsychotics both work to treat symptoms of schizophrenia and the manic phase of bipolar disorder.

Several atypical antipsychotics have a "broader spectrum" of action than the older medications, and are used for treating bipolar depression or depression that has not responded to an antidepressant medication alone.

To find additional antipsychotics and other medications used to manage psychoses and current warnings and advisories, please visit the FDA website.

How do people respond to antipsychotics?

Certain symptoms, such as feeling agitated and hallucinating, usually go away within days of starting an antipsychotic medication. Symptoms like delusions usually go away within a few weeks, but the
full effects of the medication may not be seen for up to six weeks. Every patient responds differently, so it may take several trials of different antipsychotic medications to find the one that works best. Some people may have a relapse—meaning their symptoms come back or get worse. Usually relapses happen when people stop taking their medication, or when they only take it sometimes. Some people stop taking the medication because they feel better or they may feel that they don't need it anymore, but no one should stop taking an antipsychotic medication without talking to his or her doctor. When a doctor says it is okay to stop taking a medication, it should be gradually tapered off— never stopped suddenly. Many people must

stay on an antipsychotic continuously for months or years in order to stay well; treatment should be personalized for each individual.

What are the possible side effects of antipsychotics?

Antipsychotics have many side effects (or adverse events) and risks. The FDA lists the following side effects of antipsychotic medicines:

Drowsiness
Dizziness
Restlessness
Weight gain (the risk is higher with some atypical antipsychotic medicines)
Dry mouth
Constipation
Nausea
Vomiting
Blurred vision
Low blood pressure
Uncontrollable movements, such as tics and tremors (the risk is higher with typical antipsychotic medicines)
Seizures

A low number of white blood cells, which fight infections. A person taking an atypical antipsychotic medication should have his or her weight, glucose levels, and lipid levels monitored regularly by a doctor.

Typical antipsychotic medications can also cause additional side effects related to physical movement, such as:

Rigidity
Persistent muscle spasms
Tremors
Restlessness

Long-term use of typical antipsychotic medications may lead to a condition called tardive dyskinesia (TD). TD causes muscle movements, commonly around the mouth, that a person can't control. TD can range from mild to severe, and in some people, the problem cannot be cured. Sometimes people with TD recover partially or fully after they stop taking typical antipsychotic medication. People who think that they might have TD should check with their doctor before stopping their medication. TD rarely occurs while taking atypical antipsychotics. Antipsychotics may cause other side effects that are not included in this list above.

Mood Stabilizers

What are mood stabilizers?

Mood stabilizers are used primarily to treat bipolar disorder, mood swings associated with other mental disorders, and in some cases, to augment the effect of other medications used to treat depression. Lithium, which is an effective mood stabilizer, is approved for the treatment of mania and the maintenance treatment of bipolar disorder. Mood stabilizers work by decreasing abnormal activity in the brain and are also sometimes used to treat:

Depression (usually along with an antidepressant)
Schizoaffective Disorder
Disorders of impulse control
Certain mental illnesses in children

Anticonvulsant medications are also used as mood stabilizers. They were originally developed to treat seizures, but they were found to help control unstable moods as well. One anticonvulsant commonly used as a mood stabilizer is valproic acid (also called divalproex sodium). For some people, especially those with "mixed" symptoms of mania and depression or those with rapid-cycling bipolar disorder, valproic acid may work better than lithium. Other anticonvulsants used as mood stabilizers include:

Carbamazepine
Lamotrigine
Oxcarbazepine

What are the possible side effects of mood stabilizers?

Mood stabilizers can cause several side effects, and some of them may become serious, especially at excessively high blood levels. These side effects include:

Itching, rash
Excessive thirst
Frequent urination
Tremor (shakiness) of the hands
Nausea and vomiting
Slurred speech
Fast, slow, irregular, or pounding heartbeat
Blackouts
Changes in vision
Seizures
Hallucinations (seeing things or hearing voices that do not exist)

55

Loss of coordination
Swelling of the eyes, face, lips, tongue, throat, hands, feet, ankles, or lower legs.

If a person with bipolar disorder is being treated with lithium, he or she should visit the doctor regularly to check the lithium levels his or her blood, and make sure the kidneys and the thyroid are working normally.

Lithium is eliminated from the body through the kidney, so the dose may need to be lowered in older people with reduced kidney function. Also, loss of water from the body, such as through sweating or diarrhea, can cause the lithium level to rise, requiring a temporary lowering of the daily dose. Although kidney functions are checked periodically during lithium treatment, actual damage of the kidney is uncommon in people whose blood levels of lithium have stayed within the therapeutic range.

Mood stabilizers may cause other side effects that are not included in this list.

For more information on the side effects of Carbamazepine, Lamotrigine, and Oxcarbazepine, please visit MedlinePlus Drugs,

Herbs and Supplements.

Some possible side effects linked anticonvulsants (such as valproic acid) include:

Drowsiness
Dizziness
Headache
Diarrhea
Constipation
Changes in appetite
Weight changes
Back pain
Agitation
Mood swings
Abnormal thinking
Uncontrollable shaking of a part of the body
Loss of coordination
Uncontrollable movements of the eyes
Blurred or double vision
Ringing in the ears
Hair loss

These medications may also:

Cause damage to the liver or pancreas, so people taking it should see their doctors regularly

Increase testosterone (a male hormone) levels in teenage girls and lead to a condition called polycystic ovarian syndrome (a disease that can affect fertility and make the menstrual cycle become irregular)

Medications for common adult health problems, such as diabetes, high blood pressure, anxiety, and depression may interact badly with anticonvulsants. In this case, a doctor can offer other medication options.

Special Groups: Children, Older Adults and Women

Pregnant Women All types of people take psychiatric medications, but some groups have special needs, including:

Children and adolescents
Older adults
Women who are pregnant or who may become pregnant

Children and Adolescents

Many medications used to treat children and adolescents with mental illness are safe and effective. However, some medications have not been studied or approved for use with children or adolescents. Still, a doctor can give a young person an FDA-approved medication on an "off-label" basis. This means that the doctor prescribes the medication to help the patient even though the medicine is not approved for the specific mental disorder that is being treated or for use by patients under a certain age. Remember: It is important to watch children and adolescents who take these medications on an "off-label: basis.

Children may have different reactions and side effects than adults. Some medications have current FDA warnings about potentially dangerous side effects for younger patients.

In addition to medications, other treatments for children and adolescents should be considered, either to be tried first, with medication added later if necessary, or to be provided along with medication. Psychotherapy, family therapy, educational courses, and behavior management techniques can help everyone involved cope with disorders that affect a child's mental health.

Older Adults

People over 65 must be careful when taking medications, especially when they're taking many different drugs. Older adults have a higher risk for experiencing bad drug interactions, missing doses, or overdosing.

Older adults also tend to be more sensitive to medications. Even healthy older people react to medications differently than younger people because older people's bodies process and eliminate medications more slowly. Therefore, lower or less frequent doses may be needed for older adults. Before starting a medication, older people and their family members should talk carefully with a physician about whether a medication can affect alertness, memory, or coordination, and how to help ensure that prescribed medications do not increase the risk of falls.

Sometimes memory problems affect older people who take medications for mental disorders. An older adult may forget his or her regular dose and take too much or not enough. A good way to keep track of medicine is to use a seven-day pill box, which can be bought at any pharmacy. At the beginning of each week, older adults and their caregivers fill the box so that it is easy to remember what medicine to take. Many pharmacies also have pill boxes with sections for medications that must be taken more than once a day.

For more information and practical tips to help older people take their medicines safely, please see National Institute on Aging's Safe Use of Medicines booklet and Taking Medicines on NIH SeniorHealth.gov.

Women who are pregnant or who may become pregnant

The research on the use of psychiatric medications during pregnancy is limited. The risks are different depending on which medication is taken, and at what point during the pregnancy the medication is taken. Decisions on treatments for all conditions during pregnancy should be based on each woman's needs and circumstances and based on a careful weighing of the likely benefits and risks of all available options, including psychotherapy (or *"watchful waiting"* during part or all of the pregnancy), medication, or a combination of the two. While no medication is considered perfectly safe for all women at all stages of pregnancy, this must be balanced for each woman against the fact that untreated serious mental disorders themselves can pose a risk to a pregnant woman and her developing fetus. Medications should be selected based on available scientific research, and they should be taken at the lowest possible dose.

Pregnant women should have a medical professional who will watch them closely throughout their pregnancy and after delivery. Most women should avoid certain medications during pregnancy. For example:

Mood stabilizers are known to cause birth defects. Benzodiazepines and lithium have been shown to cause *"floppy baby syndrome,"* in which a baby is drowsy and limp, and cannot breathe or feed well. Benzodiazepines may cause birth defects or other infant problems, especially if taken during the first trimester. According to research, taking antipsychotic medications during pregnancy can lead to birth defects, especially if they are taken during the first trimester and in combination with other drugs, but the risks vary widely and depend on the type of antipsychotic taken. The conventional antipsychotic haloperidol has been studied more than others, and has been found not to cause birth defects. Research on the newer atypical antipsychotics is ongoing.

Antidepressants, especially SSRIs, are safe during pregnancy. However, antidepressant medications do cross the placental barrier and may reach the fetus. Birth defects or other problems are possible, but they are very rare. The effects of antidepressants on childhood development remain under study. Studies have also found that fetuses exposed to SSRIs during the third trimester may be born with *"withdrawal"* symptoms such as breathing problems, jitteriness, irritability, trouble feeding, or hypoglycemia (low blood sugar). Most studies have found that these symptoms in babies are generally mild and short-lived, and no deaths have been reported. Risks from the use of antidepressants need to be balanced with the risks of stopping medication; if a mother is too depressed to care for herself and her child, both may be at risk for problems.

In 2004, the FDA issued a warning against the use of certain antidepressants in the late third trimester. The warning said that doctors may want to gradually taper pregnant women off antidepressants in the third trimester so that the baby is not affected. After a woman delivers, she should consult with her doctor to decide whether to return to a full dose during the period when she is most vulnerable to postpartum depression.

After the baby is born, women and their doctors should watch for postpartum depression, especially if a mother stopped taking her medication during pregnancy. In addition, women who nurse while taking psychiatric medications should know that a small amount of the medication passes into the breast milk. However, the medication may or may not affect the baby depending s on the medication and when it is taken. Women taking psychiatric medications and who intend to breastfeed should discuss the potential risks and benefits with their doctors.

Non-Narcotic Medication

The most common non-narcotic analgesics are: Aspirin, Acetaminophen and Ibuprofen (Julien, 1995. pp.260-264).

- **Aspirin:** Aspirin is the most effective non-narcotic analgesic, antipyretic and anti-inflammatory medication. Aspirin can inhibit the aggregation of platelets and therefore reduce the formation of intravascular clotting. Low dose aspirin (80-85 mgs) are now widely used for preventing heart attacks and strokes in individuals under seventy years of age. The one caution with aspirin is its association with the fever that accompanies chicken pox or influenza with the subsequent development of Reye's syndrome, which can be life, threatening.

- **Acetaminophen (Tylenol)**: Similar action as aspirin but its anti-inflammatory effect is minor. It is not useful in preventing vascular clotting or helpful against heart attacks or strokes. Alcoholics as well as all chemically dependent individuals should avoid acetaminophen because of its potential negative effect on the liver. Tylenol is generally used for individuals for whom aspirin is poorly tolerated.

- **Ibuprofen:** This includes Advil, Motrin, Nuprin, Medipren and compounds similar to ibuprofen like Naproxin (Aleve, Naprosyn and Anaprox). All these compounds are as effective as aspirin. The effect is comparable to or better than aspirin with codeine or proporyphene (Darvon). (Julien, 1995.p 263) Ibuprofen should be used with caution in clients who suffer from peptic ulcer disease or bleeding abnormalities. This medication is not recommended for women during pregnancy.

Throughout the balance of this text various traditional treatment plans are presented that represent specific guidelines for developing short- and long-term strategies based on DSM criteria (medical model). In behavioral health, the medically focused treatment plan refers to a written document that outlines the evidence-based progression of helping individuals gain increasing control of their life processes. A traditional treatment plan may be highly formalized or may consist of loosely handwritten notes, depending on the documentation requirements of the health care provider, the preference of the helper and the severity of the presenting challenges. No matter how formalized, however, the treatment plan is always subject to change as the person progresses through their healing process. In general, traditional effective treatment plans make sure that the person seeking support is always involved in developing their treatment plan. This is often accomplished through informal discussion of a person's situation. Many helpers present a written copy of the treatment plan to the individual. The traditional treatment plan usually forms the basis for not only the intervention strategies but also provides documentation for reimbursement of services provided by the individual and/or the health care agency. These medically driven treatment plans should not be confused with recovery plans which will be discussed in the chapters on the social model of recovery.

Below is the first of these traditional treatment plans that reflect the challenges associated with prescription drug use.

Prescription Drug Abuse Treatment Plan. (DeGood, Crawford and Jongsma, 1999).

Challenge to individual:

1. Consistent overuse of medication originally intended for control of medical symptoms.

2. Conflicts with physicians over type and amount of use of prescription drugs, often leading to Doctor shopping for a source that will prescribe a specific drug.

3. Excessive worry about health and well-being when not taking medication.

4. Spends excessive money on both prescription and non-prescription medications.

Long-Term Goals

1. Clarify the nature of the drug-seeking pattern of behavior and then eliminate this self-destructive pattern.

2. If mood altering type of dependency, actively participate in a recovery program leading to total abstinence.

3. Develop a safe and effective medication regime appropriate to medical condition

4. Develop the ability to use medications as prescribed.

Short-Term Goal #1

1. Honestly describe history and current use of substances and motivation for drug seeking behavior.

Short-Term Intervention #1

1. Obtain history of past and present prescription medication or illicit use from client and from medical and psychological history assess the type of drug dependency present.

2. Explore client attitudes and expectations regarding the use of mood-altering drugs; challenge assumption that there is a chemical solution for every incident of physical pain or emotional suffering.

Short-Term Goal #2

1. Accurately self-monitor all medication use.

Short-Term Intervention #2

1. Teach the client to maintain accurate self-monitoring records of medication use. (also Goal # 3)

2. Insist on client exercising great care in handling all medications and pointing out consequences of carelessness resulting in loss, destruction, or incorrect use.

Short-Term Goal #3

1. Use medication only as prescribed and report benefits and problems to counselor and physician.

Short-Term Intervention #3

1. Elicit client's cooperation in setting firm limits on use of emergency treatment leading to prescriptions being given that are not part of systematic treatment plan.

2. If narcotic use is medically justified have clients sign narcotic use contract specifying agreement to use a medication only as prescribed and have medication prescribed by only one physician or treatment program (also Goal #4).

3. Teach the client to maintain careful self-monitoring records of medical use (also Goal #2)

4. Monitor client's drug use, reviewing self-monitoring records and assess for any abuse or side effects.

Short-Term Goal #4

1. Verbalize an understanding of the rationale and mutual responsibilities involved if physician or treatment program requires signing a medication use agreement.

Short-Term Intervention #4

1. If narcotic use is medically justified, have clients signed narcotic use contract specifying agreement to use medication only as prescribed and to have medication prescribed by only one position or treatment program (also Goal #3).

2. Explain the rationale for a signed contract regarding medication use and urge client cooperation with the procedure.

Chapter 4
Screening and Assessment in Recovery

Screening and assessment are used to identify a client's strengths and problems. Normally, screening and assessment occur at intake, and both processes usually continue throughout the course of treatment. Routine screening and assessment can identify problems that may arise or manifest after initial intake and can help pinpoint a client's strengths—such as strong marriage or family ties, strong motivation to change, or the absence of a current crises. Routine administration of these processes is imperative, as the counselor's understanding of a client's strengths and problems significantly influences the type and duration of interventions applied as clients enter treatment in various behavioral health settings*.

Screening evaluates for the possible presence of a problem but does not diagnose or determine the severity of a disorder. For instance, screening a person for substance abuse might entail asking an individual a few interview questions about drug use and related problems and using a brief screening scale for substance abuse and/or substance dependence. When positive indicators are found, one usually schedules the individual for an assessment. Screening determines the likelihood that a client has co-occurring substance use and mental disorders or that his or her presenting signs, symptoms, or behaviors may be influenced by co-occurring issues. Screening is a formal process that typically is brief and occurs soon after the client presents for services.

SAMHSA recommends the following goals for initial screening:

❖ **Crisis intervention.** Identification of and immediate assistance with crisis and emergency situations

❖ **Eligibility verification.** Assurance that an applicant satisfies Federal and State regulations and program criteria for admission.

❖ **Clarification of the treatment alliance.** Explanation of client and program responsibilities

---

*For more detail about women in treatment see: Center for Substance Abuse Treatment. (2009). *Substance Abuse Treatment: Addressing the Specific Needs of Women.* Treatment Improvement Protocol (TIP) Series, No. 51. HHS Publication.

For more detail on men in treatment see: Substance Abuse and Mental Health Services Administration. *Addressing the Specific Behavioral Health Needs of Men* (2013). Treatment Improvement Protocol (TIP) Series 56. HHS Publication No. (SMA) 13-4736. Rockville, MD: Substance Abuse and Mental Health Services Administration.

❖ **Education.** Communication of essential information about treatment requirements, and discussion of the benefits of treatment

❖ **Identification of treatment barriers.** Determination of factors that might hinder an applicant's ability to meet treatment requirements, for example, lack of childcare or transportation.

Finally, the purpose of screening is not to establish the presence or specific type of a disorder, but to establish the need for an in-depth clinical assessment.

Client Motivation and Readiness for Change

Client motivation to engage is a predictor of early retention (Joe et al. 1998) and is associated with increased participation, positive treatment outcomes, improved social adjustment, and successful treatment referrals (CSAT 1999*a*).

Starting with initial contact and continuing throughout treatment, clinical assessment should focus on client motivation for change (CSAT 1999*a*). Clinical staff members help clients move beyond past experiences by focusing on making a fresh start, letting go of old grievances, and identifying current realities, ambivalence about change, and goals for the future. It often is helpful to enlist recovering clients in motivational enhancement activities.

Whether the counselor is screening or assessing an individual it is necessary is that the clinician:

❖ Engage the client

❖ Upon receipt of appropriate client authorization(s), identify and contact collaterals (family, friends, other treatment providers) to gather additional information

❖ Screen for and detect COD

❖ Determine severity of mental and substance use disorders

❖ Determine appropriate care setting (e.g., inpatient, outpatient, day-treatment)

❖ Determine diagnoses

❖ Determine disability and functional impairment

- ❖ Identify strengths and supports

- ❖ Identify cultural and linguistic needs and supports

- ❖ Identify additional problem areas to address (e.g., physical health, housing, vocational, educational, social, spiritual, cognitive, etc.)

- ❖ Determine readiness for change

- ❖ Plan treatment

Clinical Assessment*

Clinical assessment is a more in-depth evaluation that confirms the presence of a problem, determines its severity, and specifies treatment options for addressing the problem. It also surveys client strengths and resources for addressing life problems. Clinical assessment typically examines not only possible diagnoses, but also the context in which a disorder manifests. A substance abuse assessment, for example, assesses the severity and nature of the substance use disorder and may also explore the possibility of co-occurring disorders; the client's family, marital, interpersonal, physical, and spiritual life; financial and legal situations; and any other issues that might affect treatment and recovery. **Assessment generally involves in-depth interviews and the use of various assessment instruments**.

The third component to compliment screening and assessment is treatment planning develops a comprehensive set of staged, integrated program placements and treatment interventions for each disorder that is adjusted as needed to consider issues related to the other disorder. The treatment plan is matched to the individual needs, readiness, preferences, and personal goals of the client. It integrates screening, both medical, psychiatric and socio-cultural assessments, and develops a treatment planning that addresses all behavioral health challenges.

A vast amount of literature exists on screening, assessment, and treatment planning in substance abuse treatment and an equally vast amount in mental health settings. Considerably less material has been published on screening, assessment, and treatment planning specifically addressing persons with (or suspected of having) co-occurring disorder (COD). However, a clinically meaningful and useful screening, assessment, and treatment planning process will necessarily include procedures, practices, and tools drawn

---

*Center for Substance Abuse Treatment. *Screening, Assessment, and Treatment Planning for Persons with Co-Occurring Disorders.* COCE Overview Paper 2. (2006). DHHS Publication No. (SMA) 06-4164 Rockville, MD: Substance Abuse and Mental Health Services Administration, and Center for Mental Health Services.

from both the substance abuse and mental health fields.

Although diagnostic certainty cannot be the basis for service planning and design. For example, some clients' mental health and substance abuse problems may not, at a given point in time, fully meet the criteria for diagnoses in categories from the *Diagnostic and Statistical Manual of Mental Disorders*, 5th edition (DSM- 5) (American Psychiatric Association, 2013). Nonetheless, they would be included in a broad definition of COD to allow responses to the real needs of consumers.

The process of integrated screening, assessment, and treatment planning will vary depending on the information available at the time of initial contact with the client. The special challenge of screening, assessment, and treatment planning in COD is to explore, determine, and respond to the effects of two mutually interacting disorders. Because neither substance abuse nor mental challenges should be considered primary for a person with COD (Lehman et al., 1998; Mueser et al., 2003), an existing diagnosis of mental illness or substance abuse is a point of departure only.

The complexity of COD dictates that screening, assessment, and treatment planning cannot be bound by a rigid formula. Rather, the success of this process depends on the skills and creativity of the clinician in applying available procedures, tools, and laboratory tests and on the relationships established with the client and his or her intimates.

Although there has been little research into the differences between men's and women's responses to screening and assessment, some literature (e.g., Cochran 2005) suggests that men and women present uniquely similar and distinctively different challenges. Masculine gender role socialization can lead some men to minimize difficulties or underreport problems—and some problems, such as depression, can manifest differently in men as opposed to women, thus disguising the disorder and leading to under diagnosis or misdiagnosis (see Chapter 5 for discussion of this and other co-occurring mental disorders). In addition, different screening or assessment settings (e.g., prisons, outpatient programs, primary care offices) influence whether and how men and women present their struggles. Culture also plays a role; men from some nonmainstream cultures may be reluctant to share information about difficulties or illnesses. Counselors must be sensitive to these nuances and create an environment in which men and women feel open to sharing their vulnerabilities or perceived shortcomings. Clinicians should show sensitivity to the values, attitudes, and behavioral dispositions of both men and women, as well as differences related to age, ethnicity, socioeconomic status, geographic location, disability status, and sexual orientation. All clinicians must consider ways in which men and women are alike, clinicians must also account for other characteristics that make them different from one another.

67

Data should be collected in a respectful way, taking into consideration a client's current level of functioning. Motivational interviewing techniques (Miller and Rollnick 2002) can help engage applicants early. The information collected depends on program policies, procedures, and treatment criteria; State and Federal regulations; and the client's stability and ability to participate in the process. The psychosocial history can reveal addiction-related challenges in areas that might be overlooked, such as strengths, abilities, aptitudes, and preferences. Most information can be analyzed by using standardized comprehensive assessment instruments tailored to specific populations or programs, such as those described by Dodgen and Shea (2000).

SAMHSA regulations require that individuals *"accepted for treatment shall be assessed initially and periodically by qualified personnel to determine the most appropriate combination of services and treatment"* (42 CFR, Part 8 § 12(f)(4) [*Federal Register* 66(11):1097]). Treatment plans should be reviewed and updated, initially every 90 days and, after one year, biannually or whenever changes affect a client's treatment outcomes. Ongoing monitoring should ensure that services are received, interventions work, new problems are identified and documented, and services are adjusted as problems are solved. Clients' views of their progress, as well as the treatment team's assessment of clients' responses to treatment, should be documented in the treatment plan.

Co-Occurring Disorders and Current Mental Status

Mental status assessments identify the threshold signs of co-occurring disorders (COD) and require familiarity with the components of a mental status examination (i.e., general appearance, behavior, and speech; stream of thought, thought content, and mental capacity; mood and affect; and judgment and insight). Finally, a mental status assessment also should look for perceptual disturbances and cognitive dysfunction. (a mental health status is addressed in Chapter Five of this text).

Qualified professionals should train all staff members involved in screening and assessment to recognize signs and symptoms of change in clients' mental status. This training should be ongoing. After reviewing their observations with the program physician, staff members should refer all clients still suspected of having co-occurring disorders for psychiatric evaluation. This evaluation should identify the types of co-occurring disorders and determine how they affect clients' comprehension, cognition, and psychomotor functioning. Persistent neuropsychological problems warrant formal testing to diagnose their type and severity and to guide treatment. Consultations by psychologists or physicians should be requested or referrals made for testing.

Substance Use Assessment

A client's lifetime substance use and treatment history should be documented thoroughly. The following areas should be assessed:

- ❖ Periods of abstinence (e.g., number, duration, circumstances)
- ❖ Circumstances or events leading to increased use or relapse
- ❖ Effects of substance use on physical, psychological, and emotional functioning
- ❖ Changing patterns of substance use, withdrawal signs and symptoms, and medical sequelae.
- ❖ Reports of psychiatric symptoms during abstinence helps clinicians differentiate drug withdrawal from mental disorder symptoms (Substance dependency vs Substance induced disorders) and can reveal important clues to effective case management, for example, the need to refer an individual for treatment of co-occurring disorders.

Substance Abuse Screening for Men*

As mentioned earlier in this chapter the primary goal of screening is to identify men and women who need a comprehensive problem assessment. In a screening intake, the behavioral health clinician gathers facts by asking simple questions that evaluate whether a person requires further assessment. For screening, clients often fill out self-reports prior to a clinical interview. In such cases, the screener should be sensitive to possible language or literacy barriers by asking clients if they want assistance with forms or if they prefer to fill them out by themselves.

Substance Abuse Assessment for Men

When screening suggests the presence of a substance use disorder, problem assessment will help better define the nature of the client's problems. In many ways, assessment procedures for men and women do not differ significantly. Nevertheless, at each stage of the assessment process, providers should consider how gender may have affected some past behaviors and how it may affect current treatment. Assessment for substance abuse or dependence should focus on:

---

*For more detail on men in treatment see: Substance Abuse and Mental Health Services Administration. *Addressing the Specific Behavioral Health Needs of Men.* (2013). Treatment Improvement Protocol (TIP) Series 56. HHS Publication No. (SMA) 13-4736. Rockville, MD: Substance Abuse and Mental Health Services Administration.

- ❖ Historical and situational factors contributing to the onset of the substance use.
- ❖ Patterns of use.
- ❖ Common signs and symptoms of a substance use problem.
- ❖ Consequences of use.

Because some men are more comfortable analyzing visual information, visually representing substance use and consequences of substance use along a timeline or on a calendar may be a better method of collecting and displaying information for male clients. Laboratory studies may also be used to document recent use, obtain markers of chronic use, and document medical consequences of chronic use. Most standardized assessment instruments were developed largely with male client populations, and most are normed for men. Readers are referred to resource guides developed by NIAAA (Allen and Columbus 2003) and the National Institute on Drug Abuse (1994), which contain listings of clinical and research tools that can be used during problem assessment. The Center for Social Work Research at The University of Texas at Austin has also assembled a valuable list of screening and assessment instruments (http://www.utexas.edu/research/cswr/nida/instrumentListing.html).

Women Patterns of Use: From Initiation to Treatment*

Numerous factors influence the reasons for initiation of substance use among women, and a number of these factors are more prevalent among women than men. Women often report that stress, negative affect, and relationships precipitate initial use. In fact, women are often introduced to substance use by a significant relationship such as boyfriend, family member, or close friend. Though genetics also may be a significant risk factor for women, more research supports familial influence—a combination of genetic and environment effects. Less is known about familial influence of illicit drugs, but parental alcohol use increases the prevalence of alcohol use disorders among women by at least 50 %. Family of origin characteristics play a role too. Exposure to chaotic, argumentative, and violent households, or being expected to take on adult responsibilities as a child, are other factors associated with initiation and prevalence of substance use disorders among the female population.

Women are significantly influenced by relationships, relationship status, and the effects of a partner's substance abuse. Women dependent on substances

*For more detail about women in treatment see: Center for Substance Abuse Treatment. (2009). *Substance Abuse Treatment: Addressing the Specific Needs of Women*. Treatment Improvement Protocol (TIP) Series, No. 51. HHS Publication No. (SMA) 15-4426. Rockville, MD: Center for Substance Abuse Treatment. Executive Summary.

are more likely to have partners who have substance use disorders. At times, women perceive shared drug use with their partner as a means of connection or of maintaining the relationship. Often, rituals surrounding drug use are initiated by a male partner, and women bear more risk in contracting HIV/AIDS and hepatitis by sharing needles or having sexual relationships with men who inject drugs. Relationship status similarly influences use and potential development of substance use disorders. Marriage appears protective, whereas separated, never married, or divorced women are at greater risk for use and the development of substance use disorders. Relationship influence does not stop at the point of treatment entry; relationships also significantly influence treatment engagement, retention, and outcome among women.

Other risk factors associated with initiation of use and the prevalence of substance use disorders include sensation-seeking, symptoms of depression and anxiety, posttraumatic stress and eating disorders, and difficulty in regulating affect. Women with a history of trauma, including interpersonal and childhood sexual abuse, are highly represented in substance abuse samples. In addition, sociocultural issues play a significant role across the continuum beginning with enhanced risk for substance use. Degree of acculturation, experiences of discrimination, and socioeconomic status are prominent risk factors from the outset but continue to influence women's substance use, health status, treatment access, and help-seeking behavior. Among women, six patterns of substance use clearly emerge from empirical data. **First**, the gender gap is narrowing for substance use across ethnicities, particularly among young women. **Second,** women are more likely to be introduced to and initiate substance use through significant relationships, while marital status appears to play a protective role. **Third,** women accelerate to injecting drugs at a faster rate than men, and rituals and high-risk behaviors surrounding drug injection are directly influenced by significant relationships. **Fourth,** women's earlier patterns of use (including age of initiation, amount, and frequency) are positively associated with higher risks for dependency. **Fifth,** women are more likely to temporarily alter their pattern of use in response to caregiver responsibilities. And **Sixth,** women progress faster from initiation of use to the development of substance-related adverse consequences.

Substance use is not as prevalent among women as it is among men, but women are as likely as men to develop substance use disorders after initiation. Women who are pregnant are likely to reduce or remain abstinent during pregnancy; however, continued use is associated with a wide range of issues and effects—from less prenatal care to potential irreparable harm to the child from fetal exposure. Among those entering treatment, women are more likely to report drug use as the main reason for admission.

71

Physiological Effects of Alcohol, Drugs, and Tobacco on Women

Women develop substance use disorders in less time than men. Some factors that either influence or compound the physiological effects of drugs and alcohol include ethnicity, health disparity, socioeconomic status, developmental issues, aging, and co-occurring conditions. Although research on the physiological effects of alcohol and illicit drugs on women is limited and often inconclusive, significant differences have been found in the way women and men metabolize alcohol. Women have more complications and more severe problems from alcohol use than do men, and these complications and problems develop more rapidly. This phenomenon is known as *"telescoping."* Complications include liver disease and other organ damage; cardiac-related conditions such as hypertension; reproductive consequences; osteoporosis; cognitive and other neurological effects; breast and other cancers; and greater susceptibility and progression of infections and infectious diseases, including HIV/AIDS and hepatitis C virus (HCV).

Although many physiological effects of licit and illicit drugs have not been well studied, research has shown that abuse of substances such as stimulants, opioids, and some prescription (e.g., anxiolytics, narcotic analgesics) and over-the-counter (e.g., laxatives, diuretics, diet pills) drugs causes adverse effects on women's menstrual cycles and gastrointestinal, neuromuscular, and cardiac systems, among others. Regarding nicotine use, women who smoke increase their risk of lung cancer. Currently, cancer is the second leading cause of death among women, with mortality rates higher for lung cancer than breast cancer. Other physiological consequences of tobacco use include, but are not limited to, increased risks for peptic ulcers, Crohn's disease, estrogen deficiencies, strokes, and atherosclerosis. Women who smoke are more likely to have chronic obstructive pulmonary disease and coronary heart disease.

Women who use alcohol, drugs, or tobacco while pregnant or nursing expose their fetuses or infants to these substances as well. The most thoroughly examined effect of alcohol on birth outcomes is fetal alcohol syndrome, which involves growth retardation, central nervous system and neurodevelopmental abnormalities, and craniofacial abnormalities. Alcohol and drug use by pregnant women is associated with many complications, including spontaneous abortion, prematurity, low birth weight, premature separation of the placenta from the uterine wall, neonatal abstinence syndrome, and fetal abnormalities. Likewise, women who are pregnant and use tobacco are more likely to deliver premature and low birth weight infants.

Screening and Assessment of Women

Understanding the extent and nature of a woman's substance use disorder and its interaction with other areas of her life is essential for accurate diagnosis and successful treatment planning. This understanding can be acquired through screening and assessment. As mentioned earlier in this chapter, screening is typically a brief process for identifying whether certain conditions may exist and usually involves a limited set of questions to establish whether a more thorough evaluation and referral(s) are needed. Sociocultural factors—ethnicity, culture, acculturation level, language, and socioeconomic status—are particularly relevant in screening and assessment selection, in determining the appropriateness of the instruments, and in interpreting the subsequent results. Sociocultural and socioeconomic characteristics of the client can affect testing expectations and behavior of both the counselor and client during the screening and assessment process; e.g., the client's distrust and subsequent reluctance in the testing process or the counselor's expectation that a woman with lower socioeconomic status will have a positive screening for alcohol or drug use.

For women, general alcohol and drug screening that determines current or at-risk status for drug and alcohol use during pregnancy is essential. However, healthcare professionals sometimes overlook the necessity of drug and alcohol screening for older, Asian, and/ or middle- and upper-class women who are pregnant. Screening is more likely based on preconceived beliefs concerning greater prevalence of substance abuse among women from diverse ethnic groups. Counselors and intake personnel may also alter their behavior when working with diverse populations, such as eye contact, body language, and communication styles, that ultimately affect clients' responses and trust in the screening process.

Other screenings involve the determination of co-occurring risks, conditions, or disorders, including general mental disorders, mood and anxiety disorders, risk of harm to self or others, history of childhood trauma and interpersonal violence, and eating disorders. Considering women's likely involvement with health care providers, screening for substance use and abuse should be a standard practice. Yet, the implementation of screening, regardless of setting, is only as good as the protocol in providing feedback, referral, and follow-up. Screening is not an intervention. What makes the difference is how a woman's positive endorsement of screening questions leads to feedback, referral, further assessment, and intervention, if warranted.

As noted earlier in this chapter, the difference between screening and assessment is that assessment examines several domains in a client's life in detail so that diagnoses can be made for substance use disorders and possible co-occurring mental health challenges. Assessment is an ongoing process in which the counselor forms an increasingly clearer picture of the client's issues, how they can best be addressed, and how the client is changing over time. An assessment interview, such as a structured psychosocial interview, an unstructured psychosocial and cultural history, and/or the Addiction Severity Index, needs sufficient time to complete. The degree to which it is possible or advisable to probe in depth in different areas of functioning depends on the individual issues, the needs of the woman, the complexity of her issues, and the level of rapport between the client and clinician. Equally important, assessment processes should explore coping styles, strengths, and available support systems. An assessment process would not be complete without a health assessment and medical examination.

In sum, screening and assessment for women and men must be approached from a perspective that allows for and affirms cultural relevance and strengths. Whenever possible, instruments that have norms established for specific population groups should be used. Counselors' sensitivity to the clients' cultural values and beliefs, language, acculturation level, literacy level, and emotional ability to respond facilitates the assessment process and helps women and men engage in treatment.

Treatment Engagement, Placement, and Planning for Women Services

Women face many obstacles and challenges in engaging in treatment services: lack of collaboration among social service systems, limited options for women who are pregnant, lack of culturally congruent programming, few resources for women with children, fear of loss of child custody, and the stigma of substance abuse. On one hand, intake personnel and counselors can help women tackle and overcome personal barriers to treatment (such as issues of motivation and shame); yet, on the other hand, programming and administrative policies must address obstacles surrounding program structure, interagency coordination, and service delivery to improve treatment engagement. In recent years, more effective engagement strategies have been implemented. Outreach services, pretreatment intervention groups, and comprehensive and coordinated case management can effectively address the numerous barriers and the array of complex problems that women often express in their role as caregivers.

Treatment placement decisions are based not only on the woman's individual needs and the severity of her substance use disorder but also on the treatment options available in the community, her financial circumstances, and available healthcare coverage. To determine treatment placement, the American Society of Addiction Medicine's Patient Placement Criteria are used widely, and the levels determined by these criteria are useful to standardize treatment placement (see Chapter 7 of text for more detail) . To date, empirical literature supporting specific placement criteria for women is limited. The treatment levels suggested by SAHMSA and supported by ASAM criteria include pretreatment or early intervention; detoxification; outpatient treatment; intensive outpatient treatment (IOT); residential and inpatient treatment; and medically managed, intensive inpatient treatment. Specific placement criteria must also account for pregnancy, child placement, and children services. Treatment services for women must extend beyond standard care to address specific needs for women, pregnant women, and women with children such as medical services, health promotion, life skills, family- and child-related treatment services, comprehensive and coordinated case management, and mental health services.

When clients participate fully in decisions related to treatment, they are more likely to understand the process and develop realistic expectations of treatment. Active involvement of clients in all aspects of treatment planning and placement significantly contributes to both recovery and empowerment and is essential to the development of meaningful, effective person-first services for women.

Substance Abuse Among Specific Population Groups and Settings

Women who are of different racial and ethnic groups, different sexual orientations, in the criminal justice system, living in rural areas, older, and who speak languages other than English are among the population groups that may experience unique challenges that affect their substance use or abuse and its treatment.

The risk for substance abuse and its consequences and optimal processes for treatment and recovery differ by gender, race, ethnicity, sexual orientation, and other factors. The complex interplay of culture and health—as well as the influence of differing attitudes toward, definitions of, and beliefs about health and substance use among cultural groups—affects the psychosocial development of women and their alcohol, drug, and tobacco use and abuse. Women's risks for substance abuse are understood best in the social and historical context in which the influences of gender, race and ethnicity, education, economic status, age, geographic location, sexual orientation, and other factors converge. Understanding group differences across segments of the population of women is critical to designing and implementing effective substance abuse treatment programs for women.

Training helps staff members recognize the individual and group strengths and resiliency factors that can assist women from diverse identity groups in recovery. These include beliefs regarding health care and substance abuse; the value the individual or identity group places on family and spirituality;

75

the effects of group history on current behaviors; how women are socialized in a particular culture; and the flexibility of gender norms, communication styles, rituals, the status of women, the stigma the group or individual faces, and attitudes toward self-disclosure and help-seeking behavior.

Substance Abuse Treatment for Women

Gender does not appear to predict retention in substance abuse treatment. Women are as likely as men to stay in treatment once treatment is initiated. Factors that encourage a woman to stay in treatment include supportive therapy, a collaborative therapeutic alliance, onsite child care and children services, and other integrated and comprehensive treatment services. Socio-demographics also play a role in treatment retention. Studies suggest that support and participation of significant others, being older, and having at least a high school education are important factors that improve retention. Criminal justice system or child protective service involvement also is associated with longer lengths of treatment. Women are more likely to stay in treatment if they have had prior successful experiences in other life areas and possess confidence in the treatment process and outcome. Although pregnancy may motivate women in initiating treatment, studies suggest that pregnant women do not stay in treatment as long and that retention may be significantly affected by stage of pregnancy and the presence of co-occurring psychiatric disorders.

Limited research is available highlighting specific therapeutic approaches for women outside of trauma-informed services. In recent years, more attention has been given to effective women's treatment programming across systems with considerable emphasis on integrated care and the identification of specific treatment issues and needs for women. Gender specific factors that influence the treatment process and recovery evolve around the importance of relationships, the influence of family, the role of substance use in sexuality, the prevalence and history of trauma and violence, and common patterns of co-occurring disorders. Among women with substance use and co-occurring mental disorders, diagnoses of posttraumatic stress and other anxiety disorders, postpartum depression and other mood disorders, and eating disorders are more prevalent than among men who are in treatment for substance use disorders. Consequently, clinical strategies, treatment programming, and administrative treatment policies must address these issues to adequately treat women. Likewise, women often need clinical and treatment services tailored to effectively address pregnancy, child care, children services, and parenting skills.

Recovery Management and Administrative Considerations for Women

Empirical data suggest that women are as likely as men to attend continuing care services. Transition from a more intensive level of care to less intensive services has proven to be challenging for all clients, but evidence suggests that women will continue with services stay within the same agency and/or effort is made to connect them to the new service provider prior to transition.

Gender does not consistently predict treatment outcome. For example, women have comparable abstinent rates with men and are as likely to complete treatment. Even so, women are more likely to have positive treatment outcomes in the following ways: less incarceration, higher rates of employment, and more established recovery-oriented social support systems. Women and men do not differ in relapse rates. It is more likely that individual characteristics hold the key in determining who may be a greater risk for relapse. However, there is a delineation of the types of risks and triggers that make women versus men more vulnerable to relapse, and women exhibit different emotional and behavioral responses during and after relapse. Women report more interpersonal problems and strong negative affect, including symptoms of depression, severe traumatic stress reactions to early childhood trauma, and low self-worth, as precipitants of relapse. They also display a lack of coping skills, greater difficulty in severing their connections with individuals who use, and a failure in establishing new recovery-oriented friends. Conversely, women who relapse are more likely to seek help and have shorter relapse episodes.

Other considerations in providing treatment to women involve programmatic and administrative issues. First, participation of clients as partners in treatment is important, and both the program and client will benefit if they are involved in program development and serve in an advisory capacity. Programs will likely improve the quality of services and clients will benefit from an increase in self-efficacy, the attainment of specific skills, and a reduced stigma from substance abuse treatment. Gender-responsive treatment involves a safe and non-punitive atmosphere, where staff hold a hopeful and positive attitude toward women and show investment in learning about women's experiences, treatment needs, and appropriate interventions. Administrators need to invest in staff training and supervision and show a commitment to training beyond immediate services. Training should include other social and healthcare facilities and personnel within the community to enhance awareness, identify women with substance use disorders, and increase appropriate referrals. As research, programming, and clinical experience expand along gender lines in substance abuse treatment, clinicians and administrators alike will have considerable opportunities in adapting new standards of care for women.

Sexual orientation and history

The assessment and treatment needs of hetero-sexual and LGB populations are similar and should focus on stopping the substance abuse that interferes with clients' well-being. Assessment of risk factors associated with sexual encounters and partners is essential. What often differs for an LGB population is the importance of assessing clients' sexual or gender orientation concerns, such as their feelings about their sexual orientation. Treatment staff should pay strict attention to confidentiality concerns for LGB clients because they may be at increased risk of legal or other actions affecting employment, housing, or child custody. Treatment modalities and programs should be accessible to all groups, and programs providing ancillary services should be sensitive to the special needs of all patients regardless of sexual orientation (CSAT 2001b).

Gender-Aware Personal Assessment

Once the nature of the substance abuse problem has been clearly established, the assessment process moves to the personal assessment phase. A comprehensive personal assessment routinely includes a complete physical examination, an exploration of significant events in the client's life that could affect treatment and recovery, the client's history of mental health or developmental challenges, and an evaluation of his close relationships. In each of these areas, client strengths should also be assessed. Personal assessment aims to distinguish values, attitudes, and behavioral dispositions that the individual may share with other men or women that makes him or her different from other men and women.

Core Areas of Assessment

The first step should be a broad-based, gender-aware screening to identify at least seventeen (17) core areas in need of more detailed assessment, such as those described below:

❖ **Employment status and work history:** Employment before and during treatment has been associated with better retention and improved treatment outcomes (Platt 1995; Sterling et al. 2001), especially for men (Arndt etal. 2004). Clinicians should talk with clients about current and past employment and education to get a better understanding of what roles these factors may have played in the clients' substance abuse as well as how they might be used in promoting recovery.

❖ **Client stabilization issues:** Until clients are stabilized, employed clients often experience substance-related difficulties at the workplace, including lack of concentration, tardiness and absences,

78

inability to get along with coworkers, on-the-job accidents, and increased claims for workers' compensation. Early identification of these difficulties can help staff and clients create a more effective treatment plan.

* **Family relationship issues:** The effect of substance use on an individual's family cannot be overestimated, and family problems should be expected for most clients entering treatment. The comprehensive assessment should include questions about family relationships and problems, including any history of domestic violence, sexual abuse, and mental disorders. When possible, the assessment should include input from relatives and significant others. Because families with members who abuse substances have problems directly linked to this substance abuse, at least one staff member should be trained in family counseling or in making appropriate referrals for family intervention. During assessment, clinical staff should be sensitive to various family types represented in the client population. For example, programs treating significant numbers of single parents should consider onsite childcare programs. Structured childcare services also enable staff to observe and assess a client's family functioning, which can be valuable in treatment planning.

* **Spousal or partner abuse:** Generally, if a client believes that she or he is in imminent danger from a batterer, the treatment provider should respond to this situation before addressing any others and, if necessary, suspend the screening or assessment interview to do so. He or she should refer a client to a shelter, legal services, or a domestic violence program if indicated. Providers should be familiar with relevant Federal, State, and local regulations on domestic violence (e.g., the Violence Against Women Act [visit: www.ovw.usdoj.gov]) and the legal resources available (e.g., restraining orders, duty to warn, legal obligation to report threats and past crimes, confidentiality)

* **Housing status and safety:** A significant number of clients entering substance abuse treatment lack adequate housing or are at risk of losing housing. (SAMHSA 2013.TIP 55). Based on year 2000 estimates, approximately 10 percent of clients are homeless or living as transients when admitted to treatment (Joseph et al. 2000). Moreover, those who are not homeless often live with people who are addicted or in areas where substance use is common. Early intervention to arrange safe, permanent shelter for these clients should be a high priority, and a client's shelter needs should be ascertained quickly during screening and assessment. Treatment programs should establish special support services to help clients

secure appropriate living arrangements, such as referral agreements with housing agencies or other programs to locate housing that addresses the special needs of homeless individuals.

❖ **Criminal justice involvement and legal issues:** Clinicians should understand what outstanding legal problems clients face, any past history of involvement with the criminal justice system, and the roles these issues have played in their clients' lives. Counselors should also ask if a client is currently on probation or being monitored in the criminal justice system, how often the client is required to report to probation or parole officers, and the conditions under which the counselor might be required to report the client's progress to the criminal justice system. During assessment, clinicians need to inform the client of what information he or she is required to provide to representatives of the criminal justice system (e.g., probation officers), such as the results of positive urine drug screens or threats to self or others.

❖ **Military or other service history**: A client's military or other service history can highlight valuable areas in treatment planning. Was military service generally a positive or negative experience? If the former, treatment providers can help clients identify areas of strength or personal achievement, such as the ability to cope under stress, receipt of medals for service accomplishments, and honorable discharge; clients can learn to build on past strengths in current challenging situations and to progress in treatment. If the latter, clinicians should review clients' negative military experiences, including loss of friends and loved ones, onset of substance use, war-related injuries, chronic pain, PTSD, and co-occurring disorders (e.g., depression). The above information might indicate patterns of behavior that continue to affect recovery. Clients' military history also might reveal their eligibility for medical and treatment resources through U.S. Department of Veterans Affairs programs and hospitals or social service agencies.

❖ **Health status/physical health:** Because chronic substance abuse is associated with poor physical health, comprehensive substance abuse assessment *must* include a complete physical examination (and is required for admission to most healthcare facilities). Ideally, the examination will include laboratory studies to screen for health problems associated with the use of specific substances (e.g., hepatitis C and HIV/AIDS for men who use injection drugs, cirrhosis and pancreatitis for men who abuse alcohol) and those health problems most common among men. Clinicians should work with clients to help them access needed care through other channels, such as public health clinics.

❖ **Functional limitations:** Assessment should determine if the client has any functional limitations due to co-occurring physical and/or cognitive disabilities (Schrimsher et al. 2007). The behavioral health service provider must be able to accommodate a client with special needs. For example, a provider can accommodate a client who has lower back pain (which may not necessarily be described as a disability by the client) that is exacerbated by sitting for extended periods by giving the client permission to stretch or stand during long group therapy sessions. Similarly, a person with limited skills in reading or writing English may require modified versions of written client material. TIP 29, *Substance Use Disorder Treatment for People with Physical and Cognitive Disabilities* (CSAT 1998e), offers more information on screening individuals for functional limitations.

❖ **Co-occurring mental disorders:** Rates of co-occurring mental challenges among substance abuse treatment clients (both male and female) are high, and these clients often require special behavioral health services for effective treatment. Chapter Five of this text discusses screening specifically for COD and provides some insight into assessing and treating specific disorders in this population.

❖ **Trauma histories:** Men with substance use disorders often have experienced multiple traumatic events during their lives. Men are more likely than women to be exposed to trauma, and substance abuse may increase the risk of trauma exposure (Breslau 2002). Even if past traumas have not resulted in a mental disorder, such as posttraumatic stress disorder, traumatic events can have lasting effects. Behavioral health service providers should be aware of a client's trauma history to better understand his substance abuse and better aid him/her in recovery.

❖ **Spirituality:** At minimum, spiritual assessment should determine the client's denomination, beliefs, and spiritual practices, if any, and should identify how these might affect his treatment or pose barriers to participation in mutual-help groups or other treatment practices (e.g., meditation). Specific questioning about how spirituality has helped a client through difficult times can elicit spiritual strengths that might positively influence substance abuse treatment. Clinicians can ask clients such questions as, "Who or what provides you with strength and hope? How do you access your sense of 'higher power'? Is a belief in a higher power important in your life? Has it ever been?" (Joint Commission on Accreditation of Healthcare Organizations 2004). Gorsuch and Miller (1999) provide valuable insights into assessing spirituality in a mental health or substance abuse treatment setting. The Spirituality Competency Resource

81

Center outlines a spiritual assessment that behavioral health counselors may find useful in discussing spirituality with clients' Other assessment areas include beliefs about masculinity and femininity, family history, sexuality, and shame. (http://www.spiritualcompetency.com/recovery/lesson7.html).

❖ **Motivation to change:** A client's motivation to seek and comply with treatment is a key factor in predicting a successful outcome. TIP 35, *Enhancing Motivation for Change in Substance Abuse Treatment* (CSAT 1999*b*), includes valuable information on a variety of assessment instruments that evaluate a client's level of motivation and readiness for treatment.

❖ **Relapse risk and recovery support:** Although it may be left to later stages of treatment, an assessment that evaluates a client's risk factors for relapse and supports for recovery can reduce relapse risk and promote long-term recovery.

❖ **Peer relations and support:** The extent of social deterioration, interpersonal loss, and isolation that clients have experienced should be documented thoroughly during screening and assessment. Assessment of a client's support systems, including past participation in mutual-help groups (e.g., Alcoholics Anonymous, Narcotics Anonymous, Voices and Faces in Recovery), is critical to identifying peer support networks that provide positive relationships and enhance treatment outcomes.

❖ **Recreational and leisure activities:** Recreational and leisure activities are important in recovery; therefore, assessment should determine any positive activities in which clients have participated before or during periods of substance use. Identifying existing recreational and leisure time preferences and gaining exposure to new ones can be significant steps in developing a recovery-oriented lifestyle.

❖ **Clients ability to manage money:** Financial difficulties are common among clients in substance abuse treatment, who often have spent considerable money on their substance use that otherwise would have paid for rent, food, and utilities. Financial status and money management skills should be assessed to help clients understand their fiscal strengths and weaknesses as they become stabilized. Clients often need assistance to adjust to loss of income caused by reduced criminal activity and develop skills that enhance their legitimate earning power. Once financial factors are clarified, individuals may be better prepared to devise realistic strategies to achieve short- and long-term goals.

❖ **Insurance status**: Clients' resources to cover treatment costs should be determined during screening and assessment. Often they are uninsured or have not explored their eligibility for payment assistance. Treatment personal are responsible for helping clients explore payment options so that they have access to a full range of treatment services, including medical care. In situations of inadequate funding or client ineligibility for funds, another source of payment should be identified. Treatment staff should assist patients in applying for public assistance or inquiring whether personal insurance will reimburse costs. Counselors can help patients make decisions about involving their insurance companies and address fears that employers will find out about their substance use or that benefits for health care will be denied.

In general, all clinical assessment should be ongoing with periodic reassessment throughout treatment, but the initial personal assessment can occur over a longer period than an initial problem assessment for substance abuse and dependence. Circumstances could require a personal assessment to be deferred. For example, if problem assessment shows alcohol dependence with the need for detoxification, then medically supervised detoxification in a hospital or residential setting should be pursued immediately—personal assessment should be deferred until the individual returns to an ambulatory setting. Similarly, if a problem assessment done in a medical, behavioral health, legal, occupational, or social service setting shows a need for substance abuse treatment, personal assessment should be deferred to the substance abuse treatment setting. A client's sensitivity to some of the topics discussed in the following sections might also lead to deferral of in depth exploration until the therapeutic alliance is sufficient to allow the client to be comfortable talking about such issues. In exploring gender and sexuality, clinicians should be sensitive to the degree of discomfort clients might experience. However, if a client shows that these issues are meaningful for him, further exploration enables the clinician to solidify the relationship with the client while also letting him discuss issues of likely importance for his recovery.

Domestic Violence and Child Abuse

The relationship between domestic violence and substance abuse is well documented (Caetano et al. 2001; Chase et al. 2003; Chermack et al. 2000; Cohen et al. 2003; Easton et al. 2000; Schumacher et al. 2003; Stuart 2005). The use of certain substances (e.g., alcohol, cocaine, methamphetamine) is associated with increased domestic violence, whereas use of others (e.g., marijuana, opioids) is not (Cohen et al. 2003). Some estimates suggest that up to 60 percent of men seeking treatment for alcohol abuse have perpetrated partner violence (Chermack et al. 2000; O'Farrell et al. 2004; Schumacher et al. 2003). A DOJ survey found that more than half of both prison and jail inmates convicted of a violent crime against a current or former partner had been drinking or using drugs at the time of the offense (Greenfeld et al. 1998).

A survey conducted by the National Committee to Prevent Child Abuse found that up to 80 % of child abuse cases are associated with the use of alcohol and/or drugs by the perpetrator (McCurdy and Daro 1994). Many individuals who abuse their children were themselves abused in childhood. The rate at which violence is transmitted across generations in the general population has been estimated at 30 to 40 percent (Egeland et al.1988; Kaufman and Zigler 1993). These probabilities suggest that as many as 4 of every 10 children who observe, or experience family violence are at increased risk for becoming involved in a violent relationship in adulthood, either as perpetrator or as victim.

Substance use is also associated with being the victim of domestic abuse for both men and women (Chase et al. 2003; Cohen et al. 2003; Cunradi et al. 2002; Miller et al. 1989; Weinsheimer et al. 2005). Other risk factors for both genders include being young, having a high number of relationship problems, and having high levels of emotional distress (Chase et al. 2003). Violence between intimate partners tends to escalate in frequency and severity over time, much like patterns of substance abuse. Thus, identifying and intervening in domestic violence situations as early as possible is paramount. Staff members should understand relevant State and Federal laws regarding domestic violence and their duty to report. More information on the legal issues relating to domestic violence and duty to report can be found in TIP 25, *Substance Abuse Treatment and Domestic Violence* (CSAT 1997*b*), along with other valuable information on this topic. TIP 36, *Substance Abuse Treatment for Persons with Child Abuse and Neglect Issues* (CSAT 2000*b*), discusses child abuse and neglect issues for clients in treatment who have been abused as children and/or have abused their own children.

Relapse can be a particularly high-risk time for domestic violence, although it is unclear which event (relapse or domestic violence) precipitates the other. Regardless of causality, both issues need to be addressed. During a relapse crisis, it can be easy for the counselor to decide to deal with the violence at a later date. Several complications arise, however, as a result. Not addressing the violent behavior may imply that it is not significant or important. It also invites the client to ignore the behavior and not address it at a later date. Not addressing the violence may also signal to other family members that the violent behavior should not be brought into the open and discussed.

When issues like domestic violence or child abuse are discussed, all behavioral health clinicians should be aware of confidentiality laws and any

84

exceptions to those laws that may apply in specific instances. Providers should also be aware of applicable Federal regulations (notably, the Confidentiality of Alcohol and Drug Abuse Patient Records laws contained in 42 CFR Part 2) and specific State regulations or laws (e.g., "Megan's Laws"). Appendix B in TIP 25 (CSAT 1997*b*) and Appendix B in TIP 36 (CSAT 2000*b*) provide detailed discussions of these topics. In addition, the SAMHSA (2004) publication, *The Confidentiality of Alcohol and Drug Abuse Patient Records Regulation and the HIPAA Privacy Rule: Implications for Alcohol and Substance Abuse Programs* discusses these regulations as well as Health Insurance Portability and Accountability Act regulations that affect confidentiality of patient records.

Child abuse

All States require mandatory reporting of child abuse by helping professionals—particularly State-licensed physicians, therapists, nurses, and social workers (CSAT 2000*d*). Most States require that this reporting be immediate and offer toll-free numbers. Most also require that reports include the name and address of a parent or caretaker, the type of abuse or neglect, and the name of the alleged perpetrator. **Failure to report indications of abuse that results in injury to a child can lead to criminal charges, a civil suit, or loss of professional licensure.** Mandated reporters generally are immune from liability for reports made in good faith that later are found to be erroneous (CSAT 2000*d*). Staff members who suspect domestic violence should investigate immediately whether a client's children have been harmed. Inquiries into possible child abuse can occur only after notice of the limitations of confidentiality (42 CFR, Part 8 § 12(g)) has been given to the patient, who must acknowledge receipt of this notice in writing. Clients also must be informed, during orientation and when otherwise applicable, that substance abuse treatment providers are required to notify a children's protective services agency if they suspect child abuse or neglect.

Men as victims of domestic violence

Although women are commonly perceived as the victims of domestic violence, the reality is that men can also be victimized by either male or female partners. In the National Violence Against Women Survey, 15.4 % of men who lived with male partners and 7.7 % of men who lived with female partners reported stalking, physical assault, and/or sexual assault by their partners (Tjaden and Thoennes 2000). Other studies, which contextualized domestic violence as family conflict rather than criminal behavior, report higher rates of female-on-male violence, although the types of violence perpetrated and the likelihood of it resulting in injury were inconsistent (George 2003). In a meta-analysis of physical aggression between opposite-sex partners, Archer (2002) found that men were more likely to cause injury to partners but that men still sustained one third of injuries resulting from such acts.

Studies of clients in substance abuse treatment have found high levels of intimate partner violence perpetrated by women against men. Cohen and colleagues (2003) interviewed 1,016 men and women in treatment for methamphetamine dependence: 26.3 % of men (compared with 63.2 % of women) reported that their partners had threatened them, and 26.3 % of men (compared with 80 % of women) reported that their partners had been physically violent. In a study of 103 women with alcohol use disorder seeking couples-based outpatient treatment, women were more likely to report having committed serious violence toward their partners (50 %) than having been victims of such violence (22 %), although this was not the case in a study of women seeking individually based treatment for alcohol abuse (Chase et al. 2003). It should also be noted that unmarried intimate partners appear to be more likely to commit violent acts toward one another than married partners (Straus 1999).

Because stereotypes of masculinity stress self-sufficiency and strength, men who have been abused by their partners may be even less willing to seek help than women. Additionally, there are fewer resources available for male victims of domestic violence than for female victims. The majority of domestic violence programs are designed for women, and many will not provide assistance to male victims; also, many men who are abused by their partners do not feel that the justice system will support them even if they do report the crime (McNeely et al. 2001). The problem is further complicated by traditional beliefs that men should be the head of the household and men's fear of ridicule for not filling that role; the shame men may feel at disclosing family violence is compounded by the shame of not being able to keep their partners under control (Straus 1999). Often, providers presume that men in treatment should be screened as potential abusers but not as victims of domestic abuse, especially when the man's partner is a woman (CSAT 1997*b*).

Limited data are available on the rates of intimate partner abuse among gay male couples: for example, the National Violence Against Women Survey (Tjaden and Thoennes 2000) found that men with male partners were twice as likely to experience domestic violence as men with female partners. Bartholomew and colleagues (2000) compared factors associated with partner abuse in heterosexual and gay couples, concluding that they were largely the same and that substance use played a significant role in both situations. In a review of 19 studies that examined partner violence in gay and lesbian couples, Burke and Follingstad (1999) only found three that gathered data from gay male couples and one that extrapolated data on rates of abuse for heterosexual men. Still, these limited studies suggest that men

86

in same-sex relationships are at least as likely to experience violence from their partners as men in opposite-sex relationships.

Limited data are available on the rates of intimate partner abuse among gay male couples: for example, the National Violence Against Women Survey (Tjaden and Thoennes 2000) found that men with male partners were twice as likely to experience domestic violence as men with female partners. Bartholomew and colleagues (2000) compared factors associated with partner abuse in heterosexual and gay couples, concluding that they were largely the same and that substance use played a significant role in both situations. In a review of 19 studies that examined partner violence in gay and lesbian couples, Burke and Follingstad (1999) only found three that gathered data from gay male couples and one that extrapolated data on rates of abuse for heterosexual men. Still, these limited studies suggest that men in same-sex relationships are at least as likely to experience violence from their partners as men in opposite-sex relationships.

Limited data are available on the rates of intimate partner abuse among gay male couples: for example, the National Violence Against Women Survey (Tjaden and Thoennes 2000) found that men with male partners were twice as likely to experience domestic violence as men with female partners. Bartholomew and colleagues (2000) compared factors associated with partner abuse in heterosexual and gay couples, concluding that they were largely the same and that substance use played a significant role in both situations. In a review of 19 studies that examined partner violence in gay and lesbian couples, Burke and Follingstad (1999) only found three that gathered data from gay male couples and one that extrapolated data on rates of abuse for heterosexual men. Still, these limited studies suggest that men in same-sex relationships are at least as likely to experience violence from their partners as men in opposite-sex relationships.

Romans and colleagues (2000) identified the following methods for exploring potential domestic violence situations, which can be incorporated into effective assessment tools:

❖ Always interview clients in private about domestic violence. Begin with direct, broad questions and move to more specific ones; inquire how disagreements or conflicts are resolved (e.g., "Do you want to hit [him or her] to make [him or her] see sense?"); ask whether clients have trouble with anger or have done anything when angry that they regret; combine these questions with other types of lifestyle questions.

❖ Ask about violence by using concrete examples and specific hypothetical situations rather than vague, conceptual questions.

❖ Display information about domestic violence in public (e.g., waiting room) and private (e.g., restroom) locations.

❖ Use opportunities during discussions (e.g., comments about marital conflict situations or poor communication with partners) to probe further.

❖ Obtain as complete a description as possible of the physical, sexual, and psychological violence perpetrated by or on a client recently; typically, those who commit domestic violence minimize, deny, or otherwise obscure their acts.

A comprehensive assessment should include clients' values and assumptions; linguistic preferences; attitudes, practices, and beliefs about health and well-being; spirituality and religion; and communication patterns that might originate partly from cultural traditions and heritage (Office of Minority Health 2001). Staff knowledge about diverse groups is important for effective treatment services. Of importance are experiences and coping mechanisms related to assimilation and acculturation of groups into mainstream American culture that may affect how they perceive substance abuse. Gathering pertinent information often must rely on subjective sources (e.g., interviews and questionnaires). Even so, staff members involved in screening and assessment should be cautioned against making value judgments about cultural or ethnic preferences or assumptions about *"average"* middle-class American values and beliefs.

A shared staff–client cultural identity is attractive to some individuals entering treatment. To the extent possible, client preferences for staff members who share their cultural identity should be honored. Multilingual educational materials and displays of culturally diverse materials help clients feel more at ease when English is not their primary language.

Spirituality and Religion in Assessment*

Most clients in substance abuse treatment usually have some religious and/or spiritual beliefs, based on research in medical settings (Koenig 2001*b*) and among the general population (Public Broadcasting Service 2002; Robinson 2003). Spiritual and religious activity should generally be encouraged; research has repeatedly confirmed that people who participate in

*Center for Substance Abuse Treatment. *Medication-Assisted Treatment for Opioid Addiction in Opioid Treatment Programs.* (2005). Treatment Improvement Protocol (TIP) Series 43.HHS Publication No. (SMA) 12-4214.Rockville, MD: Substance Abuse and Mental Health Services Administration.

spiritual/religious activities are less likely to abuse substances (Koenig 2001*b*). Also, religious practices and beliefs (at least those from established religions) seem to affect physical health by improving coping, reducing emotional distress, improving attitude and mood, increasing social support, and reducing problem behaviors (Koenig 2001*a*).

Due to the influence of 12-Step groups like Alcoholics Anonymous, spiritual beliefs play an important role in many substance abuse treatment programs. Many clients find that spiritual and/or religious beliefs play an important role in their recovery, so counselors should be prepared to discuss these beliefs with clients if they so choose.

Counselors in behavioral health settings can use a client's religious or spiritual beliefs to motivate change and, sometimes, to counter the negative effects of certain cultural beliefs about masculinity and alcohol use. For example, a client who believes that not drinking will jeopardize his masculinity and status among his peers may be better able to reconcile his decision to maintain abstinence as a culturally appropriate one if it is supported by a priest or clergyman. Faith can also help recovering clients as they reenter their communities; support from a church, synagogue, mosque, or other faith-based institution can improve their chances of recovery and reduce the odds of relapse (CSAT 1999*b*).

Although substances (such as wine or peyote) may be used in some religious rituals, all major religions have made adaptations for individuals with substance use disorders, enabling them to participate in the religion without partaking of those substances.

Behavioral health services providers should become familiar with their clients' spiritual beliefs, practices, and experiences just as they learn about their occupations, families, habits, and mental health.

Defining the Difference Between Religion and Spirituality

It is useful to distinguish between spirituality and religion, as some men seeking treatment view themselves as spiritual but not necessarily religious. Religion is organized, with each religion having its *own "theology, doctrine, creeds, catechisms, and liturgical practices, all of which are intended to enhance each member's spirituality"* (Chappel 2003, p. 970). Spirituality, on the other hand, is a personal matter involving the individual's search for meaning, and it does not require an affiliation with any religion. People can have spiritual experiences or develop their own spirituality regardless of the presence or absence of any religious connection (Chappel 2003). In recovery from substance abuse, focusing on spirituality rather than religion can help some people accept the need for a higher power or a power greater than themselves (which could be other people, nature, a spiritual being, or a

89

deity) when they might otherwise be resistant toward organized religion (Hazelden Foundation 2003). beliefs.) In a therapeutic relationship of mutual respect and tolerance, differences between counselor and client in spiritual beliefs need not become problematic. A clinician can serve as an orchestrator of resources when it comes to a client's religious or spiritual beliefs (Koenig 2001b). Just as the clinician or other appropriate staff person can help clients get the physical services they need (e.g., housing, medical care), they can also help clients meet their spiritual needs by arranging visits with spiritual advisors or clergy, as well as by providing access to religious services during treatment upon client request. Clinicians must be able to refer clients to spiritual advisors from many different faiths (reflecting the population with which the clinician works) *

Spirituality of ordinary people

"Spirituality of ordinary people" refers to willing involvement in socially desirable activities or processes that are beyond the immediate details of daily life and personal self-interest. Attention to the ethics of behavior, consideration for the interests of others, community involvement, helping others, and participating in organized religion are expressions of spirituality. A client's spirituality can be an important treatment resource, and persons recovering from addiction often experience increased interest in the spiritual aspects of their lives. A study by Flynn and colleagues (2003) of 432 patients admitted to 18 treatment programs found that those who remained in recovery for five years credited religion or spirituality as one factor in this outcome. Staff should assess clients' connections with religious institutions because these institutions often provide a sense of belonging that is valuable in the rehabilitative process.

Miller (1998) found a lack of research exploring the association between spirituality and addiction recovery but concluded that spiritual engagement or reengagement appeared to be correlated with recovery. In studies reviewed by Muffler and colleagues (1992), individuals with a high degree of spiritual motivation to recover reported that treatment programs that included spiritual guidance or counseling were more likely to produce positive outcomes than programs that did not. Treatment programs should assess spiritual resources adequately. Counselors and other mental health professionals could benefit from training in client spirituality.

---

*For a more detailed discussion of religion and spirituality go to: Scoles, P. (2020). **Faith, Spirituality and Resilience in Recovery.** Kindle Publishing.

In summary, all clients should have a comprehensive medical and psychosocial assessment conducted over multiple sessions. This assessment should include, but not be limited to, the individuals' recollections of and attitudes about previous substance abuse treatment; expectations and motivation for treatment; level of support for a substance-free lifestyle; history of physical or sexual abuse; military or combat history; traumatic life events; and the cultural, religious, and spiritual basis for any values and assumptions that might affect treatment. This information should be included in an integrated summary in which data are interpreted, clients' strengths and weaknesses are noted, and a treatment plan is developed that matches each client to appropriate services.

Chapter Five
Assessment: The DSM

The influence of Newtonian physics and Pre-Darwinian biology on the biomedical movement of modern medicine had an inordinate impact on the development of twentieth century Psychiatry and much of Psychology. The biomedical perspective (as opposed to the psychosocial and/or spiritual) of psychoanalytic theory helped the emerging mental health professions join the mainstream of "medical science". In order to be recognized by the 19th century medical community the science of mental health had to develop a system in which complex psychic phenomena (emotional problems in living) were explained in terms of simpler, component behavior with physically measurable data that followed scientific laws and were reasonably predictable. Historically, if the above "science" did not develop, the study of mental disorders would be reduced to non-scientific or mystical explanations, which in turn would negate the evolution of the assessment and treatment of mental problems and have a major impact on the legitimacy of psychiatry. Historically, Freud's break with Jung was more about the materialistic effort to separate mental illness from religion and spirituality, in order to join the mainstream scientific medical community. The need for a diagnostic nomenclature, which attempts to explain life in a singular dimension, primarily physical and mechanical, with little or no consideration to one's spirituality, was a necessity if the emerging profession of psychiatry was to become established as a part of medicine. Although psychiatry has tried to merge biomedical and psychosocial perspectives in the diagnosis of mental disorders, the language does not sufficiently disguise its biomedical bias. Surely psychiatric labels do help us converse with our professional colleagues and comply with managed care requirements (reimbursement agents), but the person, in front of the therapist is more than a label and greater than modern science.

Earlier in the text the reader was introduced to a broader cultural concern than just the Western scientific perspective. Culture is a way of trying to understand one's relationship to a problem and how their cultural history interprets and serves the consumer of a given service (Kaplan 1984). Early in my clinical career, I was working in a large Community Mental Health Center and was assigned a case by my supervisor, a psychiatrist. The record indicated that the individual had *"paranoid delusions"*, his affect was intense and labile with a wide range of emotions, his reality occupied much of his personal and social life, and he had poor impulse control and had a distorted sense of self and others. The psychiatric transfer summary indicated that he was a 38-year-old African American male who was considered dangerous because he "carried a knife with him at all times". The transfer note indicated that the client rarely went out at night and even in the summer he locked all his windows and doors and was extremely suspicious

92

of anyone he didn't know. Finally, the report concluded that he had mistrust for all *"White people"*. After meeting with this individual for four or five sessions, I basically agreed with his perspective on life and felt that his mistrust was justifiable and culturally congruent. I recommended he be discharged from therapy and the community mental health agency work with local groups to provide better protection in their neighborhood (catchment area). During my clinical supervision, the psychiatrist objected to my recommendations, even though I informed him that the client lived in a high crime area of the city and his mistrust of the neighborhood was culturally consistent with growing up in Philadelphia as an African American. Furthermore, the client's need to physically protect himself by carrying a weapon and being suspicious of "White people" appeared within "normal limits" of some racial/ethnic groups in America. Incidentally, a year or so after this incident I read a book entitled, **Black Rage** by Grier and Cobbs (1968) and realized that the client was expressing a kind of 'healthy paranoia". At the time, I was not aware of this idea and attributed my thinking to *"cultural relativity"*. I can only assume that the supervising psychiatrist had a more traditional medical interpretation because a few weeks after our consultation I was transferred from the outpatient clinic and assigned a research associates position under the Director of Grants Management.

Culture, Ethnicity and Assessment

The above example reflects the continuing controversy over the value of assessment and diagnosis of clients seeking help. The purpose of diagnosis is to identify areas of disruption in an individual's life that have a negative impact on current behavior and lifestyle. A danger in this perspective is that the clinician will fail to consider ethnic and cultural factors that influence one's behavior. The need for a more culturally sensitive classification system, one that acknowledges the role that cultural factors play in mental disorders and clinical judgments about them, is a topic of much debate. Historically, this cultural insensitivity has led to labeling individuals with inappropriate disorders. Certain behaviors and personality styles when taken out of their ethnic or cultural context could be viewed as deviant or dysfunctional, when in fact they are culturally congruent. There is increasing pressure for clinicians to become more knowledgeable, comfortable and skilled in working with individuals from different races, ethnic backgrounds, sexual and religious minorities as well as other populations that are not bound by contemporary Western standards.

The DSM-5 discusses no real distinct cultural and/or ethnic patterns that could influence the diagnostic process and in turn bias an evaluator from pursuing these patterns of influence. The DSM-5 does not deal with cultural variations in the expression of maladaptive behavior, despite the fact that culture and ethnic background of the individual does influence symptoms

93

and etiology of many disorders. Cory (2001) cautions the clinician about misdiagnosis:

> *Diagnostic assessment can be especially challenging when a clinician from one ethnic or cultural group uses the DSM classification to evaluate an individual from a different ethnic or cultural group. A clinician that is unfamiliar with the nuances of an individual's cultural frame of reference may incorrectly judge as psychopathology those normal variations in behavior, belief, or experience that are particular to the individual's culture. (Cory 2001, p.69)*

Many social scientists believe that ethnic identity is a significant cultural variable that impacts on a person's s concept and sense of belonging with other members of a subgroup and defines the individual's relationship to the dominant culture. These shared influences can affect a person's willingness to seek help concerning a mental health problem and impact on the way in which the problem is described to a professional worker. Olandi (1992) defined culture as shared traditions, customs, arts, folklore, history, values, norms and institutions of a given people (p. VI). Ethnicity and racial heritage is an integral part of one's culture and must become an integral part of one's recovery. At the present time, there is insufficient research on the relationship of ethnic and cultural differences and their effect, positive or negative, on the assessment, diagnosis and treatment of dysfunctional behavior. In some respects members of minority groups may view and react to the world just like all other people, in other respects, they may feel differently, believing their problems are a result of exposure to racism and/or poverty. In recent years, research on personality and maladaptive behavior has increased with regard to similarities and differences and the impact these differences have on individuals living in different communities. (Jackson, 1991; Uba, 1994). One's difference becomes relevant in that practitioners must be, knowledgeable about the world views of their clients and attempt to understand these views without making negative judgments (Jeff, 1994; Moore, 1994). Unless clinicians consider the social and cultural context of their client it is almost impossible to understand their clients struggle. For example, research on cross-cultural comparisons of emotional disturbance and its expression has shown that depression often has very different meanings and forms of expression in different societies. Most cases of depression worldwide are experienced and expressed in bodily terms of aching backs, headaches, fatigue, and a wide assortment of other somatic symptoms that lead individuals to regard this condition as a physical problem. Only in contemporary Western societies is depression seen principally as an intrapsychic experience (Jenkins, 1991). Clinicians need to take account of cultural factors with regard to cultural variations in emotional expression, body language, and religious beliefs and rituals within particular societies such as the United States.

94

In conclusion, evaluators and counselors must have an appreciation for their own culture, the culture of their client and the sociopolitical system, in which they both work and live before they can effectively evaluate other individuals

It is not necessarily important that the evaluator/counselor be in recovery or a member of a minority group in order to help an individual. What is more important is that the clinician be receptive to a similar set of feelings and struggles. Sometimes our differences are as important as our similarities. Race clearly affects the process of evaluation but there is no clear evidence that racial difference necessarily impairs outcome (Davis & Proctor; 1989). If an evaluator is oblivious, apathetic and unskilled regarding a clients values, beliefs and customs, his/her race, ethnicity or recovery has little if any bearing on the individuals' competence. Insensitive Euro-Americans (Whites) are just as problematic as insensitive African Americans, Asian Americans, Latinos or Native Americans. Corey (2000) in discussing culture in clinical practice established some practical guidelines for working effectively with diverse client populations:

> ➢ Learn more about your own culture and how it has influenced your behavior and thoughts about others.

> ➢ Identify for yourself basic assumptions about culture, race, ethnicity, gender, etc.

> ➢ Expand your knowledge and experience with other cultural groups.

> ➢ Learn to find your common ground with people of diverse backgrounds.

> ➢ Recognize the importance of being flexible in the application of techniques that benefit different cultures. (Cory, pp.30-31).

Two factors should be emphasized in relation to the above guidelines:

1. Too many Euro-Americans (Whites) have limited experiences with minority communities, cultures and concerns. Generally, Americans continue to go to different schools, live in non-integrated neighborhoods, attend segregated churches and socialize in different parts of the city. Social scientists, as well as many others, believe that groups, who live separately, don't know or understand each other, have difficulty trusting one another and know very little about social and cultural realities of individuals different from their own world view. Book knowledge about culture or race is not the same as living with different cultures and experiencing race. Too often counselors enter the helping professions with no meaningful contact or

exposure to other cultures except the superficial information of books or their meaningless interaction with a few people of color in college.

2. The interpersonal relationship or the development of effective therapeutic relationships fosters the kind of respect; professional courtesy and competence that helps experienced skilled practitioners work effectively with racially and culturally dissimilar clients. Expertise in assessment and treatment requires that the counselor have sufficient breadth and depth in (1) cultural awareness and sensitivity, (2) a body of multicultural knowledge and experience, as well as, (3) a specific set of practice skills. (Leong and Kim 1991)

Since diagnostic categories clearly represent the medical model clinicians must be aware that the symptoms do not necessarily mean the same thing or dictate the same type of intervention. They are a guide and provide generally acceptable boundaries of discourse and intervention.

Many recovering individuals and addiction counselors can't understand why mental disorders and spirituality are not integrated into one unified holistic approach. A brief historical perspective may shed some light on why the field of psychotherapy struggles with the mind, the body and the spirit (biopsychospiritual approach). Although one can recount as far back as Hypocrites, who believed that all illness was the result of psychic or spiritual influence, it was the teachings of Jesus and the early Christians and their instant cures through the power of faith or spiritual guidance that lead to the first psychotherapeutic spiritual interventions (Micozzi, 1996). For many centuries, the church "diagnosed" and treated the "mentally ill" who were possessed, in trance states or under some "satanic" influence. Due to increasing pressure, the Church ceased practicing this healing art and abrogated it to the new "priests" or "shamans" of modern medicine, the physicians. Descartes assertion that the mind and body were separate entities fostered the development of physical explanations for all emotional difficulties. By the end of the 19th century, biomedical science was taking histories, searching the biochemical and structural parts of the body and reducing signs and symptoms of illnesses to single diagnostic categories. (Micozzi, 1994) In 1841, the United States classification for Mental Disorders was but a single category, *"Idiocy"* (Reid and Wise, 1995 p.3). It took almost ninety years and the evolution of modern Psychiatry to produce the first Diagnostic and Statistical Manual of Mental Disorders (DSM-I) in 1952. The DSM-II was published in 1968, the DSM-III in 1974, with the more detailed manual, the DSM III-R being published in 1987. The DSM-IV was published in 1994. (Reid and Wise, 1995) the DSM IV-TR in 2000 and the new DSM-5 in 2013.

Before proceeding to a review of the medical approach (DSM) discussion it is important to note that labeling of individual behaviors into symptoms

96

complexes known as diagnostic groups reflects two of the three explanatory paradigms: (1) the Biomedical and (2) the Psychosocial. The Biomedical model emphasizes the physical body and the connections and communications between nerves, bones, muscles and the rest of what is often referred to as one's physical presentation. Much of Western medicine and to a large extent American psychiatry is grounded in this model, being represented primarily by allopathic medicine (M.D's) and to a lesser extent by osteopathic medicine (D.O's). The acceptance of Chiropractic healing, the younger relative to osteopathy appears to be the most radical of the traditional Western practices. Even Psychiatry is considered more "mainstream" than the natural principles of chiropractic healing, which finds much comfort in the recovery process. The holistic approach to chiropractic healing indicates that a balanced diet and regular exercise foster the human body's innate healing potential and that pharmaceutical suppression of symptoms can compromise the body's ability to heal itself and that natural non-pharmaceutical measures should be the approach of first resort, not last. (Micozzi, 1996. p.20) This approach appears to make sense when one views "pathology" from a broader ecosystem perspective. For the reader's information, the one Eastern or Chinese medical practice that appears to compliment the Western biomedical approach to health is Acupuncture, which analyses the physical body through meridians or pathways. The energy that flows through the material body is called *"Chi."* The objective of acupuncture is to allow unimpeded energy flow, through the body, its organs and the channel pathways therefore producing a balanced state of health. Illness usually results from an interruption or imbalance in the flow of *"Chi"*. Acupuncture is employed to remove the obstructions.

The second exploratory paradigm, Psychosocial includes much of the domain of psychotherapists and is often referred to as the mind, body, emotion relationship. In Western medicine it is rooted in traditional psychiatric practice or the non-medical psychological therapies. Historically, the Freud/Jung schism was more of a reflection of the times and had more to do with the identification of psychiatry as a branch of modern medicine with little or no association with the historical religious or spiritual traditions. Jung's persistent interjection of theological and archetypal explanations of psychic phenomena threatened the new marriage between psychoanalysis and modern medicine.

The Diagnostic and Statistical Manual of Mental Disorders is primarily an outgrowth of the biomedical model of sickness, discomfort or malfunction. Although non-medical practitioners (psychologists, clinical social workers, etc.) have inappropriately identified with the medical model, primarily to join the third party parity with medical doctors, one hopes that the non-medical mental health community will continue to view problems in living as more than medical and psycho-social in nature. One hopes that the influence of spirituality in therapy will transcend the physical body of our

97

clients and reach out to a more transpersonal relationship with our "illness". Certainly there are mental conditions that require diagnosis and medical and psychosocial interventions. Surely, if one is to survive in the "Behavioral Health field", we must know and contribute to the diagnostically driven payment system of healthcare. However, clinicians must never lose sight of their primary mission, which is physical, psychosocial and spiritual in nature. To ignore any one of these aspects is to splinter an individual's reality.

The presentation of the DSM has value in completing insurance forms, in communicating with clients or other practitioners about common symptoms and by assigning meaning to an experience that helps others explain a general course of action. By its very nature, this labeling denies the existence of multiple realities with credit only given to the scientific fact.

Co-occurring Disorders and Differential Diagnoses*

A hallmark of CODs is the highly interactive nature of mental and substance use disorders and how each disorder affects the symptoms, course, and treatment of the other disorder. The American Psychiatric Association (2013) describes a number of different ways in which the two sets of disorders are interdependent and interactive:

❖ One disorder may predispose a person to another type of disorder

❖ A third type of disorder (e.g., such as HIV/AIDS) may affect or elicit the onset of mental or substance use disorders

❖ Symptoms of each disorder may be augmented, as these often overlap between mental and substance use disorders (e.g., anxiety, depression [APA, 2013])

❖ Other disorders, such as borderline personality disorder (BPD, as classified by DSM), may predispose individuals to more severe mental disorders such as major depressive disorder and substance use disorders

❖ Alcohol or other drugs may induce, or more frequently mimic or resemble, a mental disorder

*Substance Abuse and Mental Health Services Administration. (2015). Screening and Assessment of Co-occurring Disorders in the Justice System. HHS Publication No. (SMA)-15-4930. Rockville, MD: Substance Abuse and Mental Health Services Administration.

Because of the intertwined nature of mental and substance use disorders among people, it is critically important to assess the recent and historical use of substances to determine whether there were direct effects (e.g., symptom exacerbation) that resulted from substance use. For example, it is important to determine if mental health symptoms appeared **after** engaging in substance use. Similarly, assessment should consider whether engaging in substance use was motivated by attempts to **alleviate** symptoms of mental disorders (e.g., agitation, anxiety, depression, sleep disturbance). Other strategies to ascertain an accurate diagnostic picture include establishing a temporal framework to better understand the relationship between substance use and mental health symptoms; for example, investigating the presence of mental health symptoms following periods of abstinence (either voluntary or coerced) can help determine if there is a causal relationship between the mental and substance use disorders. Similar steps during assessment should be taken to *"rule out"* mental disorders occurring due to a general medical condition.

Evidence-based screening and assessment strategies for individuals who have CODs recognize the interactive nature of the disorders and the need for ongoing examination of the relationship between the two disorders. Attention to the interactive nature of the disorders should be reflected in ongoing assessment activities and use of repeated measures to assess changes in the diagnostic picture and in symptoms and levels of impairment related to the two sets of disorders. Treatment planning, must consider the interdependent nature of the disorders. This approach does not necessarily entail providing concurrent services for the disorders in equal intensity, but instead prioritizes the sequence of services according to the presence of acute crises (e.g., suicidal behavior, intoxication) and areas of functional impairment (e.g., cognitive impairment) that affect treatment participation. The focus of treatment at any given time should be on remediating areas of functional impairment caused by one or both disorders, and the sequence of interventions should be dictated accordingly.

The following cautions should be noted when using the DSM:

1. Diagnosis does not assume causation. One can identify a symptom complex from many psychological perspectives.

2. Diagnostic categories only describe a disease process not a person. Individuals with similar disorders may have certain things in common but they also may require different intervention strategies for the same diagnostic category.

3. Don't assume that there are distinctive, sharp boundaries between disorders. Many disorders fit within a broad range of symptoms that identify a pathologic state.

4. The DSM is clearly a medical model of illness. (Morrison, 1995 p.8)

Typically, a clinical assessment can vary from two to three hours and be completed over a few sessions. In most cases, assessment involves a combination of a clinical interview, personal history information, some biological/medical testing and paper and pencil testing. Assessment has a number of specific goals and purposes:

- It helps determine the extent and severity of Alcohol and other drug abuse problems.

- It helps determine the client's level of maturity and readiness for treatment.

- It ascertains the coexistence of chemical dependency and mental illness.

- It determines what type of intervention will be necessary to address the problems.

- It begins the client's treatment process.

Assessment instruments are standardized tools that are used along with the clinical interview. These instruments provide another data source for the assessor to use in evaluating the client.

The following instruments can provide useful and valuable information as well as providing a uniform approach to client assessment.*

Structured Clinical Interview for the DSM (SCID).

The SCID is a semi structured interview designed specifically to determine the diagnoses of all of the fifty (50) major DSM psychiatric diagnoses (including the above substance abuse and dependency disorders) in Axis I, and the twelve (12) types of personality disorder in Axis II. The DSM criteria for each disorder are presented alongside the interview questions. A User's Guide includes illustrative case vignettes to demonstrate how the SCID can be used to determine one's disorder. Although inter rater reliabilities are in the process of being established, research with the SCID at the Center for Cognitive Therapy at the University of Pennsylvania Medical

---

*for a more detailed discussion of a variety of clinical instruments go to: Substance Abuse and Mental Health Services Administration. (2015). Screening and Assessment of Co-occurring Disorders in the Justice System. HHS Publication No. (SMA)-15-4930. Rockville, MD: Substance Abuse and Mental Health Services Administration.

School, indicates that satisfactory levels of inter rater agreement can be achieved. The SCID takes approximately seventy-five (75) minutes to administer by a trained interviewer. A training program, which is several days in duration, is required for someone with clinical experience, preferably a psychiatrist, psychologist, or clinical social worker.

The Mini-SCID

The Mini-SCID is a computerized, shortened version of the SCID, for a quick method of screening for many of the major psychiatric disorders, such as mood disorders and anxiety disorders, in addition to substance abuse and dependency disorders. The client can complete the Mini-SCID in twenty-five (25) minutes, after a brief tutorial introduces the client to the keyboard; the software allows a choice between responding by using simple highlighted menu bars, or by pressing the letter to indicate choice of response.

The Mini-SCID provides three different report options: complete summary of patient responses; concise summary of possible diagnoses that you should consider; and an expanded version of the concise summary that includes additional diagnostic tips, which are your "next steps" in the diagnostic process.

Remember: Treatment referral through 2017 remained unchanged from 2008 with only approximately 6% seeking substance use treatment services; only 7% of co-occurring disorders are in treatment with depression as the predominant presenting symptoms (NSDUH, 2017).

Mental Status Evaluation: Behavioral and Cognitive Aspects

The Mental Status Exam is a structured way of determining an individual's assessment and level of care. Generally, the evaluator focuses on two large areas of investigation: (1) Behavioral and (2) Cognitive. (Morrison, 1995a; Morrison, 1995 and APA, 1994)

<u>Behavioral Aspects of Mental Status Exam</u>

> **General Appearance and Behavior**

(1) Physical Characteristics and Hygiene

Many clients tell you a lot about them by their general appearance. The way they introduce themselves, when they shake hands, is their grip firm or halfhearted? Is their posture erect or slumped over? Do they have unusual characteristic such as scars, tattoos, missing limbs, poor dental care and body odor? Do they look older than their stated age? Do they appear to be in reasonably good shape? Are they slender? Obese? Is the client clothing clean or dirty? Bright colors, outrageous jewelry may suggest mania. Bizarre dress, such as an adult wearing a Boy Scout uniform, may suggest psychosis. Is their hair color odd? Does the hairstyle seem age appropriate or is he/she a forty-year-old in a twelve-year-old person's haircut?

(2) Alertness or consciousness

Be aware of conscious fluctuations during the interview. Clients should be fully alert and aware of their environment without being overly suspicious and "scanning the environment" for danger.

- Does the client know where he/she is today and what the time and date are?
- Does the client look drowsy?
- Is the client coherent?
- Is the client alert and aware of his/her surroundings?

Chemical dependency could lead to a variety of symptoms that may mimic serious psychiatric conditions. Some disturbances of consciousness could indicate delirium, dementia, disassociation, paranoia, drug withdrawal, drug intoxication etc. Also, someone who is awake but not fully alert could reflect a greater pathology like major depression or psychosis

(3) Psychomotor Activity

- During the interview does the client appear relaxed or tense?

- Does he/she listen to your speech or talk over your sentences?

- Does the client appear to take a long time to respond to questions?

- Does he/she exhibit any inappropriate scratching, rubbing or touching?

- Does the client pick at clothing or skin? Does he/she have any odd mannerisms?

- Does the client frequently leave his/her chair and move around the office?

- Does the client maintain eye contact?

- Does the client stare into space for no apparent reason?

102

- Can the client control his/her impulses?
- Can the client delay gratification of impulses?
- Does he/she know the differences between feelings, thoughts and actions?
- When threatened does client flee, confront, or overreact to the problem?

(4) Facial Expression and Voice

- Does the client show normal facial expressions?
- Are there any contradictory behaviors with the facial expressions and the verbal message? For example, does he/she have a sad face but claims to be in a good mood?
- Does the client have a natural pitch, volume and clarity to their voice? Is he/she monotonous and dull?
- Does he/she use language that is educationally appropriate?
- Does the client stutter, lisp, mumble or demonstrate other speech problems?
- Does he/she use certain phrases habitually?
- Is his/her voice generally angry, sad or friendly?

(5) Attitude toward Evaluator

- Does the client appear cooperative or obstructionist?
- Friendly or hostile?
- Open or secretive?
- Involved or apathetic?
- *Seductive or evasive?*

➢ Mood

The term mood usually refers to the way a person claims to be feeling. Mood is long lasting and more stable than affect. Affect is like the weather, very changeable and someone's mood is like the climate much more stable and more predictable. When evaluating affect the interviewer should be concerned about the following questions.

- Is the individuals affect consistent with his/her thinking? (For example, the client appears happy when relating information on the birth of their child and sad at the death of a loved one).

- Does this client show a broad or a very narrow range of feelings? Does his/her affect change rapidly (lability)?

- Does this client have difficulty-controlling affect? (For example, does he/she exhibit uncontrollable crying, anger, or fear?)

- What quality is there about this client's affect? Is it flat (no feeling) or blunted (diminished feeling)? Are the client's emotional responses disproportionate to the questions asked? (For example, the client gets uncontrollably angry in response to a non-threatening question.)

- What is the client's mood? Is he/she, angry, tearful, fearful, aloof excited, and alienated?

- Does the client have any problem with controlling mood?

- Does he/she have a history of depressed mood?

- If so, how long does this mood last? Does he/she have a history of excited mood (mania)?

- Is the client's mood appropriate given the circumstances of his/her life?

- Does the individual show an appropriate range of feelings such as, anxiety, anger, irritation, joy, sadness, shame, guilt, fear, surprise disgust, etc.

➤ Flow of Thoughts

This usually refers to the flow of thoughts through speech. We assume that speech reflects thought.

- Does this client eventually get to the point when responding to a question, or does he/she ramble and lose track of his/her thinking (circumstantial or tangential)?

- Is it hard to follow the logic of this client's responses to questions?

- Is it confusing, disconnected, or disjointed?

- Does this client have problems completing thoughts (blocking)? Are there long silences in the middle of thoughts?

- Does this client keep saying the same thing over and over in response to different questions (verbigeration)?

- Does one thought seem to run into another (derailment-loose association)?

- Do words or phrases from one thought stimulate the client to take off on another thought (derailment-flight of ideas)?

- Does the client speak rapidly and often at considerable length, being hard and difficult to interrupt (pressured speech)?

Cognitive Aspects of Mental Status Exam

This part of the interview requires that the evaluator be very systematic and review all of the topics. Thought content includes at least a review of delusions and thoughts of violence. It is important to focus on what the individual talks about as well as how the client thinks. Content of thought and perception problems are usually associated with psychotic disorders. Psychotic disorders produce the kind of behaviors that were formally known as insanity, lunacy or madness. The principal DSM psychotic disorders are Schizophrenia, Schizoaffective disorder, Delusional disorder, Brief psychotic disorder, shared psychotic disorder and Substance-induced psychotic disorder. Although thought and perceptual problems do exist in other disorders like, depression they do not occupy a central feature in the symptom complex as they do in the traditional psychotic disorders. This part of the evaluation should reflect the best of your counseling skills. (warmth, empathy, genuineness, etc.)

Content of Thought

The most serious content of thought disorder is a delusion, a fixed false belief or idea that is obviously false to others who share a similar culture. The clients' belief system must be unshakable despite strong evidence that it does not exist.

The most frequently reported delusions are:

Reference-people are working against them, slandering them or spying upon them. Delusions of Reference are usually found in mistrusting (paranoid) individuals.

Grandeur-person has a false belief that he is some exalted individual like God or Einstein, etc. This also includes individuals who feel they have a power or gift not possessed by others such as eternal life or an ability to speak to the dead, etc. Grandeur is typically found in manic (bipolar) individuals.

Guilt-these clients feel that they committed some serious sin or error that they deserve to be punished for. Guilt is found often in major depression.

Persecution-Clients believe they are being interfered with through constant discrimination, threat or ridicule. Persecution is closely associated with delusions of Reference.

Thought Broadcasting -the client's thoughts are being transmitted across the nation or to local individuals.

Thought Control feelings or thoughts are being put into or removed from the person's mind. Thoughts of violence either homicidal or suicidal are an important and necessary screening. Previous history and current thinking must be taken seriously.

Some questions to ask regarding delusional/violent ideas:

- Does the client appear preoccupied with any particular concern, such as his/her health or other aspects of his/her life?

- What are the individual's fears? Are they normal? Severe? Irrational? If yes what are they?

- Does this client have recurring homicidal or suicidal ideas? If yes what are they?

- Does this client have bizarre thoughts? If yes what are they?

- Does this individual show paranoid thinking? If yes what are they?

- Does the person feel so angry that he/she thinks about harming oneself or others?

All positive answers must be followed up immediately and completely.

Perception

Perception refers to an individual's awareness of their environment and ones internal psychic state. A variety of problems can lead to disturbances in a client's perception. The evaluator must pay particular attention to disturbances associated with psychosis. Many clients are reluctant to disclose hallucinations, phobias, obsessions and compulsions or serious anxiety states for fear that other people will consider them "bazaar or crazy".

(1) Hallucinations

Hallucinations are projections of internal impulses and experiences onto perceptual images in the external world, in the absence of external stimuli. Hallucinations can involve any of the five senses with auditory hallucinations being the most common. Visual hallucinations are the second most common with touch (Tactile), smell (Olfactory) and taste (Gustatory) being more associated with brain tumors, toxic psychosis or seizures disorders.

Some questions to consider asking:

- Does the client report-hearing voices, seeing things, or feeling things that the counselor cannot detect or understand?

- Does the individual see things other people cannot see? If so what do the things look like?

If the person hears voices;

- Where do they come from?

- Whose voices are they?

- Is there more than one voice?

- Do the voices give commands?

- What is the content of the client's voices?

- How does the client react to the voices?

- Does the client complain that he/she feels like a stranger to him/herself (depersonalization)?

(2) Phobias

A phobia is an intense unreasonable fear associated with some situation or object. Unlike general anxiety, phobic individuals know exactly what they are afraid of in the environment. Phobic clients recognize how unreasonable their fears are while delusional individuals do not. Torgersen (1979) categorized phobic fears into five distinct groups:

Separation fears-crowds, traveling alone, being alone at home;

Social fears- Eating with strangers, being watched while writing, being watched while working;

Animal fears-Mice, Rats, Insects;

Nature fears-mountains, oceans, cliffs, heights;

Mutilation fears-open wounds, blood surgical operations.

Some questions to consider asking:

- Does the individual have any of the five distinct fear groups mentioned above?

- Does the client have fears that seem unreasonable or out of proportion to you?

(3) Anxiety

Anxiety is usually defined as vague, diffuse, very unpleasant feeling of fear and apprehension that are not caused by anything specific. The anxious person worries a lot about unknown dangers. Many individuals report symptoms of nervousness, tension, dizziness, feeling tired, heart palpitations, frequent urination, feeling faint, sweating, trembling, sleeplessness, worry and apprehension, difficulty concentrating, hyper vigilance, etc.
Some questions to consider:

- Does the client worry about things excessively?

- Does family or friends tell the client that he worries too much?

- Does the client feel anxious or tense most of the time?

- Does the individual ever feel panicked, suddenly overwhelmed or frightened for no reason?

(4) Obsessions and Compulsions

Obsessions usually involve doubt, hesitation, fear of one's own aggression, or fear of contamination. Obsessive thoughts are often distasteful and shameful. An obsession is a belief, idea, or thought that dominates a client's thought content with persistence. Compulsive behaviors are elaborate patterns of activity performed repeatedly that the client realizes is inappropriate. Compulsive behavior without obsessive thoughts is rare.

Some questions to ask:

- Does the client have obsessive thoughts? If so what are they?

- Does the individual have behaviors that he/she feels must be performed over and over again? If so what are they?

- How neat of a person is the client? At home? In personal attire?

Consciousness and Cognition

This part of the evaluation is related to the individual's ability to absorb, communicate and process information. It is important to have an understanding of the client's capacity for processing information. A disturbance in consciousness almost always indicates a cognitive condition such as delirium, dementia, or intoxication.

(1) Intelligence

Clients who show borderline intelligence or mild mental retardation can have great difficulty in treatment programs, especially recovery programs, which stress education, lectures and other high-level communication. Some questions to ask:

- Can this client understand your questions?

- Does he/she show common sense?

- Does this client have enough common everyday knowledge to deal with day-to-day living?

- Does this client have a good vocabulary? (Vocabulary is the best general measure of intelligence.)

109

- Is this client able to see similarities and relationships (abstract thinking)?

(2) Memory

A disturbance in memory may be a sign of a cognitive disorder or may be secondary to other symptoms, such as poor attention span. Attention is defined as the ability to focus on a certain task or topic. Concentration is the ability to sustain that focus over a period of time.

Some questions to ask:

- Does the individual remernber such basic information as his/her birthday, social security number, and phone numbers?

- Does the client seem excessively forgetful and apologetic about his/her memory?

- Does the client remember prior events of the day?

(3) Language

Language refers to one's ability to read, write, comprehend and repeat things, name things and fluency. If an individual has problems with any language issues they should be referred for educational and/or neurological evaluation.

(4) Abstract Thinking

This is the ability to abstract a principle from a specific example. Commonly asked abstractions include the interpretation of proverbs, differences, etc.

Some questions to ask:

"Can you tell me what this means?"
"A rolling stone gathers no moss"
"How are an apple and an orange alike?"

Note: _Abstract thinking depends heavily on culture, intelligence and education._

Finally, the mental status exam should be completed for any legal or forensic exam, if there is a need for any major diagnosis or in the event of suicidal or homicidal ideation.

To incorporate, update and formulate changes to the DSM-III-R, the DSM IV was published in 1994.The following major changes were noted:

1. Fifty-six (56) new Substance-Related Disorders were listed in addition Substance-Induced Disorders were relocated in similar phenomenological sections. (e.g. Substance-Induced Mood Disorder is now located in the "Mood Disorders" section).

2. New appendices dealing with Culture-Bound Syndromes,

3. Selected Diagnoses and Medications along with the expansion material for further study.

4. AXIS IV now lists Psychosocial and Environmental Problems that influence disorders

5. The term "organic" was eliminated.

6. DSM IV-TR now lists Specific Learning Disorders, Motor Skill Disorders, Pervasive Developmental Disorders and Communication Disorders. (Reid and Wise, 1995).

All of the above changes were completed in order to help clinicians identify important collections of symptoms that cause individuals stress and disability or increase their risk to develop what modern medicine has identified as mental illness. The DSM-5 which was published in May of 2013 made the following revisions to the DSM-IV-TR

DSM-5 Classification System

The American Psychiatric Association (APA) publication of the fifth edition of *Diagnostic and Statistical Manual of Mental Disorders* (DSM-5) became available in 2013. One of the major changes in the DSM-5 is the removal of the current multiaxial system in favor of nonaxial documentation of diagnosis. This change will combine the former DSM-IV-TR Axes I, II, and III with separate notations for psychosocial and contextual factors (formerly Axis IV) and the GAF (formerly Axis V).

Substance Use Disorders- The DSM-5 eliminates the separate categories of Substance Abuse and Substance Dependence and replacing them with one unified category **Substance Use Disorders**. In addition, the manual for the first time would include gambling as an addiction within the category — *"behavioral addiction — not otherwise specified"* (A more detailed analysis of this change is indicated below under the heading Substance Use Disorders).

Personality Disorders-They will maintain the categorical model and criteria as identified in the DSM-IV-TR for the ten (10) personality disorders included in DSM-IV and will include the new trait-specific methodology.

Posttraumatic stress disorder (PTSD) It will be included in a new chapter in DSM-5 on Trauma- and Stressor-Related Disorders. DSM-5 pays more attention to the behavioral symptoms that accompany PTSD and now includes four (4) distinct diagnostic clusters instead of three. PTSD will also be more developmentally sensitive for children and adolescents.

Gender identity disorder. Individuals who believe their biological gender doesn't match their gender identification will no longer be labeled with a disorder. Instead, if they seek psychiatric treatment, they can be labeled with *"gender dysphoria."*

Bereavement exclusion in major depression. The DSM-5 does away with the restriction that a diagnosis of major depression cannot be given to individuals reporting severe grief from the death of a loved one **if the death occurred within the preceding two months.**

Catatonia as a psychotic diagnosis. The group has reworked the diagnostic criteria for catatonia and removed it as a subtype of schizophrenia. Instead, catatonia is now a specifier in schizophrenia and several other psychiatric diagnoses. The DSM-IV diagnosis of catatonia related to a general medical condition will be retained, and DSM-5 will also create a new *"Catatonia NEC"* diagnosis for individuals showing catatonia of uncertain origin or associated with neuro-developmental conditions such as autism.

NOS diagnoses. Most psychiatric disorder in DSM included a NOS (not otherwise specified) diagnosis that served as a catchall for patients who appeared to have disorder but who didn't fit into the established categories. In DSM-5, NOS categories are either gone entirely or replaced with NEC for *"not elsewhere classified."* NEC categories will include a list *of "specifiers,"* each with a specific diagnostic code that will convey clinical information. For example, Depressive Disorder NEC comes with five (5) specifiers such as *"short duration"* that indicate the individual's clinical condition and why it doesn't meet criteria for one of the main depression syndromes.

Substance Use Disorders

As mentioned above the DSM-5 eliminates the separate categories of Substance Abuse and Substance Dependence and replacing them with one unified category Substance Use Disorders. The DSM-5 rationale for lumping together what in DSM IV are the separate categories of Substance Abuse and Substance Dependence comes from studies (factor analytic and latent class analyses) that suggest that there is no sharp boundary between the two concepts and are more uni-dimensional and lack a clear

112

demarcating boundary between them. The new guidelines would eliminates the diagnostic category of "*substance abuse*," which is generally defined by short-term problems like driving drunk, and "*substance dependence*," which is chronic and marked by **tolerance** and **withdrawal.** These categories would be replaced by a combined "*Substance use and addictive disorders.*" This would also merge the criteria used to diagnose disorders related to the use of alcohol, cigarettes, illicit, or prescription drugs, as well as other substances that can be addicting. This list includes issues such as being unable to cut down or control the use of substance and failing to meet obligations, such as school, work, or family. An individual will be given a diagnosis, depending on how many different criteria they meet. The APA notes that previous substance abuse criteria required only 1 symptom whereas the DSM-5's mild substance use disorder requires 2 to 3 symptoms. This increase in the number of symptoms is believed **to** strengthen the diagnosis by increasing the amount of symptoms needed to show distress. The APA believes that the characterization of the severity levels for these conditions, rather than the current artificial distinction between abuse and dependence, would better guide the type and intensity of prevention and treatment services. The only change to the list was the removal of legal problems. This change was made because of marked variations in local U.S. jurisdiction standards which at times appear to be biased towards certain ethnic groups.

The symptoms listed in DSM-IV under "substance abuse" and "substance dependence" was combined to create the list for substance use disorders. Workgroup chairman Charles O'Brien, MD, of the University of Pennsylvania indicated that no longer are physical tolerance and withdrawal symptoms a criteria for a disorder diagnosis because tolerance and withdrawal reflect the body's adaptation to chemicals and are not necessary to a diagnosis.

With the DSM-5, a person can have an "*alcohol use disorder*" or a "*drug use disorder*" but not specifically abuse of or dependence on alcohol or other drugs. Under this change, current substance abusers would not be categorized as "addicts." They would receive a diagnosis of mild, moderate, or severe substance use disorder. It should be noted that the word "*addiction.*" is not used in any DSM-5 names. Instead, they are labeled "*use disorders,*" as in "*opioid use disorder.*"

In addition, theDSM-5 manual for the first time would include gambling as a behavioral disorder. There is a significant body of research that supports the position that pathological gambling and substance-use disorders are very similar in the way they affect the brain and neurological reward system. This is the only behavioral disorder (non-substance diagnosis) change. Gambling disorder has been included in previous editions of the DSM as "*pathological gambling.*" Internet use disorder is currently proposed for inclusion in

Section 3, an area of DSM-5 for conditions requiring further study before they should be considered disorders.

Also, new to the DSM-5 are diagnostic criteria for *"cannabis withdrawal,"* which the APA says is caused by *"cessation of cannabis use that has been heavy and prolonged,"* results in *"clinically significant distress or impairment in social, occupational, or other important areas of functioning,"* and is characterized by at least three of these symptoms: irritability, anger or aggression; nervousness or anxiety; sleep difficulties (insomnia); decreased appetite or weight loss; restlessness; depressed mood; and or physical symptoms such as stomach pain, shakiness or tremors, sweating, fever, chills, and headache.

Finally, a new category for addictive diseases would include a variety of *"substance-use disorders"* broken down by drug type, such as *"cannabis use disorder"* and *"alcohol use disorder."* Diagnostic criteria for these disorders in DSM-5 would remain *"very similar"* to those found in the current DSM-IV. However, the symptom of ***"drug craving"*** would be added to the criteria, while a symptom that referred *to "problems with law enforcement"* would be eliminated *"because of cultural considerations that makes the criteria difficult to apply internationally,"* (APA statement 2012).

Drug Craving –This concept is now becoming **a** key innovation in the diagnosis of substance use disorders and is a requirement that the individual report or demonstrate craving for a particular substance. In general, Cravings are responses to environmental signals that have been connected to drug use through an individual's life experience and have major impact on brain functioning. Drug cravings can be triggered by seeing objects or experiencing moments, such as, music or group events, etc. that can be associated with the drug or usage of a given substance. All the environmental cues associated with taking a drug can become rewarding. For example, if one usually take a drug in a certain room, or at a certain time in the day, or with certain equipment, just being in that space with all the familiar objects can stimulate the Dopamine levels in your brain. That brain change alone can force your craving for a given drug and take one into cognitive relapse followed by drug behavior. Within the recovery community it is one of the main reasons why people, places, things and situations need to change.

Finally, drug craving symptoms can occur intermittently, but are not always present. They are made worse by stress or other triggers and may arise at unexpected times and for no apparent reason. They may last for a short while or longer. Any of the following may trigger a temporary return or worsening of the symptoms of craving. Stressful and/or frustrating situations, such as, multitasking, feelings of anxiety, fearfulness or anger, social conflicts or unrealistic expectations of oneself may precipitate drug craving.

Substance related disorders encapsulate a wide variety of psychoactive chemicals. Disorders in this category are divided into two groups: (1) Substance Use Disorders and (2) Substance-Induced Disorders.

DSM-5-Substance Use Disorders

Please find below a list of disorders that are currently proposed for the diagnostic category, Substance Use and Addictive Disorders. This category contains diagnoses that were listed in DSM-IV under the chapter of Substance-Related Disorders. It is being proposed that this diagnostic category include both substance use disorders and non-substance patterns of behavior. Gambling Disorder has been moved into this category, which was listed in DSM-IV under the chapter, Impulse-Control Disorders Not Elsewhere Classified.

Substance-Induced Disorders:

Substance-Induced Psychotic Disorder
Substance-Induced Bipolar Disorder
Substance-Induced Depressive Disorder
Substance-Induced Anxiety Disorder
Substance-Induced Obsessive-Compulsive or Related Disorders
Substance-Induced Dissociative Disorder
Substance-Induced Sleep-Wake Disorder
Substance-Induced Sexual Dysfunction
Substance-Induced Delirium
Mild Neurocognitive Disorder Associated with Substance Use
Major Neurocognitive Disorder Associated with Substance Use

Substance Use Disorders

Definition

. A maladaptive pattern of substance use leading to clinically significant impairment or distress, as manifested by 2 (or more) of the following, occurring within a 12-month period:

   1. recurrent substance use resulting in a failure to fulfill major role obligations at work, school, or home (e.g., repeated absences or poor work performance related to substance use; substance-related absences, suspensions, or expulsions from school; neglect of children or household)

2. recurrent substance use in situations in which it is physically hazardous (e.g., driving an automobile or operating a machine when impaired by substance use)
3. continued substance use despite having persistent or recurrent social or interpersonal problems caused or exacerbated by the effects of the substance (e.g., arguments with spouse about consequences of intoxication, physical fights)
4. tolerance, as defined by either of the following: a. a need for: (a) markedly increased amounts of the substance to achieve intoxication or desired effect and (b) markedly diminished effect with continued use of the same amount of the substance. (Note: Tolerance is not counted for those taking medications under medical supervision such as analgesics, antidepressants, ant-anxiety medications or beta-blockers.)
5. withdrawal, as manifested by either of the following:
   a. the characteristic withdrawal syndrome for the substance (refer to Criteria A and B of the criteria sets for Withdrawal from the specific substances)
   b. the same (or a closely related) substance is taken to relieve or avoid withdrawal symptoms. (Withdrawal is not counted for those taking medications under medical supervision such as analgesics, antidepressants, or anti-anxiety medications.
6. the substance is often taken in larger amounts or over a longer period than was intended
7. there is a persistent desire or unsuccessful efforts to cut down or control substance use
8. a great deal of time is spent in activities necessary to obtain the substance, use the substance, or recover from its effects
9. important social, occupational, or recreational activities are given up or reduced because of substance use
10. the substance use is continued despite knowledge of having a persistent or recurrent physical or psychological problem that is likely to have been caused or exacerbated by the substance
11. Craving or a strong desire or urge to use a specific substance.

Severity specifiers:

> Moderate: 2-3 criteria positive
> Severe: 4 or more criteria positive

Specify if:

> With Physiological Dependence: evidence of tolerance or withdrawal (i.e., either Item 4 or 5 is present)

Without Physiological Dependence: no evidence of tolerance or withdrawal (i.e., neither Item 4 nor 5 is present)

Course specifiers (see text for definitions):

Early Full Remission

Early Partial Remission

Sustained Full Remission

Sustained Partial Remission

On Agonist Therapy

In a Controlled Environment

Example: Alcohol Use Disorder

A. A maladaptive pattern of substance use leading to clinically significant impairment or distress, as manifested by 2 (or more) of the following, occurring within a 12-month period:

1. recurrent substance use resulting in a failure to fulfill major role obligations at work, school, or home (e.g., repeated absences or poor work performance related to substance use; substance-related absences, suspensions, or expulsions from school; neglect of children or household)
2. recurrent substance use in situations in which it is physically hazardous (e.g., driving an automobile or operating a machine when impaired by substance use)
3. continued substance use despite having persistent or recurrent social or interpersonal problems caused or exacerbated by the effects of the substance (e.g., arguments with spouse about consequences of intoxication, physical fights)
4. tolerance, as defined by either of the following:

   a. a need for markedly increased amounts of the substance to achieve intoxication or desired effect

   b. markedly diminished effect with continued use of the same amount of the substance (Note: Tolerance is not counted for those taking medications under medical supervision such as analgesics, antidepressants, ant-anxiety medications or beta-blockers.)

117

5. withdrawal, as manifested by either of the following:

    ✓ the characteristic withdrawal syndrome for the substance (refer to Criteria A and B of the criteria sets for Withdrawal from the specific substances)

    ✓ the same (or a closely related) substance is taken to relieve or avoid withdrawal symptoms. (Note: Withdrawal is not counted for those taking medications under medical supervision such as analgesics, antidepressants, anti-anxiety medications or beta-blockers.)

6. the substance is often taken in larger amounts or over a longer period than was intended
7. there is a persistent desire or unsuccessful efforts to cut down or control substance use
8. a great deal of time is spent in activities necessary to obtain the substance, use the substance, or recover from its effects
9. important social, occupational, or recreational activities are given up or reduced because of substance use
10. The substance use is continued despite knowledge of having a persistent or recurrent physical or psychological problem that is likely to have been caused or exacerbated by the substance.
11. Craving or a strong desire or urge to use a specific substance.

Severity specifiers:

    Moderate: 2-3 criteria positive

    Severe: 4 or more criteria positive

Specify if:

    With Physiological Dependence: evidence of tolerance or withdrawal (i.e., either Item 4 or 5 is present)

    Without Physiological Dependence: no evidence of tolerance or withdrawal (i.e., neither Item 4 nor 5 is present)

Course specifiers (see text for definitions):

    Early Full Remission

    Early Partial Remission

    Sustained Full Remission

    Sustained Partial Remission

On Agonist Therapy

In a Controlled Environment

Other Substance Use and Intoxication Disorders:

- R 01 Amphetamine Use Disorder
- R 02 Cannabis Use Disorder
- R 03 Cocaine Use Disorder
- R 04 Hallucinogen Use Disorder
- R 05 Inhalant Use Disorder
- R 06 Opioid Use Disorder
- R 07 Phencyclidine Use Disorder
- R 08 Sedative, Hypnotic, or Anxiolytic Use Disorder
- R 09 Tobacco Use Disorder
- R 10 Other (or Unknown) Substance Use Disorder
- R 11-21 Substance Intoxication
- R 11 Alcohol Intoxication
- R 12 Amphetamine Intoxication
- R 13 Caffeine Intoxication
- R 14 Cannabis Intoxication
- R 15 Cocaine Intoxication
- R 16 Hallucinogen Intoxication
- R 17 Inhalant Intoxication
- R 18 Opioid Intoxication
- R 19 Phencyclidine Intoxication
- R 20 Sedative, Hypnotic, or Anxiolytic Intoxication

R31-Gambling Disorder (this diagnosis is being reclassified from Impulse-Control Disorders Not Elsewhere Classified to Substance-Related Disorders which will be renamed Addiction and Related Disorders)

A. Persistent and recurrent maladaptive gambling behavior as indicated by five (or more) of the following:

1. is preoccupied with gambling (e.g., preoccupied with reliving past gambling experiences, handicapping or planning the next venture, or thinking of ways to get money with which to gamble

2. needs to gamble with increasing amounts of money in order to achieve the desired excitement

3. has repeated unsuccessful efforts to control, cut back, or stop gambling

4. is restless or irritable when attempting to cut down or stop gambling

5. gambles as a way of escaping from problems or of relieving a dysphoric mood (e.g., feelings of helplessness, guilt, anxiety, depression)

6. after losing money gambling, often returns another day to get even ("chasing" one's losses)

7. lies to family members, therapist, or others to conceal the extent of involvement with gambling

8. has jeopardized or lost a significant relationship, job, or educational or career opportunity because of gambling

9. relies on other to provide money to relieve a desperate financial situation caused by gambling

B. The gambling behavior is not better accounted for by a Manic Episode.

Information about various substances use patterns

Alcohol

Alcohol Substance Intoxication. There must be recent ingestion of alcohol, as well as significant maladaptive behavioral or psychological change. At least one (1) or more of the following signs develop during, or shortly after, alcohol use:

- slurred speech
- incoordination
- unsteady gait
- involuntary rapid eye movement (nystagmus)
- impaired attention or memory
- coma or stupor.

Alcohol (uncomplicated) Substance Withdrawal. Two (2) or more of the following develop within several hours to a few days of cessation or reduction:

- autonomic over activity-sweating or rapid heartbeat
- worsened tremor of hands

- insomnia
- nausea or vomiting
- short-lived hallucinations or illusions-visual, tactile, or auditory
- psychomotor agitation
- anxiety
- grand mal seizures.

Alcohol Information

Even though alcoholic beverages are legal and widely available, alcohol is nonetheless a powerful psychoactive drug, which in small doses relaxes and sedates but in large doses is a poison (toxin). Grain alcohol (ethyl alcohol or ethanol) is the psychoactive component in alcoholic beverages. It is the least toxic of the hundreds of different alcohols. Any beverage with more than 2% alcohol content is considered an alcoholic beverage. Alcohol occurs naturally as a result of yeast feeding on sugars in honey, fruit, berries, vegetables, or grain.

History of Alcohol Use

The king of Persia in the sixth century B.C. had the distinction of being one of the first alcoholics on record. In 1250 Europeans developed the technique of distillation making it possible to produce more potent alcohol beverages. Until the 16th century distilled or spirituous liquors were made from wine. Alcohol was known as the "water of life" with extraordinary healing powers. During the 16th century excessive use of alcohol and public drunkenness was mentioned for the first time in England. In the colonies drunkenness is prominent but it is not considered a major problem, alcohol is held in high esteem both in England and in colonial America. In England alcohol continues to be very popular and is integrated into every phase of life, a condition that continues well into the 18th century. In 1637 Massachusetts ordered in each town there be established a man to sell wine so that the public will not suffer from a lack of proper accommodations. Taverns and Inns were required to provide beer for entertainment. Concern over drunkenness begins to increase as the use of distilled spirits (rum and whiskey) rises in colonial America. Drinking becomes primarily a male pastime spent away from home. The English tradition continues to prevail in America allowing many colonials to view drunkenness as a natural and essentially harmless consequence of drinking. In 1743 the Methodist Church included a prohibition against drunkenness and the buying, selling, or drinking of spirits. During the colonial revolution Benjamin Rush was one of the first to challenge popular belief in the health benefits of spirits. He recommended temperance. Congressional attempts to impose a tax on distilled spirits resulted in the whiskey revolution of 1794.Between 1825 and 1850 the temperance movement demands increased attention to total absence from all intoxicants not just temperance in the use of spirits. The Washington Temperance Society was formed in 1840. Following the Civil War, the National Prohibition Party and the Women's Christian Temperance Union were found. Between 1875 and 1900 the Prohibitionist Movement broadens its attack and becomes influential in attempts to restrict alcohol in the United States. In the early part of the 20th century Anti-Saloon League grows in strength and concentrates on the election of prohibition supporters. In January 1919 the 18th amendment to the Constitution was ratified establishing national prohibition. The possession of alcohol for personal use is still permitted; enforcement was left to the states. By 1925 widespread illicit liquor trade was well established, increased enforcement and penalties had little effect, the Depression further strengthens the repeal sentiment. The 18th amendment was repealed in 1933.

Social Consequences of Alcohol Consumption

Alcohol use is directly involved in:

- 60 % of all suicides
- 64% of all murders
- 20% of all freezing deaths
- 25% of all choking deaths
- 36% of all pedestrian deaths
- 50% of all deaths from falls
- 52% of all fire deaths
- 50% of all teen motor vehicle deaths
- 69% of all drowning
- 76% of all recreational aircraft deaths
- 33% of all motor vehicle injuries
- 65% of all motorcycle crashes
- 69% of all recreational boating injuries
- 34% of all child abuse cases
- 72% of all assaults and robberies
- 80% of all criminal court cases
- 50% of all rapes

Effects of Alcohol

Types of Alcoholic Beverages are **wine** (produced from fermenting fruits), **beer** (from fermenting grain), and **distilled spirits** (from distilled whiskey, wine, or other alcoholic beverages).

Beer is produced by adding malt and barley, roasting them, and combining the result with a mixture of water, grain, hops, and yeast.

Wine is made from grapes or other fruit and contains from 8% to 14% alcohol. Wines with more than 14% alcohol content (the natural limit of fermentation) are fortified wines with spirits added.

Distilled Spirits (liquors) are the result of boiling wine or other alcoholic beverages and collecting the condensate. Distilled beverages have much higher alcohol content than wine or beer and have led to periodic outbreaks of alcoholism.

Processing of Alcohol

Digestion is the process of dismantling food so that raw materials required by the body can be attained from the food. Alcohol does contain calories but contains no nutrients, vitamins, or minerals. Therefore alcohol calories are "empty calories." Alcohol is in a liquid form and requires no digestion or mechanical action so that it can get into the bloodstream. Alcohol is absorbed into the blood stream.

Alcohol absorption begins almost immediately. The capillaries in the mouth absorb some alcohol. The majority is swallowed and enters the stomach. Some alcohol is absorbed through the lining of the stomach. Most of the alcohol passes out of the stomach, through the pyloric valve and enters the small intestine. About 20% of alcohol is absorbed by the stomach walls, the remaining 80% being absorbed in the small intestine where it passes into the bloodstream and then throughout the body. Psychoactive effects occur once the alcohol reaches the brain. The speed of absorption is influenced by the amount drunk, the rate of drinking, the concentration of the drink, and a variety of other factors

In the stomach Alcohol is an irritant (solvent), which increases the flow of hydrochloric acid in the stomach. Presence of food in the stomach acts to slow down the rate of alcohol absorption. Absorption rate also varies with the concentration of alcohol. The higher the concentration, the quicker the absorption. Carbonation will also speed up the rate of absorption. The pyloric valve controls the passage of stomach contents into the small intestine. The valve is sensitive to alcohol and large concentrations will cause it to spasm closed. Alcohol is then trapped in the stomach and its irritation may result in vomiting. Once the alcohol is absorbed, it enters the blood stream and is circulated to all body parts.

Blood Alcohol Concentrations (BAC) are the percentage of alcohol in a person's blood. Because alcohol is metabolized at a defined continuous rate (about 1/4-1/3 oz. per hour), the blood alcohol concentration can be calculated on the basis of the sex and weight of the drinker, the number of drinks consumed, and the duration of the drinking episode.

Alcohol is diluted in the blood stream and carried to all parts of the body. Alcohol is soluble in water and can pass through cell walls. The alcohol is distributed uniformly throughout the water of all body tissues. Tissue alcohol content varies in proportion to amount of water present. Individuals with higher body weight have more blood volume for alcohol to be diluted in than individuals with lower body weight. The liver can only burn up alcohol at a constant rate of one drink per hour. **Alcohol Poisoning (overdose)** occur when large amounts of alcohol are consumed too quickly. Depression of various systems can lead to unconsciousness coma, and death, usually at a BAC 0.40% or higher, although asphyxiation and death can result with BAC levels of 0.20% or higher.

Small amounts of alcohol leave the body unmetabolized through sweat, urine, and breath. The majority of alcohol must be changed chemically through metabolism.

The drug Antabuse blocks the secretion of acetaldehyde dehydrogenase. This results in a buildup of acetaldehyde in the body. Acetaldehyde is very toxic and causes nausea, flushing, and heart palpitations.

Alcohols Effect on the Human Body

Alcohol is a depressant drug in all amounts because it slows down the central nervous system. Often not considered a drug by the general public because it can be legally purchased and is socially acceptable. Erroneously thought to be stimulant because it reduces judgment and lowers inhibitions and behavior comes out that normally would not. The physiological effects of alcohol on the body are specific, predictable, and progressive.

- **Digestive System:** Alcohol is a solvent and irritates the digestive system. Also, alcohol stimulates the production of increased amounts of hydrochloric acid in the stomach. Increasing amounts of alcohol can impede or stop digestion by causing vomiting or closing of the pyloric valve.

- **Circulatory System**: Small amounts of alcohol have little affect on heartbeat and blood pressure. In moderate amounts alcohol causes

124

vasodilatation of surface vessels and body heat is lost. The sensation of warmth experienced from drinking distilled alcohol results from the solvent property of alcohol and burns the esophagus and stomach.

- **Kidneys:** Increased urine output occurs. Consuming a liquid and alcohol affects the pituitary gland, which regulates the production of urine. Alcohol reduces the amount of pituitary hormone that controls the production of urine by the kidneys. The pituitary releases too little hormone and the kidneys form too much urine.

- **Liver:** The liver maintains proper blood sugar level. Blood sugar (glucose) is the only source of energy brain cells can use. When alcohol is present all liver attention is directed to alcohol metabolism. When metabolizing alcohol, the liver does not manufacture or release glucose (sugar). A drop in blood sugar could occur -- resulting in a hypoglycemic state. When the brain is deprived of proper nourishment the following symptoms may occur: weakness, nervousness, sweating, headache, and tremors. Drinking on an empty stomach or for lengthy periods so alcohol is still present after a meal has been digested are two situations likely to produce a hypoglycemic state.

- **Central Nervous System:** Alcohol is a central nervous system depressant. The brain is the body organ most sensitive to the presence of alcohol. Alcohol interferes with brain cell activity and lowers the activity of the brain.

- **Reproductive System.** *Female:* Chronic alcohol abuse disturbs the menstrual cycle and leads to early menopause. It can cause pathologic changes in the ovaries and subject women to greater chances of infertility and spontaneous abortion and lessen the frequency of orgasms. *Male:* Alcohol abuse decreases testosterone, causing male breast enlargement, testicular atrophy, and low sperm count. About 8% of alcoholics are impotent.

Amphetamines, Cocaine and other Stimulants

Amphetamines and/or Cocaine: Substance Intoxication.

There must be recent use of amphetamine or related substance, as well as significant maladaptive behavioral or psychological change (at least two (2) or more of the following signs develop during or shortly after use):

- slowed or rapid (tachycardia) heart rate
- dilated pupils

125

- raised or lowered blood pressure
- chills or sweating
- nausea or vomiting
- weight loss
- psychomotor agitation or retardation
- muscle weakness
- shallow or slowed breathing
- chest pain or heart arrhythmias
- coma or confusion
- impairment of normal movement (dyskinesia)
- impairment of muscle tone (dystonic) or seizures.

Amphetamines and/or Cocaine: Substance Withdrawal.

Restless mood (dysphoria) AND two or more of the following physiological changes develop within a few hours to several days:

- Fatigue
- unpleasant vivid dreams
- hypersomnia or insomnia
- increased appetite
- psychomotor agitation or retardation.

Caffeine: Substance Intoxication.

Recent use of caffeine, usually in excess of 2-3 cups (250 mgs), at least five (5) of the following signs develop during or shortly after use; restlessness, nervousness, excitement, insomnia, red face, increased urination, gastro-intestinal upset, muscle twitching, rambling speech, rapid (tachycardia) or irregular heart beat (arrhythmia), periods of tirelessness, or psycho-motor agitation. It should be noted that caffeine use and abuse is identical to Amphetamine and Cocaine

Nicotine Withdrawal.

Daily use of nicotine for at least several weeks. Abrupt cessation of nicotine use or reduction in the amount followed by four (4) or more of the following signs:

- dysphoria or depression

- insomnia,

- anger-frustration-irritability

- trouble concentrating, restlessness

- decreased heart rate

- increased appetite or weight gain.

Stimulant Information

Stimulants include powerful drugs like methamphetamines and *"crack"* cocaine and milder substances like caffeinated soft drinks and cigarettes. Stimulants range from natural substances, such as tobacco leaf and coca leaf, to refined ones, like nicotine and cocaine, and to synthetic ones, such as diet pills and amphetamines.

There are three general groups of stimulant drugs: (1) the Xanthenes which include caffeine (coffee), tobacco (nicotine), and theobromine (chocolate), (2) the Amphetamines which include all of the diet tablets and (3) cocaine. All of the stimulants have similar effects but vary by dose, amount, and type of administration.

History of Stimulants

Coffee (caffeine) was first roasted in Ethiopia in the 1300's. Prior to that coffee was very expensive, the beans were chewed or the leaves were eaten. The technique of roasting made coffee cheaper, more available and more pleasant to consume. Between 1450 and 1475 the drinking of coffee spread rapidly throughout Arabia. Coffee houses were established and flourished throughout the 15th century in many Islamic countries. Because of the stimulant effect of coffee many Holy men began to attack the use of coffee as being contrary to the Koran. Between 1515 and 1525 the drinking of coffee was forbidden and coffee houses were viewed by politicians and religious authorities as centers of sin and seduction. Civil disorder in Mecca in 1524 caused the closing of coffee houses. Between 1525 and 1550 coffee was known as the *"Wine of Islam"* and became a regular part of one's diet. Coffee continued to spread throughout the Ottoman Empire and between 1575 and 1600 the Ottoman Empire began to rely on coffee as an important source of revenue. It was during this period that coffee was introduced to Europeans. In the early part of the 1600's coffee was consumed in England as a cure for widespread drunkenness. Between 1650 and 1675 coffee houses became popular in most European countries with coffee houses being seen as places to exchange news and intellectual and political debates. During the struggle for independence coffee becomes popular in the colonies. The Boston Tea Party of 1773 fostered an abstinence from tea and the drinking of coffee. Coffee drinking was considered patriotic. Coffee continued to flourish in the United States and it was not until the early part of the 20th century that coffee was classified as an addiction similar to morphine and alcohol.

Caffeine (coffee) is the most popular stimulant in the world. It is found in tea, coffee, soft drinks, chocolate, and hundreds of medications. Caffeine is a mild stimulant but 5-7 cups per day can cause anxiety, insomnia nervousness, and other complications. Higher doses can cause increased heart rate, palpitations, muscle twitching, and other stimulant type problems. Tolerance does occur but dosage varies. Withdrawal symptoms include headaches, fatigue, depression, and irritability. About 6 cups of coffee, 8 cups of tea, or 10 cola drinks per day can result in caffeine dependence or addiction. Generally, coffee creates a milder dependency than amphetamines.

Tobacco (nicotine) was introduced into Western Europe in 1556 when seeds were brought from Brazil to France. Jean Nicot described its medical properties to the French court and was so persuasive that tobacco became known as nicotiana (nicotine). In England smoking became popular in the mid 1570's when Sir Walter Raleigh introduced it as a fashionable activity. In the early 1600s tobacco was cultivated in the colonies. Tobacco soon became a major crop in the New World. In England smoking spread rapidly becoming an expensive habit among the court and nobility. Between 1600 and 1625 smoking tobacco was introduced to Turkey, Russia and Japan. In Turkey Sultan Amend prohibited its use and considers tobacco forbidden by the Koran. During the Ottoman Empire Sultan Murad IV established the death penalty for anyone caught smoking. By the 17th century the band was repealed and cultivation spread into Turkey. Between 1717 and 1725 Western Europeans began using snuff among the nobility and clergy, this practice became firmly established over the next fifty years. Around 1845 the United States launched an anti-tobacco crusader in conjunction with the early Temperance Movement. During and after the Civil War a federal excise tax was imposed on all sales. Following the war the tobacco industry expanded rapidly. The cigarette industry initiated major advertising campaigns and formed a cartel. Sales increased dramatically, public acceptance of smoking, particularly among women was socially acceptable and by 1927 the tobacco industry was firmly entrenched as an American way of life. Between 1925 and 1950 both taxation and use continued to increase and the United States begin to see the first early health problems. The Surgeon General's report of 1964 raised some concerns regarding negative health habits but the tobacco production continued to increase through the '70s.

Nicotine (tobacco) Cigarettes account for 95% of all tobacco use in the United States. Tobacco affects the same areas of the brain as cocaine and amphetamines. Cigarettes contain over 400 toxins, 43 of which are carcinogens. Nicotine is the chemical, which accounts for the most important cardiovascular and psychoactive effects of tobacco. It disrupts the balance of neurotransmitters and as a result, it constricts blood vessels, raises heart rate, depresses appetite, produces a mild euphoria, and deadens senses. Tobacco is very addicting. Surveys indicate that 9 out of 10 smokers want to quit or limit their intake but continue to smoke. Daily use among individuals in the United States is about 29%. In other countries, it is 40% to 50%. Nicotine craving is more subtle than other cravings but still extremely powerful. Many people smoke to maintain their habit, that is, maintain a familiar state that is neither pleasurable nor objectionable.

Twenty percent of premature deaths worldwide are caused by tobacco use. Also, secondhand smoke kills 50,000 worldwide. Tobacco takes decades for its worst effects to be felt and they can be severe, including cardiovascular disease, respiratory impairment, and cancer. Early on, there are no severe warning signals, so users receive no early warning signs. A two-pack-a-day smoker lives on average eight years less.

- **Cardiovascular** effects include plaque formation on the arteries and hardening of the arteries, the leading causes of heart attacks.

- **Fetal** effects include lower birth weight and higher incidence of crib death.

- **Respiratory** effects include lung cancer (as a result of tars inhaled) and other bronchopulmonary disease. Children living with smokers have health problems resulting from inhaling secondhand smoke. The chances of cancer are increased 15-fold in male smokers and 9-fold in female smokers

Amphetamines were first synthesized in 1887. They were initially developed and used as nasals sprays known as Benzedrine inhalers. Smith Kline and French laboratories introduced them in 1932. Besides enlarging the nasal passage they raise blood pressure and stimulate the central nervous system. In Sweden in 1938 amphetamines were placed on the market and widely advertised as pep pills. During World War they were extensively used by the military, both in the United States and Japan. Following the war widespread use occurred due to its presentation as a safe, euphoric, mental energy and cure for such problems as depression, fatigue and weight loss. In Japan, after World War II its use increased as a spiritual anecdote to the loss of the war. In the United States, in the late 1940's there developed a black-market drug subculture, which practiced non-medical use of the amphetamines. During the 1950s and 1960s diet pills (pep pills) were used to elevate mood and suppress appetite. The Surgeon General Report in 1964 caused a momentary decline in use, but despite health warnings use began to increase in the 1970s. Following the Controlled Substance Act of 1970 restricted sale of legal amphetamines forced the development of illegal street amphetamines, like *"Speed"*. Street chemists increased production of *"crank"* and *"crystal"* in the 1970s and 1980s. *"Ice"*, a highly potent smoke able form of methamphetamines, began to appear in the 1990s

Amphetamines act as stimulants by interacting primarily with the adrenal gland (alert reaction) and in general, the central nervous system. Over time an individual loses performance but gains hours of alertness. Many studies have demonstrated that a fatigued mind cannot learn or reason as well as an unfatigued mind. Over time stimulant abusers exercise poor judgment and overreact to stimuli. Use of amphetamines decreases appetite and fosters insomnia. The amphetamines also enhance extreme feelings of love with prolonged body contact. Finally, it is not uncommon among stimulant abusers to see symptoms of malnutrition such as abscesses, ulcers and brittle fingernails as well as hyper-suspiciousness, aggressiveness and violent behavior. Often amphetamines are taken orally. Less popular routes are injection and snorting because of the irritating effects. Smoking (ice) is becoming more widespread. Extended amphetamine use, can cause abuse and dependence.

Cocaine flourished during the Inca Empire between 1202 and 1553. The coca leaves were central to the Incas religious and social system. It was a religious gift given to the Inca culture by the Sun God. Following the destruction of the Inca Empire by the Spaniards coca leaves became widespread among lower class Indians. In 1580 the coca leaf was brought back to Europe where it did not appear to generate any interest. In the 19th century the chief alkaloid of the coca plant was isolated and called cocaine. Published articles praised cocaine's ability to lessen fatigue, stimulate and elevate spirits and enhance sexual potency. Vini Mariani, a wine mixed with coca, was introduced and became a major success. Pope Leo XIII gave a gold medal to its developer. Sigmund Freud described and praised the effect of cocaine as a magical drug and suggested a variety of medical usages. During this same period 1825 to 1900 critics' denounced cocaine as an addictive drug worse than morphine. In 1860, cocaine was refined into cocaine hydrochloride (HCL) and was added to soft drinks, wine, and patent medicines. In1884 Dr. Carl Koehler demonstrated its usefulness as an anesthetic in eye surgery. In the United States, cocaine became widely used for a variety of medical problems; it was included in such stimulant drinks as Coca-Cola (1892). In the United States, cocaine appeared ideally suited for the industrial revolution. Between 1919 and 1925 an increase in cocaine imports occurred in the United States. In 1903 Coca-Cola company removed cocaine from their product. In 1906 the Pure Food and Drug Act eliminated cocaine from all patent medicines and soft drinks. In 1914 the

Harrison Act treated cocaine as more dangerous than opium. Cocaine subsequently went underground primarily used by bohemians' and musicians in urban ghettos. During the 1970's cocaine reappears as a major drug of choice of Americans. During this time period cocaine hydrochloride was chemically altered into freebase cocaine and was smoked, a form of intake that gets the drug to the brain the fastest (5-8 seconds)

Cocaine is extracted from the coca plant; cocaine is grown primarily in South America, which accounts for 95% of the world's production. The United States accounts for about 70% of the world's consumption. In the process of making cocaine the cocoa leaves are mixed with an organic solvent, such as kerosene. After soaking and mixing the substance is known as cocoa paste. The paste can be made into cocaine hydrochloride, a salt that is stable and mixes easily in water. Some cocaine users want to smoke the cocaine and therefore convert it into freebase by extracting the hydrochloride from the cocaine. This is accomplished by either the use of a volatile organic solvent, such as ether, or by the use of baking soda. Both forms give cocaine a lower melting point, so it can be smoked without destroying the psychoactive properties. Withdrawal effects can last years. Major effects include less ability to experience pleasure, lack of energy, and intense craving for the drug. A typical cycle of compulsive use includes binge, crash, detoxification and relapse two to four weeks later is very common. Overdose can cause injury to heart and blood vessels, and even death. Long-term cardiovascular effects can cause stroke (the bursting of a blood vessel in the brain) as well as heart damage. Exposure of a fetus to cocaine greatly increases the risk of miscarriage, stroke, and sudden infant death syndrome (SIDS).

Effects of Stimulants

All stimulants are absorbed into the body and excreted unchanged through the kidneys. Since amphetamines metabolize slowly the drug is found for approximately five to seven days after ingestion. Stimulants increase chemical and electrical activity in the central nervous system, making the user of low doses more alert, active, restless, and generally more stimulated than normal.

Physiologically, most stimulants have the following effects:

1. They constrict blood vessels.
2. They increase heart rate.
3. They increase blood pressure.
4. They dilate the bronchi.
5. They relax intestinal muscle.
6. They increase blood sugar.
7. They shortened blood coagulation time.

8. They increase muscle tension.
9. They stimulate the adrenal glands.
10. They produce extreme or morbid dilation of the pupils (Mydriasis).

Remember: Among cocaine abusers there is an 18 to 20% co-occurring diagnosis of thought and or mood disorders (NSDUH, 2017).

Cannabis (Marijuana)

Cannabis: Substance Intoxication.

Recent use of cannabis (Marijuana) as well as significant maladaptive psychological or behavioral changes (within two hours of using, at least two or more of the following signs occur):

- red eyes

- increased appetite

- dry mouth

- rapid heart rate (tachycardia)

Marijuana Information: The Mild Hallucinogen

The plant, also known as Cannabis or hemp, is used to make a variety of useful products and can be smoked or eaten to alter one's mental state. As a fiber it is used in the manufacture of fine linen to make canvas and rope. The seeds have been valued as feed for birds and for the production of oil which resembles linseed oil.

History of Marijuana Use

Cannabis, hemp or **marijuana** has been used for thousands of years. It originated in central Asia in the Neolithic times. It was probably first used as a food source (for its seeds), then as a source of fiber for clothes, rope (especially after the fifteenth century in Europe), and medicines. In 1545 A.D. the Spaniards introduced Marijuana into Chile. Marijuana was grown extensively in the United States before and during the Civil War. In the 19th century hemp plantations flourished in Mississippi, Georgia, California, South Carolina, Nebraska, etc. Kentucky was the marijuana center in the United States. Between 1850 and 1875 with the arrival in Jamaica of indentured laborers from India marijuana was introduced as a multi-purpose medication called ganja. From 1900-1925 concerns among White landowners regarding the increased smoking by Jamaican natives led to the Dangerous Drug Law Act of 1924, which increased penalties for use of both ganja and opium smoking in Jamaica. In the United States, marijuana smoking began to appear in large numbers among Mexican labors in towns along the Mexican border and spread throughout the Gulf Coast. Between 1915 and 1930, twenty-nine (29) states, mostly west of the Mississippi, prohibited its non-medical use. In 1915 the United States prohibited its import for non-medical purposes. Between 1850 and 1937 marijuana was used for medical purposes listed in medical journals until 1942. As recently as 1937 over 10,000 acres of marijuana was being grown or four (4) million pounds of seeds per year was being used as birdseed.

In 1937, the Marijuana Tax Act was passed in the United States establishing a prohibitive tax and regulatory procedures. During this time the FBI began to emphasize the need for adoption of the Uniform State Narcotic Drug Act to control marijuana. Since 1937 laws have increased dramatically to restrict its use. In 1951 Federal law fixed a one-year penalty for use. In 1956 first-time offenders were given mandatory two-year penalties. In 1970 with the passage of the Comprehensive Drug Abuse Prevention and Control Act Federal penalties for marijuana were relegated to the states.

In 1960, only two percent of the people in the United States had tried any illegal drugs. By 1995, 10 million were using marijuana once a month. An estimated 200-300 million people use it worldwide.

Physical Appearance

The usual form of marijuana found in the United States is a dried green leaf substance called "grass". It is ordinarily smoked as a cigarette or smoked in a pipe. It can also be baked and eaten. At times, the leaves are steeped in hot water and the liquid is drunk like tea. Marijuana in its strongest form is known as Hashish, which physically appears in the form of a gummy powder or brick. Marijuana has a variety of street names including "pot," "buds," "herb", etc. There are many varieties of the plant. The three general species are: *Cannabis Sativa, Cannabis Ruderalis,* and *Cannabis Indica.* The most psychoactive is *Cannabis Sativa. A* typical plant produces one to five pounds of buds and smoke able leaves.

Effects of Marijuana

There are about 360 chemicals in a Cannabis plant, at least 30 of which are psychoactive. The most potent psychoactive chemical is called delta *9* THC Tetrahydrocannabinol. A variety of growing techniques has increased the THC concentration in marijuana from 1% to 3% in the 1960s to 6% to 14% in the late '70s, and through the '90s. Generally, one joint from the '90s is equal to about 10 joints used in the '60s.

133

Short Term Effects

Physical and Mental Effects include relaxation or sedation, detachment in moderate doses and giddiness, stimulation, and sensory distortion in higher doses. Effects depend on mood and surroundings. Marijuana exaggerates emotions. It can act as a stimulant or depressant and causes a loss of sense of time, making repetitive jobs go by faster. It impairs tracking ability. Smoking marijuana irritates lungs and breathing passages. It increases heart rate, decreases blood pressure, disrupts hormones, and can increase anxiety or paranoia. Residual effects can last for up to six months.

Long-Term Effects

1. Respiratory Problems. Long-Term use of marijuana damages the breathing passages and other parts of the respiratory system, leading to coughing, chronic bronchitis, and increased dangers of cancer of the lung, larynx, and tongue. Respiratory problems are partly related to reduce white blood cells in lungs, which reduces ability to remove bacteria and other foreign debris from lungs.

2. Immune System. Evidence suggests that heavy use depresses the immune system, exposing the user to increased risks of infection and disease. It also lowers resistance to viral infection.

3. Learning and Emotional Maturation. Marijuana slows learning and disrupts concentration. It impairs short term memory but seems to have little effect on long term memory. Some researchers describe an Amotivational Syndrome that accompanies long-term use. It can impede emotional development because users employ the drug as a way of finding pleasure and avoiding painful situations.

4. Acute Mental Effects are unusual from short term use but even short-term use can trigger preexisting mental problems and trigger acute anxiety or temporary psychotic reactions. Heavy doses can trigger anxiety and paranoia.

Tolerance and Withdrawal

1. **Tolerance increases rapidly**. Because marijuana is fat soluble it persists in the body of a chronic user for up to six months, residual amounts can disrupt physiological, mental, and emotional functioning for a long period.

2. Withdrawal. Recent research has demonstrated that cessation of marijuana can cause true withdrawal symptoms. Chronic use causes mild to moderate withdrawal symptoms, including anger, aches, depression, inability to concentrate, tremors, disturbed sleep, decreased appetite, sweating, and craving. Because there are relatively few receptor sites in the autonomic nervous system, it is difficult to physically overdose with marijuana.

3. Addiction occurs more frequently in the 1990s because of the increased potency of marijuana and compulsive use patterns.

The Medical Use of Marijuana

Over the past ten years, marijuana has been recommended for glaucoma, nausea, asthma, and weight gain. There are some health benefits but the mental effects are still present. Many medical practitioners are reluctant to prescribe it because other drugs have the same therapeutic effects. Marijuana smoke is dangerous because it contains irritants, carcinogens and pathogens, impairs the immune system, and clients has a potential for abuse and addiction. Caution should be taken with HIV.

In 1992, researchers found receptor sites in the brain specifically reactive to THC, implying that the brain has its own natural neurotransmitters, which affect the same areas of the brain as marijuana. In 1994, an antagonist was found that instantly blocks the effects of marijuana, enabling researchers to look for tissue dependence and withdrawal symptoms. Finally, in 1995, researchers found anandamide, the natural neurotransmitter that fits into these receptor sites.

Remember: Marijuana is the most widely used substance (37.8 million individuals, Cocaine (5.1 million) is in the second spot with Heroin at number seven (948,000) (NSDUH, 2017).

Hallucinogens (including PCP)

Hallucinogens: Substance Intoxication. Recent use of hallucinogens, as well as significant maladaptive psychological or behavioral changes (shortly after use, two or more of the following signs develop); dilated pupils (Mydriasis), rapid heart rate (tachycardia), sweating, irregular heartbeat, blurred vision, tremors, incoordination.

Hallucinogens Persisting Perception Disorder (flashbacks): Substance Withdrawal.

The re-experiencing following the end of use of a hallucinogen of one or more of the perceptual symptoms that were experienced while intoxicated with the hallucinogen. These symptoms could include flashes of color, trails of images, after images, halos, illusion that objects are larger or smaller than actual size (macropsia or micropsia), geometric hallucinations and false peripheral perception of movement.

Phencyclidine (PCP): Substance Intoxication. Recent use of PCP or related substance, as well as significant maladaptive psychological or behavioral changes within an hour or less if snorted, smoked or used intravenously, two or more of the following signs; nystagmus, rapid heartbeat or high blood pressure, numbness or decreased response to pain, trouble walking or speaking (ataxia), joint deformity (dysarthria), rigid muscles, coma or seizures, abnormally acute hearing (hyperacusis).

Phencyclidine (PCP): Substance Withdrawal. (Not in DSM Classification)

Hallucinogen Information

LSD is a synthesized form of ergot fungus toxin. Synthesized by a Swiss chemist, Albert Hoffman in 1938. LSD can be found naturally as a fungus in the heads (buds) of rye and wheat or can be extracted from morning glory seeds. It was developed in the late 1940s as a therapy for mental illness and used as a chemical warfare weapon. The drug was popularized by Dr. Timothy Leary in the 1960s who advised young people to *"Tune in, turn on, and drop out,"* and was identified with the 1960s hippie generation. By the '70s, scientific research had ceased and interest diminished. In the 1990s, there was some renewed use of LSD.

Psilocybin and Psilocin (magic mushroom) Psilocybin and psilocin are the active ingredients. The mushrooms were used ceremonially in pre-Columbian America and are still used today.

Peyote (mescaline). Mescaline is the active component of peyote in the San Pedro cacti. It was named after an Apache tribe called the Mescalero Indians. Native American people in religious ceremonies use it and the history of its use goes back to pre-Columbian times. It is derived from the tops (buttons) of the peyote cactus cut at ground level. Peyote is chemically related to adrenaline and the amphetamines but the effects take longer to peak than LSD.

PCP, (angel dust) was originally developed in the 1950's as an anesthetic for animals. Its unwanted side effects are frequent and severe including sensory deprivation and mind/body separation. It can also induce stimulation (usually low dose), depression, high blood pressure, combative behavior (moderate dose), catatonia, coma, and convulsions (high dose). The range between the amount needed for low dose mild effects and high dose severe effects is small. Effects can last up to 48 hours and occasionally recur in flashbacks.

136

Physical Appearance

Most of the hallucinogens can appear in a variety of different forms. LSD is usually in a tablet or capsule and swallowed in various small amounts (25 micrograms). It is put on blotter paper or a sugar cube and chewed or swallowed. Most frequent use is by American students in junior high and high school. It is used at "rave" parties. It is difficult to detect since dosage is hidden in blotter paper, on sugar cubes, in microdots, or on gelatin square Psilocybin, Mescaline, and PCP are generally found in two types: (1) all of the hallucinogens can be found as a white powdery substance. (2) Psilocybin in its natural form is a mushroom, which is why it is frequently referred to, as the "magic mushroom" About 75 species of mushrooms exists. The strength of psychedelic effects varies from plant to plant. Mescaline in its natural form is a bud of the cactus plant, which is frequently referred to as a "button" because of its appearance. PCP has no natural form but can appear at times as a bright green leaf, which is smoked.

Effects of Hallucinogens

Problems in determining effects include the lack of scientific documentation of effects because of the illegal status of psychedelics, the lack of standard doses, contamination, and misrepresentation. Psychedelics disrupt the functioning of neurotransmitters. The effects of psychedelics, particularly the mental effects, depend on the size of the dose, past experience with the drug, emotional makeup, mood, and surroundings.

Many of the hallucinogens have produced a variety of effect:

- *Eidetic Imagery.* Seeing physical objects, usually in motion as sharply as if you were watching a film.

- *Synesthesia.* This is a simultaneous perception of several senses. For example, "hearing" color or "seeing" sound.

- *Perception of Multilevel Reality.* An experienced where the individual sees things and experiences life from several different vantage points usually simultaneously.

- *Fluid Motion.* An experience where the universe appears to explode into a shimmering pulsating cosmos, a world in continual flux.

- *Subjective Exaggeration.* This occurs when an individual perceives more than the reality event. Sometimes this is referred to as the "Eureka Experience" or the feeling that what is usually seen and thought to be quite ordinary takes on epic proportions.

137

- *Emotional Lability.* This refers to extremes in mood

- *Feelings of Timelessness.* Generally, time ceases to exist it becomes suddenly irrelevant. A minute becomes an hour and an hour can be a minute.

- *Irrationalism.* The concepts of clarity, logic, cause and effect become insignificant. Much of what happens during the experience defies rational, logical thinking.

Physical Effects of Hallucinogens

LSD usually involves stimulation, including increased pulse rate, blood pressure, sweating, nausea, and sensitivity to sensory stimulation. Disruption of visual and auditory effects is often. There is usually a rise in heart rate, blood pressure, and body temperature.

Psilocybin effects include initially nausea followed by changes in sensations and altered states of consciousness, many of the sensations are similar to LSD but with less disassociation and panic.

Peyote effects last twelve (12) hours and are similar to LSD, especially the colorful "visions." Similar to psilocybin, each use is accompanied by severe vomiting. Singing, drumming, chanting, and spiritual visions accompany ceremonial use. The U.S. Supreme Court ruled that use of this drug is not protected in religious ceremonies.

PCP effects can be quite dramatic and are directly related to dosage levels: Stage I abuse (2 -5 mgs) the individual becomes quite combative experiencing visual illusions and occasionally auditory hallucinations. Stage II (5-10mgs) is marked by impaired judgment and paranoid delusions with agitation and auditory and visual hallucinations. This stage can be very self-destructive. In Stage III abuse (10 -20 mgs) the individual experiences psychotic episodes sometime lasting a month or more. The individual clinically resembles psychotic symptoms of schizophrenia, delusional thinking, global paranoia and depression. At this stage an individual is at high risk for suicide and/or homicide.

Mental Effects of Hallucinogens

One-time use of LSD rarely causes permanent psychotic or schizophrenic disability but LSD can precipitate or provoke a relapse in someone with an underlying disorder. Flashbacks can occur (rarely) as remembrances of earlier trips. Bad Trips (acute anxiety reactions) occur because of the disruption of the emotional center of the brain and the distortions of reality, as well as depersonalization that can trigger acute anxiety, fear, and paranoia, along with delusions of persecution.

Peyote, which includes stimulation and distortion of perception, can produce empathy with others with no illusions or hallucinations.

Drug Dosage

LSD is potent at microscopic doses (200mics) but at lower doses (20-50mics) it acts more as a stimulant. Tolerance to the psychedelic effects of LSD can occur.

Peyote at 300 to 500mics and **Psilocybin** at 20 to 60misc resembles LSD. Generally, Psilocybin is shorter acting (4-6 hours).

Other Psychedelics

Ibogaine is a long acting psychedelic in high doses and a stimulant in low doses. It is grown and used primarily in Africa.

Morning Glory Seeds contain an LSD-like substance.

DMT is a naturally occurring psychedelic usually powdered or smoked to produce short-term hallucinations. It is easily synthesized and causes intense visual hallucinations, intoxication, and loss of awareness.

Yage is made from an Amazonian vine and causes intense vomiting diarrhea, and a dreamlike condition lasting up to 10 hours.

Designer Psychedelics

This class of synthetic drugs uses variants of the amphetamine molecule. The stimulatory effects, side effects, and toxicity are like those of amphetamines.

MDMA ("ecstasy," "rave", etc.).

MDMA acts for 4-6 hours and can be swallowed or injected. Physical effects include amphetamine like stimulation, nausea, appetite loss, and clenched jaw muscles, high body temperature and blood pressure occur as do depression, and with high doses, anxiety reactions, high blood pressure, and seizures.

PCP and Other Psychedelics

Ketamine a close relative to PCP is used, as a surgical anesthetic but is not common as a street drug.

Amanita Mushrooms causes dreamy intoxication and hallucinations. Their history goes back to ancient India, Siberia, and pre-Columbian Mexico.

Nutmeg and Mace, from the nutmeg tree, in very high doses causes a wide variety of effects from a mild floating sensation to delirium. They are generally not abused for psychedelic effects because at effective doses they cause severe nausea.

Opiates and Opioids

Opioids: Substance Intoxication. Recent use of opioids, as well as significant maladaptive psychological or behavioral changes (constriction or dilation of pupils due to absence of oxygen to body tissue despite adequate blood supply (anoxia) following a severe overdose, *and* one or more of the following signs):

- drowsiness or coma
- slurred speech
- impaired memory or attention

Cessation or reduction in opioid use that caused clinically significant distress or impairment in social, occupational or other important areas of

functioning (three or more of the following develop within minutes to several days of cessation.

Opiates and Opioids Information

The Arabs introduced the opium poppy as a medical remedy, which was consumed in a beverage made from seeds around 700 A.D. China and India cultivated the opium poppy around 1100 and opium was consumed by all social classes as a household remedy for aches and pains. The medical use of opium continued through the 17th century primarily being centered in China and India. Around 1675 the English became enthusiastic advocates of opium and its therapeutic potential to relieve pain.

Between 1700 and 1725 China began smoking opium mixed with tobacco and started the recreational use of opium. The smoking of opium also became widespread in India. In 1770 use of opium in England was declared by Dr. John Jones to alleviate symptoms and as a cure for many disorders.

140

His enthusiasm made opium preparations widespread for the next 150 years. In 1757 the English, through the British East India Company, established a limited monopoly over the opium trade by attempting to popularize its use to increase revenues. Between 1775 and 1800 and British opium traders commercially imported opium to England. In1803 Morphine was isolated from opium. Through 1825 doctors, for all kinds of ailments, prescribed opium. Use increased particularly among working-class individuals because opium was cheaper than alcohol. By 1840 opium use was increasing in England but opinions differed as to how harmful opium was to the English people. During this time the Chinese become increasingly concerned about the opium trade and vigorously enforced anti-opium policies. This precipitated the first war with the British, which occurred between 1830 and 1842. China was defeated and the opium trade doubled in the next 10 years. The exporting of opium to the United States during the 1800s created major problems. The introduction of morphine, the development of the hypodermic needle in1853, the increased advertising and mass production of opium based medicines, as well as the continued smoking of opium, appeared antagonistic to the moral reforms occurring in the United States. Following the Civil War, and partly related to the immigrant Chinese laborers bringing the habit of opium smoking to the United States, opium became widespread and unregulated. In 1864 Heroin was synthesized and recommended as a more effective medicine that was less dangerous and less addicting than Morphine. Between the Civil War and World War I opiate use was widespread and uncontrollable in the United States. White, middle-class, middle-aged women as well as opium smoking among the Chinese were the two most common patterns of opium use in the United States. In 1914 the U.S. Congress passed the Harrison Act. The Act restricted the supply of opiates to users by registered physicians. Following World War I, the concept of the "American drug addict" was firmly established in the culture. During the period from 1925 to 1950 a cohesive drug subculture emerged, the typical member being a younger, urban, male heroin abuser, who used the drug for pleasure and obtained it illicitly. In the late 1960's the Federal government established treatment programs for heroin addiction by using methadone, a long acting opioid that was taken orally. The drug was abused and created a new type of addict in the 1980s.

Classification of Opiates/Opioids

Heroin is derived from Morphine roughly a one to five ratio. Morphine in turn is derived from opium, which is 10 % morphine in weight. Alkaloid products called opiates are Morphine, Heroin, Codeine, Dilaudid, Laudanum, Paregoric (4% opium), etc. Synthetic narcotics called opioids are Methadone (Dolophine), Demerol, Talwin, Darvon, etc.

Effects of Opiates and Opioids

Primarily used as painkillers or analgesics. They reduce sensory sensitivity to pleasure or pain. The drug tends to replace the need for food, sex, and emotional involvement.

Opioids prevent the transmission of substance "P," the neurotransmitter that transmits pain. They also block most of what does get through to the receiving neuron. Painkilling effects of the various opioids are similar. What vary are the strength, duration, and toxicity. Opioids artificially activate the reward/pleasure center by slotting into receptor sites meant for endorphins. Heroin has the strongest effect of any of the opioids. The desire for pain relief and euphoria are just two reasons for opioid addiction. Physical and mental effects are felt in almost every part of the body. Some effects are noticeable, like drooping eyelids, nodding, and slurred slowed speech. Other effects are less visible, like suppression of the cough center. More severe effects are felt in the digestive and hormonal systems. Neonatal effects are felt because opioids cross the placental barrier. They include greater risk of miscarriage, placental separation, premature labor, stillbirth, and seizures. A baby born to an addicted mother is also addicted. Withdrawal can be quite severe, even fatal. Withdrawal occurs after two to three weeks of continuous use followed by abstinence. Short acting opiates, like heroin and morphine, cause more severe withdrawal symptoms.

Dirty and shared needles not only inject the drug but other materials, bacteria, and viruses, including the HIV virus that causes AIDS. Robbery, prostitution, or drug dealing results from the need to support an opiate habit. Polydrug use is dangerous because opiates have additive and synergistic effects, which increase the potential for, overdose death and addiction. Some use drugs to enhance the effect of opiates (alcohol with heroin), others to counter the effects (cocaine, amphetamines with morphine or heroin)

Major Opiates

Heroin (diacetylmorphine) is a worldwide problem. Mexico has been the largest supplier ("tar" heroin) to the United States. Production has increased in Southeast Asia, particularly production of smoke able heroin. Injection is the principal means of abuse in the West.

Codeine is not as strong as morphine and is generally used for relief of moderate pain or to control coughs. It can be extracted from opium or refined from morphine and is one of the most widely abused prescription drugs.
Morphine is refined from opium and is the gold standard for pain relief.

Hydromorphone (Dilaudid), a short acting, medication prescribed as an alternative to morphine for moderate to severe pain. More potent than morphine, it has a higher abuse potential.

Major Opioids

Methadone a long acting synthetic narcotic used to treat heroin addiction.

Meperidine (Demerol) is a short acting opioid that is often prescribed for moderate to severe pain and causes more sedation and euphoria than morphine.

Pentazocine (Talwin) is prescribed for chronic pain and is abused with an antihistamine in "T's & B's."

Propoxyphene (Darvon, Darvocet) is prescribed for mild to moderate pain and lasts for four to six hours.

Fentanyl (Sublimaze) is the most powerful of the opioids (50 to 100 times as strong as morphine) and is used after surgery for severe pain.

Designer Heroin includes street versions of Fentanyl, known as "China white." Very dangerous since they can be over 100 times stronger than regular heroin.

Remember: Heroin deaths skyrocketed 630 % between 2002 and 2017 (NSDUH, 2017).

LAAM is an opioid being used for heroin replacement therapy.

Chemical Dependency Treatment Plan (Jongsma, A and M. Peterson, 1999)

Behavioral Definition:

1. Consistent use of alcohol or other mood altering drugs until high, intoxicated, or passed out.

2. Inability to stop or cut down use of mood altering drug once started, despite the verbalized desire to do so and the negative consequences continued use brings.

3. Blood work that reflects the results of a pattern of heavy substance use, for example, elevated liver enzymes.

4. Denial that chemical dependence is a problem despite direct feedback from spouse, relatives, friends, and employers that the use of the substance is negatively affecting them and others,

5. Amnesiac blackouts have occurred when abusing alcohol.

6. Continued drug and/or alcohol use despite experiencing persistent or recurring physical, legal, vocational, social, or relationship problems that are directly caused by the use of the substance.

7. Increased tolerance for the drug, as there is the need to use more to become intoxicated or to attain the desired effect.

8. Physical symptoms, that is, shaking, seizures, nausea, headaches, sweating, anxiety, insomnia, and/or depression, when withdrawing from the substance.

9. Suspension of important social, recreational, or occupational activities because they interfere with using.

10. Large time investment in activities to obtain the substance, to use it, or to recover from its effects.

11. Consumption of substance in greater amounts and for longer periods than intended.

12. Continued use of mood altering chemical after being told by a physician that it is causing health problem.

Long Term Goals

L/T Goal 1- Accept chemical dependence (be specific about what drugs) and begin to actively participate in a recovery program.

L/T Goal 2- Establish and maintain total abstinence while increasing knowledge of the disease and the process of recovery.

L/T Goal 3- Acquire the necessary skills to maintain long-term sobriety from all mood altering substances and live a life free of chemicals.

Short Term Goals

S/T Goal 1-Decrease the level of denial around using as evidenced by fewer statements about minimizing amount of use and its negative impact on life.

S/T Goal 2-Verbalize increased knowledge of alcoholism and the process of recovery.

S/T Goal 3-Verbalize an understanding of personality, social, and family factors that foster chemical dependence.

S/T Goal 4- State changes that will be made in social relationships to support recovery.

S/T Goal 5- Attend AA/NA meetings on a regular basis as frequently as necessary to support sobriety.

S/T Goal 6-Identify potential relapse triggers and develop strategies for constructively dealing with each trigger.

Action Steps (Therapeutic Interventions)

- ➤ Ask client to make a list of the ways substance abuse has negatively impacted his/her life and process it with therapist. (Goal 1).

- ➤ Assign client to ask two or three people who are close to him/her to write a letter to therapist in whom they identify how they saw client's chemical dependence negatively impacting his/her life. (Goal 1)

- ➤ Require client to attend didactic lectures related to chemical dependence and the process of recovery. Then ask client to identify in writing several key points attained from each lecture for further processing with therapist. (Goal 1, 2 & 6)

- ➤ Model and reinforce statements that reflect acceptance of chemical dependence and its destructive consequences for self and others. (Goal 1)

- ➤ Assign client to read article/pamphlet on the disease concept of alcoholism and select several key ideas to discuss with counselor. (Goal 2)

- ➤ Assess client's intellectual, personality, and cognitive functioning as to his contribution to chemical dependence. (Goal 3)

- ➤ Investigate situational stress factors that may foster client's chemical dependence. (Goal 3 & 6)

- ➤ Probe client's family history for chemical dependence patterns and relate these to client's use.(Goal 3)

- ➤ Review the negative influence of continuing old alcohol/drug related friendships and assist client in making a plan to develop new sober friendships. (Goal 4 & 6).

- ➤ Assist the client in developing insight into life changes needed in order to maintain long-term drug and alcohol free lifestyle. (Goal 4)

- ➢ Recommend client attend AA or NA meetings and report to therapist the impact of the meetings. (Goal 5)

- ➢ Help client develop an awareness of relapse triggers and alternative ways of effectively handling them. (Goal 6)

- ➢ Recommend the client read *Staying Sober: A Guide to Relapse Prevention* (Gorski and Miller) and *The Staying Sober Workbook* (Gorski).(Goal 6).

- ➢ Assist client in planning social and recreational activities that are free from association with substance abuse. (Goal 6)

Inhalants

Inhalants: Substance Intoxication. Recent intentional use of volatile inhalants, (solvents) as well as significant maladaptive psychological or behavioral changes shortly after exposure two or more of the following signs develop); dizziness, involuntary rapid eye movement (nystagmus), incoordination, slurred speech, unsteady gait, lethargy, diminished reflexes, psychomotor retardation, blurred or double vision (diplopia), tremors, generalized muscle weakness, stupor or coma, or euphoria.

Products	Chemicals
Airplane glue	Toluene, ethyl acetate
Analgesic sprays	Fluorocarbons
Anesthetic Gases	Nitrous oxide
Correction fluid thinner	Trichloroethylene, trichloroethane
Deodorants, air fresheners	Butane, propane, Fluorocarbons
Dry cleaning fluid	Tetrachloroethylene, Trichloroethane
Degreasers	Tetrachloroethylene, trichloroethane,
Fire extinguisher propellant	Bromochlorodifluoro-methane
Fuel gas	Butane
Hair Sprays	Butane, propane, fluorocarbons
Lighter fluid	Butane, isopropane
Nail polish remover	Acetone
Paint Sprays	Butane, propane, fluorocarbons, toluene, hydrocarbons
Paint Removers	Toluene, methylene chloride
Paint Thinners	Toluene, methylene Chloride, methanol
PVC Cement	Trichloroethylene

Rubber Cement	Hexane, toluene, methyl chloride, methyl ethyl ketone, methyl butyl ketone
Spot Removers	Tetrachloroethylene, trichloroethane, trichloroethylene
'Rush". "poppers"	Nitrous oxide
Whipped cream	Amyl nitrite, butyl nitrite, isopropyl nitrite

Substance-Induced Disorders:

There are eight (8)-related categories of **Substance-Induced Disorders** that warrant independent clinical attention. Substance-induced disorders are directly related to use or withdrawal and symptoms can persist for at least one (1) month before a dual diagnosis can be assured. Substance dependency can coexist with other Axis I disorders prior to the month if appropriate history indicates the other disorder existed without substance use or dependency.

Substance Intoxication Delirium:

Disturbance of consciousness as demonstrated by reduced clarity of awareness of the environment with difficulty focusing, shifting or sustaining attention. Preexisting or evolving Dementia cannot explain cognitive changes, such as deficit of language, memory, orientation, or perception. These symptoms develop rapidly (hours to days) and tend to vary during the day. History, physical examination or laboratory data suggest that the Dementia is related to Substance Intoxication.

Substance-Induced Persisting Dementia:

Cognitive deficits manifested by both memory impairment, inability to learn new information or recall previously learned information and cognitive disturbances in one or more of the following: language disturbance despite intact articulation (aphasia), impaired ability to carry out motor activities despite intact motor functioning (ataxia), failure to recognize or identify objects despite intact sensory function (agnosia), inability to plan, organize, sequence, or abstract. There is evidence from history, physical examination, or laboratory findings that the deficits are related to the effects of drugs of abuse or medication.

Substance-Induced Persisting Amnesiac Disorder:

Impaired memory due to inability to recall previously learned information or to learn new information. These symptoms significantly impair functioning. These symptoms don't occur solely during Delirium or a Dementia. There is evidence from history, physical examination, or laboratory findings that the memory disturbances are related to the effects of drugs of abuse or medication. When drug or alcohol related it is usually referred to as a "black out".

Substance-Induced Psychotic Disorder:

Prominent hallucinations or delusions (don't include hallucinations the client realizes are caused by substance use). These symptoms have developed within a month of medication or Substance Intoxication or Withdrawal. This diagnosis is made if another psychotic disorder, that is not Substance Induced, doesn't better explain the symptoms.

Substance-Induced Anxiety Disorder (generalized):

Prominent anxiety, Panic Attacks, or obsessions dominate the clinical situation with evidence from history, physical examination, or laboratory findings that the anxiety developed within one month of Substance Intoxication or Withdrawal.

Substance-Induced Mood Disorder:

A prominent and persistent disturbance in mood predominates in the clinical picture and is characterized by either (or both) of the following:

(a) Depressed mood or markedly diminished interest or pleasure in all, or almost all, activities.

(b) Elevated, expansive or irritable mood.

There is evidence from the history, physical examination, or laboratory findings of either (1) The symptoms in Criteria (a) or (b) developed during, or within, a month of, Substance Intoxication or Withdrawal or (2) medication use is etiological related to the disturbance. Finally, the disturbance is not better accounted for by a Mood Disorder that is not substance induced. Also, the disturbance does not occur exclusively during the course of a delirium and the symptoms cause clinically significant distress or impairment in social, occupational, or other important areas of functioning.

Substance-Induced Sleep Disorder:

Prominent disturbance in sleep that is sufficiently severe to warrant independent clinical attention. The chief complaint is difficulty initiating or maintaining sleep, or nonrestorative sleep. There is evidence from history, physical examination, or laboratory findings that the mood disturbance developed during, or within one month of, Substance Intoxication or Withdrawal.

Substance-Induced Sexual Dysfunction:

Clinically significant sexual dysfunction that results in marked distress or interpersonal difficulty. Sexual dysfunctions are disorders related to: sexual desire, arousal, orgasm, or pain. Finally, there is evidence from history, physical examination, or laboratory findings that the sexual dysfunction is fully explained by Substance Intoxication or medication use.

Substance-Induced Treatment Plan (Perkinson and Jongsma, 1998).

This treatment plan refers to memory impairment and cognitive disturbances that persist beyond substance intoxication or withdrawal effects. Hallucinations or delusions, as well as sexual dysfunction and sleep disturbances may be present for a significant period of time. All of the induced disorders assume an etiology from the substance of choice.

Long Term Goals

1. Recover from substance induced disorder and maintain a recovery program free from substance use.

2. Normalize memory and cognition and maintain abstinence from substance use.

3. Recover clear memory and awareness of environment, realistic perceptions, coherent communication, focused attention and maintain abstinence from substance use.

4. Understand the relationship between the substance-induced disorders and substance dependency.

5. Learn the importance of working a 12 Step program to recover from substance-induced disorders and substance dependency disorders.

Short Term Goal #1

1. Verbalize an understanding that signs and symptoms of substance-induced disorder are caused by chemical dependency.

Short Term Intervention #1

1.   Teach the client about his substance-induced disorder and directly relate signs and symptoms to chemical abuse

2.   Teach the client that his symptoms are a direct result of chemical abuse and that they will disappear if the client remains abstinence.

Short Term Goal #2

1.   Report to staff any thoughts of harming himself or others.

Short Term Intervention #2

1.   Assess the client's potential for harming himself or others and take precautionary steps if needed; encourage client to report to staff any thoughts of harming self or others.

2.   Encourage client to share his feelings surrounding substance-induced disorder and substance dependency.

Short Term Goal #3

1.   Cooperate with medical management of substance-induced disorder

Short Term Intervention #3

1.   Physician will examine the client, write treatment orders as indicated and monitor side effects and effectiveness.

2.   Counselor will monitor physicians orders and monitor clients symptoms and the side effects and effectiveness of the prescribe medication.

Other Diagnostic issues in Substance Related Disorders

1. Polysubstance Related Disorders:

The individual is using three (3) or more substances from different groups during twelve (12) month period. All three (3) substances appear to have equal dominance and the Substance Dependence criteria are met for all three (3) substances. This disorder excludes caffeine and nicotine.

2. Other (or Unknown) Substance Dependence or Abuse:

Substances considered in this category are: (1) anabolic steroids, (2)

150

nitrite inhalants, (3) over the counter drugs and (4) prescription
medication not related to drugs of abuse.

3. Remission Course Specifiers:

During the course of treatment, a person in Early Full Remission would
be an individual who for a period of one (1) to eleven (11) months or
more, *no Criteria of Dependency or Abuse* are indicated in the year
following withdrawal from all substances. Early Partial Remission would
be for individuals who during a one (1) month or more Criteria of
Dependency or Abuse are met but not the full Criteria for Dependency. If
one is on Agonist Therapy (e.g. Antabuse, etc.) or in a Controlled
Environment (e.g. locked hospital unit, etc.) for at least one (1) month the
individual is considered to not be in remission until the person is free of
the Agonist Therapy or the Controlled Environment. For example, many
individuals who are on Methadone Maintenance consider themselves in
remission (recovery) yet they are taking a synthetic narcotic to stabilize
their life style. Although, these individuals are to be commended for their
positive improvement one must consider them to not be in remission until
they are totally drug free for at least one month.

Chapter Six
Substance Use and Co-Occurring Disorders

In their analysis of data from a series of studies supported by the National Institute on Drug Abuse, the Drug Abuse Treatment Outcome Study (DATOS), Flynn et al. (2010) demonstrates that the livelihood of mental disorders with the increasing numbers of substance dependencies. Clients were assessed using the DSM criteria for lifetime antisocial personality, major depression, general anxiety disorder, and/or any combination of these disorders. Table 2 shows a general trend of increase in the rates of lifetime, antisocial personality disorders, major depression, and, general anxiety disorders as the number of substance dependencies involving alcohol, heroin, and cocaine increases (except for the relationship between alcohol dependence only and major depression and general anxiety. Since the use of multiple drugs is common in those with substance use disorders, treatment is further complicated for these people by the greater incidence of mental disorders that accompanies multiple drug use.

Table 1

Rates (%) of Antisocial Personality, Depression, and Anxiety Disorder by Drug Dependency in Treatment			
Drug Dependency	**Antisocial Personality**	**Major Depression**	**Generalized Anxiety**
Alcohol only	34.7	17.8	5.5
Heroin only	27	7	2
Heroin & Alcohol	46.3	13.2	3.2
Cocaine only	30.4	8.4	2.7
Cocaine & Alcohol	47	13.6	4.7
Cocaine & Heroin	44	10.8	2.2
Cocaine, Heroin & Alcohol	59.8	17.1	6.3

Source: NIDA sponsored DATOS study 2016.

Depressive Disorders: (Adapted from DSM)

1. Dysthymic disorder.   History of depressed mood a majority of the time.

2. Major depressive disorder.   One or more major depressive episodes.

Bipolar Disorders:

1. Cyclothymic disorder: Numerous hypomanic episodes and
                            numerous periods of depressive symptoms
                            that do not meet criteria for major
                            depressive episode.

2. Bipolar I disorder.   One or more manic episodes, and usually
                            one or more major depressive episodes.

3. Bipolar II disorder.   At least one hypomanic episode and one
                            or more major depressive episodes but no
                            manic episode or cyclothymia.

Other Mood Disorders:

1. Mood disorder due to a general medical condition.

2. Substance induced mood disorder.

Diagnostic Criteria for Dysthymic Disorder:(Adapted from DSM)

1. Depressed mood most of the day, more days than not, for at
   least two (2) years one (1) year for children and adolescents)

2. Two (2) or more of the following symptoms while depressed:
   poor appetite or overeating insomnia or sleeping too much low
   energy low self-esteem poor concentration or difficulty in
   making decisions, and feelings of hopelessness.

3. The symptoms described above have never been absent for
   more than two months in a two-year period.

4. During the first two- (2) years of the disturbance, there has
   never been a major depressive episode. If one of these episodes
   has occurred in the past, there has been a complete remission,
   or disappearance of symptoms.

5. There has never been a manic or hypomanic episode, and the
   criteria for cyclothymic disorder have not been met.

6. The disturbance is not part of a chronic psychotic disorder or the result of some chemical substance (medication or drug abuse) or a general medical condition.

7. The symptoms cause clinically significant distress or impairment in important areas of functioning.

Diagnostic Criteria for Major Depressive Disorder: (Adapted from DSM)

1. The presence of a major depressive episode, with or without a history of past major depressive episodes.

2. The episode cannot be accounted for by some other disorder,

3. There has never been a manic episode or a hypomanic episode (mild degree of mania without behavioral change), except for any that may have been the result of substance abuse, medication, or the direct physiological effects of a general medical condition.

4. If either hallucinations or delusions are present, the major depressive disorder is diagnosed as having psychotic features.

Diagnostic Criteria for Cyclothymic Disorder: (Adapted from DSM)

1. The presence of numerous periods of hypomanic symptoms and numerous periods of depressive symptoms for at least two (2) years (one year for children and adolescents). The depressive symptoms must not meet the criteria for a major depressive episode.

2. The symptoms described above have never been absent for more than two (2) months at a time during the two-year period.

3. No major depressive episode, manic episode, or mixed episode in which these episodes alternate has been present during the first two (2) years of the disorder.

Criteria for Bipolar I Disorder: (Adapted from DSM)

A Bipolar I disorder may be diagnosed after only one (1) manic episode. The most recent episode may be a major depressive episode or a hypomanic, manic, or mixed episode (a period including both manic and major depressive episodes nearly every day for a minimum of seven (7) or more days).

Clinical Criteria for a Manic Episode:

A distinct period of abnormally and persistently elevated, expansive, or irritable mood lasting at least seven (7) days (less if hospitalization is necessary).

During this mood disturbance, three (3) or more of the following symptoms must be present to a significant degree:

Inflated Self-esteem or Grandiosity

Decreased need for sleep

More talkativeness than usual, or pressure to keep talking

Flight of ideas or subjective experience of racing thoughts
Distractibility of attention

Increase in goal directed activity or psychomotor agitation.

Excessive involvement in pleasurable activities that have a high risk of negative consequences

The mood disturbance causes marked impairment in occupational or social functioning or relationships with others, or requires hospitalization to prevent self-harm, or there are psychotic features (hallucinations or delusions). The symptoms are not the result of the direct effects of some substance (drug abuse, medication) or a general medical condition.

Criteria for Bipolar II Disorder: (Adapted from DSM)

The presence or history of one (1) or more major depressive episodes.

- The presence or history of at least one (1) hypomanic episode. (A hypomanic episode is similar to a manic episode but does not meet all the criteria: it is not severe enough to cause marked impairment in functioning or hospitalization, but it is observable to others).

177

- There has never been a manic episode or a mixed episode.

- The mood symptoms are not better accounted for by another disorder.

- The symptoms cause clinically significant distress or impairment in social, occupational, or other important areas of functioning.

Low Self-Esteem (Mood Disorder) Treatment Plan (Jongsma and Peterson, 1999).

This plan is for individuals who are uncomfortable in social situations, especially large groups. They generally have an inability to accept complements. They have difficulty in saying no to others and an inability to identify positive things about themselves.

Long Term Goals

1. Elevate self-esteem.

2. Develop a consistent, positive self-image.

3. Demonstrate improved self-esteem through more pride in appearance, more assertiveness, greater eye contact, and identification of positive traits and self-taught messages.

Short Term Goal #1

1. Acknowledge feeling less competent than most others.

Short Term Intervention #1

1. Actively build the level of trust with the client in individual sessions through consistent eye contact, active listening, unconditional positive regard, and warm acceptance to help increase client's ability to identify and express feelings.

2. Explore client's assessment of self.

Short Term Goal #2

1. Increase awareness of self-disparaging statements.

Short Term Intervention #2

1.   Confront and reframe client's self-disparaging comments.

2.   Assist the client in becoming aware of how negative feelings about him/her get expressed.

Short Term Goal #3

1.   Increase insight into the historical and current sources of low self-esteem.

Short Term Intervention #3

1.   Help client become aware of the fear of rejection and its connection with past rejection or abandonment

2.   Discuss, emphasize and interpret incidence of abuse and how they have impacted feelings about the client's self-image.

Short Term Goal #4

1.   Articulated plan to be proactive in trying to get identified needs met.

Short Term Intervention #4

1.   Conduct a session with significant other in which client is supported in expression of unmet needs.

2.   Assist the client in developing a specific action plan to get needs met.

Short Term Goal #5

1.   Positively acknowledge verbal complements from others.

Short Term Intervention #5

1.   Assign mirror exercises of client talking positively abound itself.

2.   Assign client to make eye contact with whom ever he/she is speaking to.

3.   Assign client to be aware and acknowledge graciously praises and complements from others.

Short Term Goal #6

1. Form realistic, appropriate, and obtainable goals for self in all areas of life.

Short Term Intervention #6

1. Help client analyze goals to make sure they are realistic and obtainable.

2. Assign client to make a list of goals for various areas of life and a plan for steps toward gold attainment.

Short Term Goal #7

1. Use positive self-talk messages to build self-esteem.

Short Term Intervention #7

1. Verbally reinforce the use of positive statements of accomplishments.

2. Reinforce use of more realistic, positive messages to self in interpreting life events.

3. Assign client readings and ask him/her to process key ideas with counselor.

Generalized Anxiety Disorder: (Adapted from DSM)

1. Excessive anxiety and worry occurring for at least six (6) months and affecting many areas of a person's life.

2. Inability to control feelings of worry.

3. The presence of three (3) or more of the following symptoms (only one type of symptom is required by DSM-IV for children):

    a. Restlessness; feeling on edge
    b. Being easily fatigued
    c. Difficulty concentrating (mind goes blank)
    d. Irritable mood
    e. Muscle tension
    f. Sleep disturbance (difficulty falling or staying asleep)

4.   Considerable distress or impairment in social, occupational, or other important areas of life

Posttraumatic Stress Disorder: (Adapted from DSM)

I.   Exposure to a traumatic event that involved actual or threatened death or serious injury, or a threat to one's physical integrity.

A response to the event that includes intense fear, helplessness, or horror.

Persistent re-experiencing of the traumatic event in the form of recurrent and distressing thoughts or dreams, or behaving or feeling as if the traumatic event was happening again, or intense psychological or physiological reactivity when exposed to cues that symbolizes or resembles the event.

Persistent avoidance of stimuli associated with the trauma, along with numbing of general responsiveness.

Persistent symptoms of increased arousal such as hyper vigilance, irritability, sleep difficulties, difficulty in concentrating, and exaggerated startle response (not present before the trauma).

1. Symptoms of more than thirty (30) days duration that cause significant distress or impairment in social or vocational functioning.

Clinical Features of Panic Attacks:

• Shortness of breath or the feeling of being smothered

• Dizziness, unsteadiness, or faintness

• Trembling, shaking, or sweating

• Heart palpitations or a racing heart rate

• Choking, nausea, or stomach pain

• Numbness or tingling; flushing or chills

• Chest pains or discomfort

• A sense of "strangeness," of being detached from oneself or one's Surroundings

• Fear of going crazy, losing control, or dying.

Panic Disorder in Comparison with Generalized Anxiety Disorder

1. Clinical onset of Panic Disorder is later.

2. The role of heredity seems to be greater in Panic Disorders.

3. The ratio of women to men is greater in Panic Disorder.

4. Alcoholism is more common in Panic Disorder.

5. While depression is common in both, it is unusually more common in Panic Disorder.

Psychotic Disorders: (Adapted from DSM)

1. Schizophrenia: Disturbance lasts six (6) months or more. At least one (1) month of active phase, usually including at least two (2) of the following symptoms:

Delusions: A fixed, false belief not ordinarily accepted by two members of an individual's culture. In DSM IV-TR, a *bizarre delusion* is one that involves very unusual or completely implausible elements. A *delusion of reference* is one in which elements in the environment, such as comments from the news media, have particular significance and/or refer to the person.

Hallucinations: A sensory experience in the absence of external stimulation of the relevant sensory organ. Hallucinations are separate from thoughts, feelings obsessions, and illusions and are experienced as if they were real.

Disorganized speech: Speech, which appears unrelated to conversation.

Disorganized and bizarre behavior: Behavior, which is unpredictable and appears unrelated to environment.

Or one (1) of the above and at least one (1) of the following negative symptoms:

Flat affect: A compression of mood. Should be distinguished from blunted affect-a lack of emotional sensitivity.

Loss of energy: (Anergia) - Loss of strength or energy; feeling a loss of strength.

Poverty of speech: Person answers briefly when you expect elaboration. If not asked client may say nothing for long periods.

Loss of motivation: Person appears to lack initiative.

Loss of feelings of pleasure: (Anhedonia) - An inability to experience pleasure. A decline in social or occupational function must also occur.

Subtypes of Schizophrenia:

Paranoid type. A preoccupation with delusion (s) or auditory hallucinations. Little or no disorganized speech, disorganized or catatonic behavior, or inappropriate or flat affect.

Disorganized type. All the following----disorganized speech, disorganized behavior and inappropriate or flat affect are prominent in behavior, but catatonic type criteria are not met. Delusions or hallucinations may be present, but only in fragmentary or non-coherent form.

Undifferentiated type. Does not fit any of the subtypes above, but meets the symptom criteria for schizophrenia.

Residual type. Has experienced at least one episode of schizophrenia, but currently does not have prominent positive symptoms (delusions, hallucinations, disorganized speech or behavior). However, continues to show negative symptoms and a milder variation of positive symptoms (odd beliefs, eccentric behavior)

Please Note:

In assigning a subtype to the diagnosis, DSM uses the following rules: Paranoid type is assigned if delusions or hallucinations are prominent .If criteria for either the catatonic or disorganized type are met, then that diagnosis takes priority. If criteria for both disorganized type and catatonic type are present, then catatonic is the type assigned. This means that the catatonic type diagnosis is used if catatonic symptoms are present, even if behaviors characteristic of another type are also seen. If a person shows symptoms characteristic of the active phase of schizophrenia but does not meet the criteria for any of these three types, a subtype diagnosis of undifferentiated type is used.

Schizophreniform disorder. Same symptoms as schizophrenia, but lasts between 1 and 6 months. It is not necessary there be a decline in function for this diagnosis.

Schizoaffective disorder. The active-phase symptoms of schizophrenic disorder occur, together with an episode characteristic of a mood disorder. These are preceded or followed by at least two weeks of delusions or hallucinations.

Delusional disorder. Non-bizarre delusions lasting at least one month without the other symptoms that characterize the active phase of schizophrenia.

Brief psychotic disorder. A psychotic disturbance lasting more than one day but less than one month.

Shared psychotic disorder A disturbance that develops in a person influenced by someone else who has an established delusion with similar content.

Psychotic disorder due to general medical condition. Psychotic symptoms thought to be physiological results of a general medical condition or illness.

Substance induced psychotic disorder. Psychotic symptoms thought to be the physiological, result of toxin exposure medication, or drug abuse.

Psychotic Behavior Treatment Plan (Stout and Jongsma, 1998).

This treatment plan refers to individuals who have bizarre content of thought or seriously disturbed affect. In many ways these are individuals who demonstrate delusional and hallucinatory activity.

Long Term Goals

1. Control or eliminate active psychotic symptoms so that supervised functioning is possible and medications are taken consistently.

2. Significantly reduce or eliminate hallucinations and/or delusions.

Short Term Goal #1

1. Describe the history of psychotic symptoms.

Short Term Intervention #1

1. Demonstrate acceptance through calm, warm, empathetic manner. Show good active listening skills.

2. Access pervasiveness of psychotic disorder through clinical interview and/or psychological testing.

3. Determine if psychosis is of a brief reactive nature or long-term with reactive elements.

Short Term Goal #2

1. Understand the necessity for taking antipsychotic medications and agree to cooperate with medical care.

Short Term Intervention #2

1. Arrange for psychiatric evaluation and monitor medication compliance. If client is noncompliant redirect and support physician's orders.

Short Term Goal #3

1. Think more clearly as demonstrated by logical, coherent speech.

Short Term Intervention #3

1. Gently confront illogical thoughts and speech patterns to refocus disordered thinking.

2. Reinforce clarity and rationality of thought and speech patterns by client.

Short Term Goal #4

1. Verbalize an understanding of the underlying needs, conflicts, and emotions that support the client's irrational beliefs.

Short Term Intervention #4

✓ Probe causes for reactive psychosis.

✓ Assist in restructuring rational beliefs by reviewing reality based evidence and misinterpretation.

✓ Differentiate for client the source of stimuli between self-generated messages and the reality of the external world.

✓ Probe the underlying needs and feelings such as rejection, anxiety or guilt that trigger irrational thoughts.

Criteria for Dementia: (Adapted from DSM)

1. Memory impairment (inability to learn new information and to recall previously learned information).

2. One or more of the following cognitive disturbances:

   a. Deterioration of language function (speech becomes vague or empty; comprehension of spoken or written language may deteriorate).

   b. Impaired ability to execute motor activities despite intact motor function, sensory function, and comprehension of the required task (for example, impaired ability to pantomime using an object, such as combing hair).

   c. Failure to recognize or identify objects despite intact sensory function (for example, loss of the ability to recognize objects such as chairs or pencils despite normal visual acuity).

   d. Disturbance in executive functions such as planning, organizing, sequencing, and abstracting (examples of executive dysfunction include inability to recite the alphabet or state as many animals as possible in one minute).

Major Personality Disorders (adapted from DSM)

Cluster A- Eccentric Behavior

Paranoid: Tense, guarded, suspicious; holds grudges.

Schizoid: Socially isolated, with restricted emotional expression.

Schizotypal: Peculiarities of thought, appearance, and behavior that are disconcerting to others; emotionally, detached and isolated.

Cluster B- Emotional, or Erratic Behavior

Histrionic: Seductive behavior; needs immediate gratification and constant reassurance; rapidly changing moods; shallow emotions.

Narcissistic: Self-absorbed; expects special treatment and adulation; envious of attention to others.

Borderline: Cannot stand to be alone; intense, unstable moods and personal relationships; chronic anger; drug and alcohol abuse.

Antisocial: Manipulative, exploitive; dishonest; disloyal; lacking in guilt; habitually breaks social rules; childhood history of such behavior; often in trouble with the law.

Cluster C-Anxious or Fearful Behavior

Avoidant: Easily hurt and embarrassed; few close friends; sticks to routines to avoid new and possibly stressful experiences.

Dependent: Wants others to make decisions; needs constant advice and reassurance; fears being abandoned

Obsessive-compulsive: Perfectionist; over conscientious; indecisive; preoccupied with details; stiff; unable to express affection.

Clinical Features of Paranoid Personality Disorder (Cluster A)

A person having at least four (4) of these characteristics might be considered to have a paranoid personality disorder:

I. Expects, without sufficient basis, to be exploited or harmed by others.

2. Questions, without justification, the loyalty or trustworthiness of peers and associates.

3. Reads hidden demeaning or threatening meanings into benign remarks and events.

4. Bears grudge or are unforgiving of insults.

5. Is reluctant to confide in others because of unwarranted fear that the information will be used against him or her.

6. Perceives attacks on his or her character or reputation that are not apparent to others and is quick to react with anger and at times counterattack.

7. Has a recurrent suspicion, without justification, regarding fidelity of spouse or sexual partner.

Clinical Features of Schizoid Personality Disorder (Cluster A)

A person having at least four (4) of these characteristics might be considered to have a schizoid personality disorder

187

I. Neither desires nor enjoys close relationships, even with their own family.

2. Almost always chooses solitary activities.

3. Obtains pleasure from few, if any, activities.

4. Indicates little, if any desire to have sexual experiences with another person.

5. Appears indifferent to the praise or criticism of others.

6. Has no close friends or confidants (or only one).

7. Shows emotional coldness, detachment, and little variation in emotions.

Clinical Features of Schizotypal Personality Disorder (Cluster A)

A person having at least five (5) of these characteristics might be considered to have a schizotypal personality disorder:

1. Inappropriate ideas of reference (the belief that actions and other people's conversations, smiles have reference to them).

2. Excessive social anxiety that does not diminish with familiarity and tends to be associated with paranoid fears rather than negative judgments.

3. Odd beliefs or thinking that one has magical powers (e.g., people can feel his/he feelings).

4. Unusual perceptual experiences, including bodily illusions.

5. Odd speech and thinking (e.g., circumstantial, very vague).

6. Paranoid ideas or suspiciousness.

7. Odd or eccentric behavior or appearance (e.g., unusual mannerisms talking to self, odd speech).

8. No close friends or confidants other than relatives, primarily because of lack of desire for contact, pervasively uncomfortable with others.

9. Inappropriate or constricted affect (e.g., coldness, aloofness).

Clinical Features of Histrionic Personality Disorder (Cluster B)

A person having at least five (5) of these characteristics might be considered to have a histrionic personality disorder:

I. Rapidly shifting but basically shallow expressions of emotion.

2. Overly concerned with physical attractiveness.

3. Inappropriate sexual seductiveness in appearance or behavior.

4. Discomfort when not the center of attention.

5. Excessively impressionistic speech, which lacks detail.

6. Intolerance of or excessive frustration over, situations that do not work out exactly as desired.

7. Apparent view of relationships as possessing greater intimacy than is actually the case (e.g., referring to an acquaintance as a "dear, honey").

8. Exaggerated expression of emotion, with much self-dramatization.

Clinical Features of Narcissistic Personality Disorder (Cluster B)

A person having at least five (5) of these characteristics might be considered to have a narcissistic personality disorder:

1. Grandiose sense of self-importance, exaggeration of personal achievements and talents, and a need for recognition of one's superiority by others.

2. Preoccupation with fantasies of unlimited success, power, and beauty.

3. Sense that one's special qualities and only other special high-status people or institutions can appreciate their uniqueness.

4. Need for excessive admiration and attention.

5. Sense of entitlement; expects especially favorable treatment or automatic compliance with personal expectations.

6. Exploits other people and takes advantage of them.

7. Lacks empathy for other people's needs and feelings.

8. Often, envious of others or believes that others are envious of him or her (resents privileges or achievements of those regarded less special or deserving).

9. Arrogant behavior or attitudes.

Clinical Features of Borderline Personality Disorder (Cluster B)

A person having at least five (5) of these characteristics might be considered to have a borderline personality disorder:

1. Employment of frantic efforts to avoid real or imagined abandonment.

2. Unstable and intense interpersonal relationships.

3. Persistent and markedly disturbed, distorted, or unstable sense of self (e.g, believes that one is evil, a feeling that one doesn't exist).

4. Impulsiveness in such areas as sex, alcohol or drug use, crime, and reckless driving.

5. Recurrent suicidal thoughts, gestures, or behavior.

6. Emotional instability, with periods of extreme depression, irritability, or anxiety.

7. Chronic feelings of emptiness.

8. Inappropriate intense anger or lack of control of anger (e.g., loss of temper, recurrent physical fights).

9. Transient, stress related paranoid thoughts or severe dissociative symptoms.

Clinical Features of Antisocial Personality Disorder (Cluster B)

A person having at least three (3) of these characteristics might be considered to have an antisocial personality disorder:

1. Failure to conform to social norms (legal difficulties).

2. Is deceitfulness or manipulative.

3. Is impulsive and fails to plan ahead.

4. Is irritable and aggressive.

5. Has a reckless disregard for the safety of self or others.

6. Is consistently irresponsible.

7. Lacks remorse after having hurt, mistreated, or stolen from another person.

Clinical Features-Avoidant Personality Disorder (Cluster C)

A person having at least four of these characteristics might be considered to have an avoidant personality disorder:

1. Anticipates and worries about being rejected or criticized in social settings.

2. Has few friends, despite the desire for them.

3. Is unwilling to get involved with people unless certain of being liked.

4. Avoids social or occupational activities that involve significant interpersonal contact.

5. Inhibits development of intimate relationships because of fear of seeming foolish, being ridiculed or feeling shame.

6. Possesses low self-worth because of self-perceived social ineptness and a lack of qualities he or she perceives as appealing.

7. Is unusually reluctant to engage in new situations or activities for fear of embarrassment.

Dependent Personality Disorder (Cluster C)

A person should have at least five (5) of these characteristics to be considered to have a dependent personality disorder:

1. Is unable to make routine everyday decisions without excessive advice and reassurance from others.

2. Allows or encourages others to make important life decisions for him or her (e.g. where to live, what job would be best for him/her, whether to get married, whether to have children).

3. Has difficulty expressing disagreement with others because of fear of their anger or loss of support.

4. Has difficulty independently initiating activities because of lack of confidence in personal judgment or abilities.

5. Goes to excessive lengths to obtain nurturance and support from others.

6. Feels uncomfortable or helpless when alone because of exaggerated fears of inability to care for himself or herself.

7. Indiscriminately seeks another relationship to provide nurturing and support when a close relationship ends.

8. Is frequently preoccupied with fears of being left to care for himself or herself.

Obsessive Compulsive Personality Disorder (Cluster C)

A person having at least four (4) of these characteristics might be considered to have an obsessive-compulsive personality:

1. Perfectionism that interferes with completing tasks.

2. Preoccupation with details, rules, lists, and schedules.

3. Reluctance to delegate tasks or to work with others unless they follow exactly his or her way of doing things.

4. Excessive devotion to work and productivity to the exclusion of leisure activities and friendships.

5. Over conscientious and inflexible about matters of morality or ethics.

6. Perception of money as something to be saved for future catastrophes; miserliness regarding spending for self and others.

7. Inability to discard worn-out or worthless objects even when they have no sentimental value.

8. Behavior that is typically rigid and stubborn.

The **Cluster A** group is characterized by odd and eccentric traits and may lead to psychiatric conditions such as Delusional Disorder or Schizophrenia.

The **Cluster B** group is characterized by behavior that is erratic, emotional, or dramatic. Cluster B has the strongest association with substance abuse, particularly Antisocial and Borderline Personality Disorders. The **Cluster C** group is characterized by feelings of fear and anxiety. Substance abuse occurs in this group but not as frequently as in Cluster B.

When reviewing the dual problems of substance abuse and personality disorders one suspects that the interaction between them is synergistic, with the addiction sharing many characteristics of Cluster B disorders and vise-versa (Walker, pp. 226-227). Both disorders share common ground in that they have:

1. Inflexible, maladaptive, responses to stressful events.

2. Impairment in loving, working and relating to new situations.

3. Impulsivity to most life events.

4. Boundary problems.

5. Histories of persistent and pervasive anger and resentment.

Antisocial Personality Disorder (APD)

The two essential features of antisocial personality disorder (APD) are:

(1) A pervasive disregard for the violation of the rights of others,

(2) An inability to form meaningful interpersonal relationships.

Substance Abuse Disorders and APD.

The prevalence of Antisocial Personality Disorder (APD) and substance abuse is high:

- Much of substance abuse treatment is particularly targeted to those with APD, and substance abuse treatment alone has been particularly effective for these disorders

- The majority of people with substance use disorders are not sociopathic, except as a result of their addiction.

- Most people diagnosed as having APD are not true psychopaths. That is, predators who use manipulation, intimidation, and violence to control others to satisfy their needs.

- Many people with APD use substances in a polydrug pattern, involving alcohol, marijuana, heroin, cocaine, and methamphetamines.

- People with APD may be excited by the illegal drug culture and they have considerable pride in their ability to thrive in the face of the dangers of that culture. They often are in trouble with the law. Those who are more effective may limit themselves to exploitative or manipulative behaviors that do not make them as vulnerable to criminal sanctions.

Antisocial Behavior Treatment Plan (Jongsma and Peterson, 1999).

This usually involves an individual who refuses to follow rules. This person has little regard for the truth as reflected in patterns of consistently lying. His general interactions with others are irritable, aggressive and at times argumentative with authority figures. He/she verbally or physically flights often and has an inability to sustain or maintain consistent employment.

Long Term Goals

1. Become more responsible for behavior and keep behavior within the acceptable limits of societal rules.

2. Come to an understanding and acceptance of the need for limits and boundaries in behavior.

3. Accept responsibility for one's actions, including apologizing to individuals we have harmed

Short Term Goal #1.

1. Admit to the legal and/or ethical behavior that has ignored the law and/or rights and feelings of others.

Therapeutic Intervention #1

1. Explore the history of client's pattern of illegal and/or unethical behavior and confront attempts at minimizing denial or projection of blame.

2. Review the consequences for self and others of antisocial behavior.

Short Term Goal #2

1. List relationships that have been broken because of disrespect, disloyalty, aggression, or dishonesty.

Therapeutic Intervention #2

1. Review relationships that have been lost due to antisocial attitudes and practices.

2. Confront the lack of sensitivity to the needs and feelings of others.

Short Term Goal #3

1. Make a commitment to be honest and reliable.

Therapeutic Intervention #3

1. Teach the value of honesty and reliability for oneself as the basis for trust and respect in all relationships and social interactions.

2. Teach the positive effect that honesty and reliability have for others, as they are not disappointed or hurt by lies and broken promises.

3. Ask client to make a commitment to be honest and reliable.

Short Term Goal #4

1. List those who deserve an apology for hurtful behaviors.

Therapeutic Intervention #4

1. Review relationships that have been lost due to antisocial attitudes and practices (Also S/T Goal #2)

2. Confront the lack of sensitivity to the needs and feelings of others (Also S/T Goal #2)

3. Assist client to identify those who have been hurt by his antisocial behavior.

4. Teach the client the value of apologizing for his/her hurting as a means of accepting responsibility for behavior and developing sensitivity to the feelings of others.(Also S/T Goal #5)

Short Term Goal #5

1. Decreased statements of blame of others or circumstances for own behavior, thoughts, and feelings.

Therapeutic Intervention #5

1. Teach the client the value of apologizing for his/her hurting as a means of accepting responsibility for behavior and developing sensitivity to the feelings of others. (Also S/T Goal #4).

2. Confront client's avoidance of responsibility toward his/her children.

3. Confront client when making blaming statements or failing to take responsibility for actions, thoughts, or feelings.

4. Explore with client reasons for blaming others for their actions.

Do's and Don'ts of Assessment for Co-occurring Disorders

- **Do** keep in mind that assessment is about getting to know a person with complex and individual needs. **Do not** rely on tools alone for a comprehensive assessment.

- **Do** always make every effort to contact all involved parties, including family members, person to have treated the client previously, other mental health and substance abuse treatment providers, friends, significant others, probation officers as quickly as possible in the assessment process. (These other sources of information will henceforth be referred to as collaterals.)

- **Don't** allow preconceptions about addiction to interfere with learning about what the client really needs. Co-occurring disorders are as likely to be under recognized as well as over recognized. Assume initially that an established diagnosis and treatment regime from mental illness is correct, and advise clients to continue with those recommendations until careful reevaluation has taken place. **Don't** assume that all mental symptoms are caused by one's addiction.

- **Do** become familiar with the diagnostic criteria for common mental disorders, including personality disorders, and with the names and indications of common psychiatric medications. **Do** become familiar with the criteria in your own State for determining who is a mental health priority client. Know the process for referring clients for mental health case management services or for collaborating with mental health treatment providers.

- **Don't** assume that there is one correct treatment approach or program for any type of COD. The purpose of assessment is to collect information about multiple variables that will permit individualized treatment matching. It is particularly important to assess stages of change for each problem and the client's level of ability to follow treatment recommendations.

- **Do** become familiar with the specific role that your program or setting plays delivering services related to COD in the wider context of system of care. This allows you to have a clearer idea of what clients your program will best serve and helps you to facilitate access to other settings for clients who might be better served elsewhere.

- **Don't** be afraid to admit that you don't know, either to the client or yourself. If you do not understand what is going on with the client, acknowledge that to the client, indicate that you will work with the client to find the answers, and then ask for help. Identified at least one supervisor who is knowledgeable about COD as a resource for asking questions.

- **Do** remember that empathy and hope are the most valuable components of your work with the client. When in doubt about how to manage a client with, COD, stay connected, be empathic and hopeful, and work with the client and treatment team to try to figure out the best approach over time.

Chapter Seven
Assessment: General Medical Conditions

General Medical Condition

The reporting of current general medical conditions that are potentially relevant to the understanding or management of the individual's mental disorder is important and relevant to the management of an individual's behavioral health challenges. The purpose of distinguishing general medical conditions is to encourage thoroughness in evaluation and to enhance communication among health care providers.

Due to the high incidence of HIV/AIDS and Hepatitis C cases among substance use disorders particular attention will be devoted to this topic.

Medical Condition: HIV/AIDS

The first cases of acquired immunodeficiency syndrome (AIDS) were reported in the United States in the spring of 1981. By 1983 the human immunodeficiency virus (HIV), the virus that causes AIDS, had been isolated. Early in the US, HIV/AIDS pandemic, the role of substance abuse in the spread of AIDS was clearly established. Injection drug use (IDU) was identified as a direct route of HIV infection and transmission among injection drug users. The largest group of early AIDS cases comprised gay and bisexual men (referred to as men who have sex with men or MSMs). Early cases of HIV infection that were sexually transmitted often were related to the use of alcohol and other substances, and the majority of these cases occurred in urban, educated, white MSMs.

Currently, injection drug users represent the largest HIV- infected substance abusing population in the United States. HIV/AIDS prevalence rates among injection drug users vary by geographic region, with the highest rates in surveyed substance abuse treatment centers in the Northeast, the South, and Puerto Rico. From July 1998 through June 1999, 23 % of all AIDS cases reported were among men and women who reported IDU (CSAT, 2000).

IDU practices are quick and efficient vehicles for HIV transmission. The virus is transmitted primarily through the exchange of blood using needles, syringes, or other IDU equipment (e.g., cookers, rinse water, cotton) that were previously used by an HIV infected person. Lack of knowledge about safer needle use techniques and the lack of alternatives to needle sharing (e.g., available supplies of clean, new needles) contribute to the rise of HIV/AIDS. Another route of HIV transmission among injection drug users is through sexual contacts within relatively closed sexual networks, which are characterized by multiple sex partners, unprotected sexual intercourse, and exchange of sex for money (Friedman et al., 1995). The inclusion of alcohol and other non-injection substances to this lethal mixture only increases the HIV/AIDS caseload (Grella et al., 1995). A major risk factor for HIV/AIDS among injection drug users is crack use; one study found that crack abusers reported more sexual partners in the last 12 months, more sexually transmitted diseases (STDs) in their lifetimes, and greater frequency of paying for sex, exchanging sex for drugs, and having sex with injection drug users (Word and Bowser, 1997). Following are the key concepts about HIV/AIDS and substance abuse disorders that influenced the creation of the US Department of Health and Human Services Treatment Improvement Protocol:

- **Substance abuse increases the risk of contracting HIV.**

HIV infection is substantially associated with the use of contaminated or used needles to inject heroin. Also, substance abusers may put themselves at risk for HIV infection by engaging in risky sex behaviors in exchange for powder or crack cocaine. However, this fact does not minimize the impact of other substances that may be used (e.g., hallucinogens, inhalants, stimulants, prescription medications).

- **Substance abusers are at risk for HIV infection through sexual behaviors.**

Both men and women may engage in risky sexual behaviors (e.g., unprotected anal, vaginal, or oral sex; sharing of sex toys; handling or consuming body fluids and body waste; sex with infected partners) for obtaining substances, while under the influence of substances, or while under coercion.

- **Substance abuse treatment serves as HIV prevention.**

Placing the client in substance abuse treatment along a continuum of care and treatment helps minimize continued risky substance abusing practices. Reducing a client's involvement in substance abusing practices reduces the probability of infection.

- **HIV/AIDS, substance abuse disorders, and mental disorders interact in a complex fashion.**

Each act as a potential catalyst or obstacle in the treatment of the other two-- substance abuse can negatively affect adherence to HIV/AIDS treatment regimens; substance abuse disorders and HIV/AIDS are intertwining disorders; HIV/AIDS is changing the shape and face of substance abuse treatment; complex and legal issues arise when treating HIV /AIDS and

Substance abuse; HIV infected women with Substance abuse disorders have special needs.

- **Risk reduction allows for a comprehensive approach to HIV/AIDS prevention**.

This strategy promotes changing substance related and sex related behaviors to reduce clients' risk of contracting or transmitting HIV.

Origin of HIV/AIDS

Of the many theories and myths about the origin of HIV, the most likely explanation is that HIV was introduced to humans from monkeys. A recent study (Gao et al., 1999) identified a subspecies of chimpanzees native to west equatorial Africa as the original source of HIV 1, the virus responsible for the global AIDS pandemic. The researchers believe that the virus crossed over from monkeys to humans when hunters became exposed to infected blood. Monkeys can carry a virus similar to HIV, known as SIV (simian immunodeficiency virus), and there is strong evidence that HIV and SIV are closely related (Simon et al., 1998).

AIDS is caused by HIV infection and is characterized by a severe reduction in CD4+ T cells, which means an infected person develops a very weak immune system and becomes vulnerable to contracting life threatening infections (such as, Pneumocystis Carinii pneumonia). AIDS occurs late in the HIV disease.

Tracking of the disease in the United States began early after the discovery of the pandemic, but even to date, tracking data reveal only how many individuals have AIDS, not how many have HIV. The counted AIDS cases are like the visible part of an iceberg, while the much larger portion, HIV, is submerged out of sight. However, because HIV infected people generally are asymptomatic for years, they might not be tested or included in many of the recent state counts. The CDC estimates that between 650,000 and 900,000 people in the United States currently are living with HIV (CDC, 1997c).

In 1996, the number of new AIDS cases (not HIV cases) and deaths from AIDS began to decline in the United States for the first time since 1981. Deaths from AIDS have decreased since 1996 in all racial and ethnic groups and among both men and women (CDC, 1999a). However, the most recent CDC data show that the decline is slowing (CDC, 1999b). The decline can be attributed to advances in treating HIV with multiple medications, known as combination therapy; treatments to prevent secondary opportunistic infections; and a reduction in the HIV infection rate in the mid1980s prior to the introduction of combination therapy. The latter can be attributed to

200

improved services for people with HIV and access to health care. In general, those with the best access to good, ongoing HIV/AIDS care increase their chances of living longer.

HIV/AIDS is still largely a disease of MSMs and male injection drug users, but it is spreading most rapidly among women and adolescents, particularly in African American and Hispanic communities. HIV is a virus that thrives in certain ecological conditions. The following will lead to higher infection rates: a more potent virus, high viral load, high prevalence of STDs, substance abuse, high HIV seroprevalence within the community, high rate of unprotected sexual contact with multiple partners, and low access to health care. These ecological conditions exist to a large degree among urban, poor, and marginalized communities of injection drug users. Thus, MSMs and African American and Hispanic women, their children, and adolescents within these communities are at greatest risk

HIV Transmission

HIV cannot survive outside of a human cell. HIV must be transmitted directly from one person to another through human body fluids that contain HIV infected cells, such as blood, semen, vaginal secretions, or breast milk. The most effective means of transmitting HIV is by direct contact between the infected blood of one person and the blood supply of another. This can occur in childbirth as well as through blood transfusions or organ transplants prior to 1985. (Testing of the blood supply began in 1985, and the chance of this has greatly decreased.) Using injection equipment that an infected person used is another direct way to transmit HIV.

Sexual contact is also an effective transmission route for HIV because the tissues of the anus, rectum, and vagina are mucosal surfaces that can contain infected human body fluids and because these surfaces can be easily injured, allowing the virus to enter the body. A person is about five times more likely to contract HIV through anal intercourse than through vaginal intercourse because the tissues of the anal region are more prone to breaks and bleeding during sexual activity (Royce et al., 1997).

A woman is eight times more likely to contract HIV through vaginal intercourse if the man is infected than in the reverse situation. HIV can be passed from a woman to a man during intercourse, but this is less likely because the skin of the penis is not as easily damaged. Female to female transmission of HIV apparently is rare but should be considered a possible means of transmission because of the potential exposure of mucous membranes to vaginal secretions and menstrual blood (CDC, 1997a). Oral intercourse also is a potential risk but is less likely to transmit the disease than anal or vaginal intercourse. Saliva seems to have some effect in helping prevent transmission of HIV, and the oral tissues are less likely to be

201

injured in sexual activity than those of the vagina or anus. However, if a person has infections or injuries in the mouth or gums, then the risk of contracting HIV through oral sex increases.

Risks of Transmission

Another factor that increases risk is a high level of HIV circulating in the bloodstream. This occurs soon after the initial infection and returns late in the disease. New drug therapy can keep this level (called viral load) low or undetectable, but this does not mean that other individuals cannot be infected. The virus still exists it is simply not detectable by the currently available tests. Because the correlation between plasma and genital fluid viral load varies, transmission may still occur despite an undetectable serum viral load (Liuzzi et al., 1996). Once HIV passes to an uninfected person who is not taking anti-HIV drugs, the virus reproduces very rapidly. It is known that drug resistant viruses can be transmitted from one person to another. The treatment implications for a person infected with a drug resistant virus are not yet known, but treatment will likely be difficult. There are many misconceptions regarding HIV transmission. For example, HIV is not passed from one person to another in normal daily contact that does not involve either exposure to blood or sexual contact. It is not carried by mosquitoes and cannot be caught from toilet seats or from eating food prepared by someone with AIDS. No one has ever contracted AIDS by kissing someone with AIDS, or even by sharing a toothbrush (although sharing a toothbrush still is not advised).

Life Cycle of HIV (Human Immunodeficiency Virus)

It is possible to prevent transmission even after exposure to HIV. In San Francisco, post exposure prophylaxis is being offered to people who believe they have high risk for HIV transmission because of exposure with a known or suspected HIV infected individual. Treatment is started within 72 hours of exposure and includes combination therapy, which may include a protease inhibitor, for a period of 1 month and follow up for 12 months. Once an HIV particle enters a person's body, it binds to the surface of a target cell (CD4+ T cell). The virus enters through the cell's outer envelope by shedding its own viral envelope, allowing the HIV particle to release an HIV ribonucleic acid (RNA) chain into the cell, which is then converted into deoxyribonucleic acid (DNA). The HIV DNA enters the cell's nucleus and is copied onto the cell's chromosomes. This causes the cell to begin reproducing more HIV, and eventually the cell releases more HIV particles. These new particles then attach to other target cells, which become infected. Measuring HIV in the blood

Physicians can measure the presence of HIV in a person by means of (1) the CD4+ T cell count and (2) the viral load count. The CD4+ T cell count measures the number of CD4+ T cells (i.e., white blood cells) in a milliliter of blood. These are the cells that HIV is most likely to infect, and the number of these cells reflects the overall health of a person's immune system.

CD4+ T cells act as signals to inform the body's immune system that an infection exists and needs to be fought. Because HIV hides inside the very cells responsible for signaling its presence, it can survive and reproduce without the infected person knowing of its existence for many years. Even though the body can produce sufficient CD4+ T cells to replace the billions that are destroyed by untreated HIV each day, eventually HIV kills so many CD4+ T cells that the damaged immune system cannot control other infections that may make the person sick. This is the late stage of HIV, when AIDS is often diagnosed based on the presence of specific illnesses (i.e., opportunistic infections).

The viral load represents the level of HIV RNA (genetic material) circulating in the bloodstream. This level becomes very high soon after a person is initially infected with HIV, then it drops. Viral load tests measure the number of copies of the virus in a milliliter of plasma; currently available tests can measure down to 50 copies per milliliter, and even more sensitive tests can measure down to 5 copies per milliliter. To explain the relationship between CD4+ T cell count and viral load count and how together they are used to gauge a person's stage in disease progression, a "moving train" analogy can be used. The CD4+ T cell count is used to measure the person's distance to the point of high risk of contracting opportunistic infections, or death. The viral load count is used to measure the rate at which CD4+ T cells are being destroyed. Therefore, the CD4+ T cell count is the train's position on the track, and the viral load is the train's speed toward the outcome (i.e., AIDS and then death).

After a person is infected with HIV, the body takes about 6 to 12 weeks and sometimes as long as 6 months to build up proteins to fight the virus. These proteins are called HIV antibodies (disease fighting proteins) and are detected by an HIV test called the ELISA (enzyme linked immunosorbent assay). The ELISA is very sensitive--it almost always detects HIV if it is there. Rarely, ELISA tests will give false positive readings (a positive test in someone uninfected. For this reason, a positive ELISA test must always be confirmed with a second, more specific test called the Western blot. According to the CDC, the accuracy of the ELISA and the Western blot together is greater than 99 %.

The six to twelve weeks between the time of infection and the time when an ELISA test for HIV becomes positive are called the "window period." During this period, the individual is extremely infectious to any sexual or needle sharing partner but does not test positive unless a more expensive viral load test is performed.

Disease Progression

Once a person is infected with HIV, he/she should understand the progression of the disease from initial infection, through the latency period, symptomatic infections, and finally AIDS. The course of untreated HIV is not known but may go on for 10 years or longer in many people. Several years into HIV infection, mild symptoms begin to develop, and then later severe infections that define AIDS occur. Treatment appears to greatly extend the life and improve the quality of life of most patients, although estimating survival after an AIDS diagnosis is inexact.

Initial infection

The greatest spread of HIV occurs throughout the body early in the disease. Approximately 6 months after infection, the level produced every day may reach a "set point." A higher set point usually means a more rapid progression of HIV disease. Early treatment may be recommended to reduce the set point, potentially leading to a better chance of controlling the infection.

Alcohol and drug counselors should discuss symptoms that suggest initial HIV infection with their clients and encourage clients to be tested for HIV if they experience such symptoms. This not only will encourage clients who are infected to enter treatment early but also will provide an opportunity for the counselor to help uninfected clients remain that way.

Latency period

After initial infection the latency period, or incubation period develops during which untreated persons with HIV have few, if any, symptoms. This period lasts a median of about 10 years. The most common symptom during this period is swollen lymph nodes. The lymph nodes found around the neck and under the arms contain cells that fight infections. Swollen lymph nodes in the groin area may be normal and not indicative of HIV. When any infection is present, lymph nodes often swell, sometimes painfully. With HIV, they swell and tend to stay swollen but usually are not painful.

After the first year of infection, the CD4+ T cell count drops at a rate of about 30 to 90 cells per year. When the CD4+ T cell count falls below 500, mild HIV symptoms may occur. Many people, however, will have no symptoms at all until the CD4+ T cell count has dropped very low (200 or less). Bacteria, viruses, and fungi that normally live on and in the human body begin to cause diseases that are also known as opportunistic infections.

Early symptoms of infection may include chronic diarrhea, herpes zoster, recurrent vaginal candidiasis, thrush, oral hairy leukoplakia (a virus that causes white patches in the mouth), abnormal Pap tests, thrombocytopenia, or numbness or tingling in the toes or fingers. Most of these infections occur with a CD4+ T cell count between 200 and 500. Symptoms of these infections usually signal a problem with the immune system but are not severe enough to be classified as AIDS.

AIDS (Acquired Immunodeficiency Syndrome)

In the 1980s, AIDS was defined to include a depressed immune system and at least one illness tied to HIV infection. AIDS defining conditions are diseases not normally manifest in someone with a healthy immune system. These should prompt a confirmatory HIV test. The additional 1993 AIDS defining conditions led to the diagnosis of more AIDS cases in women and injection drug users. Since 1993, the list of AIDS ¬defining conditions has included pulmonary tuberculosis (TB), recurrent bacterial pneumonia, and invasive cervical cancer. HIV infected persons with a CD4+ T cell count of 200 or less are classified as persons with AIDS (CDC, 1992).

TB and invasive cervical cancer are two AIDS ¬defining conditions that warrant special mention. Pulmonary TB is the one AIDS related infection that is contagious to those without HIV It generally causes a chronic dry cough (sometimes with blood), fatigue, and weight loss. Pulmonary TB requires ongoing treatment for at least 6 months, and close associates of the infected person must be tested for TB. If TB is only partially treated (i.e., the TB patient does not take all of the medications), resistant TB will develop, which can then be passed to others. Although TB, coupled with a positive HIV test, is an AIDS defining diagnosis, it also can occur while the CD4+ T cell count is still high. If TB occurs late in the disease after the CD4+ T cell count has dropped, it may not be found in the lungs, and symptoms may include only weight loss and fever, without a cough. It should be noted, however, that the Mantoux PPD test (a test routinely administered to screen for TB by determining reaction to intra-dermal injection of purified protein derivative) might not be positive if the patient is anergic (i.e., if he has sufficient immune system damage to cause inability to respond to the PPD).

Cervical cancer may progress rapidly in women with HIV but usually is asymptomatic until it is too late for successful treatment. Women who are HIV positive should have Pap tests at least once every 6 months and more often if any abnormality is found.

AIDS symptoms

Most AIDS defining diseases are severe enough to require medical care, sometimes hospitalization. Some of these diseases, however, can be treated earlier on an outpatient basis if symptoms are reported when they are mild.

Cough is a symptom common to several AIDS related infections, the most frequent of which is Pneumocystis Carinii pneumonia (PCP not to be confused with the drug by that name, phencyclidine). A dry cough, fever, night sweats, and increasing shortness of breath characterize PCP. Recurrent bacterial pneumonia (i.e., two or more infections within a year) also is an AIDS defining condition. It often causes a fever and a cough that brings up phlegm. Coughing is also a symptom of TB. As a general guideline, if a cough does not resolve after several weeks, a medical practitioner should check it.

Several skin problems can occur in HIV/AIDS. Kaposi's sarcoma (KS), a rare malignancy outside of HIV disease, may be the best known skin condition in HIV infection. KS is a cancer of the blood vessels that causes pink, purple, or brown splotches, which appear usually as firm areas on or under the skin. KS also grows in other places, such as the lungs and mouth. KS is highly prevalent among men with AIDS, of whom 20 to 30 % may develop the condition in contrast to 1 to 3 % of women with AIDS (Kedes et al., 1997). However, since the introduction of combination anti-HIV therapy, KS is seen less frequently.

Diarrhea is a very common symptom of AIDS. Many AIDS defining conditions cause diarrhea, including parasitic, viral, and bacterial infections. HIV itself can cause diarrhea if it infects the intestinal tract. Diarrhea also is a common side effect of HIV/ AIDS medications. Weight loss can be caused by inadequate nutrition, untreated neoplasm's and opportunistic infections (which often are associated with diarrhea), and deranged metabolism (Dieterich, 1997).

Changes in vision, particularly spots or flashes (known as "floaters"), may indicate an infection inside the eye. A virus called Cytomegalovirus (CMV) is the most common cause of blindness in people with HIV/AIDS. CMV progresses very rapidly if not treated and is among the most feared of AIDS¬ related infections. Fortunately, it almost never occurs until the immune system is almost completely destroyed, so it is not usually the first symptom.

A severe headache, seizure, or changes in cognitive function may herald the onset of a number of infections or cancers inside the brain. The two most common brain infections in HIV/AIDS are cryptococcal meningitis, a fungus that usually causes a severe headache, and toxoplasmosis, which can present with focal neurologic deficits or seizure. The cancer of the central nervous system called lymphoma also can cause seizures. Progressive multifocal leukoencephalopathy (PML), a brain disease that causes thinking, speech, and balance problems and dementia also can occur as a result of HIV infection.

End stage disease

A person with HIV/AIDS can live an active and productive life, even with a CD4+ T cell count of zero, if infections and cancers are controlled or prevented. The newer antiviral medicines can even help the body restore much of its lost immune function. In the past few years, a phenomenon called the Lazarus syndrome has developed among patients with AIDS, wherein, because of optimal drug therapy, someone who had seemed very near death improves and returns to fairly normal function. Untreated, the disease eventually overwhelms the immune system, allowing one debilitating infection after another. Sometimes the possible combinations of medication are no longer effective, the side effects are intolerable, or no further therapy is available.

Hospice care is an appropriate choice for those who have run out of therapeutic options. In hospice care, the individual is treated for pain and other discomforts and allowed to die of the disease. Pain therapy at this stage invariably requires narcotics. It is crucial that the client and other treatment professionals understand that using opiates for pain is entirely different from using them to feed an addiction. The client will develop a need for high doses and will have withdrawal symptoms if the drug is stopped but will not "get high." If drugs must be stopped (which is uncommon), they can be tapered under medical supervision.

Hospice care allows the person with end stage HIV/AIDS a peaceful death and a chance to address those relationships or experiences that are important. Hospice goals involve maintaining dignity and allowing the client's significant others to dictate how they will cope with this final stage

Hepatitis C*

Hepatitis C infection is caused by the hepatitis C virus, also known as HCV, a virus that infects cells in the liver. HCV is one of several viruses (hepatitis

*NIDA Community Alert Bulletin-Hepatitis. (2019) For more detailed information go to Medicine Net.com or the National Resource Center http://www.aidsetc.org/images/masthead/aetc-logo-sub.gif.

A, hepatitis B) that can cause an inflammation of the liver. Chronic infection with HCV can result in cirrhosis (liver scarring) or primary liver cancer (hepatocellular carcinoma).

Hepatitis C Infection

- Is prevalent in many countries worldwide.

- Is the most common chronic blood-borne infection in the United

- States, infecting an estimated 4 million Americans.

- Is transmitted primarily through direct exposure to infected blood.

- Is linked to injection drug use, which accounts for most HCV transmission in the United States.

- Is estimated to be responsible for most chronic liver disease in the United States and 8,000 to 10,000 deaths annually.

- Is the single most common reason for liver transplants in the United States.

The highest rates of new infection are among persons 20 to 39 years old and the highest rates of chronic infection are among persons 30 to 49 years old.

Transmission of Hepatitis C Virus

- Sharing contaminated needles is the most common route of infection. Injection drug use is responsible for at least 60 percent of HCV infection in the United States

- The risk of sexual transmission of HCV is much lower than the risk associated with contaminated needles, but still present. Sexual transmission is estimated to account for less than 20 percent of HCV transmission. The highest rates of sexual transmission are associated with multiple sex partners, and the increased risk may be associated with traumatic sex that results in blood exposure.

- Long-term monogamous sexual partners of persons infected with HCV have very low rates of becoming infected (0 to 4 percent).

- Prior to the discovery of the virus and the development of a screening test for blood, many people were infected through contaminated

208

blood transfusions. Since 1992, infection from blood transfusions is rare in the United States.

- The average rate of transmission from an infected pregnant mother to her infant is 5 to 6 percent (range 0 to 25 percent). This risk increases if the mother is infected with both HCV and HIV, with reported transmission rates of 5 to 36 percent.

- Other potential risks for transmission include sharing contaminated straws during intranasal use of cocaine, and sharing items such as razors and toothbrushes, which may be contaminated with infected blood. Data on exposure risks from tattooing or piercing in the United States are sparse.

Injection Drug Use and Hepatitis C Infection

- Although new infections among injection drug users in the United States have declined since 1989, both the incidence and prevalence of infection remain high. Studies have shown that infection is widespread in populations of experienced injectors, with rates in many areas of the United States exceeding 80 percent. Acquisition of hepatitis C infection is very rapid among new injectors following initiation of injection, with 50 to 80 percent infected within 6 to 12 months.

- Risks for infection include needle sharing, frequent daily injection, cocaine injection, and sharing needles with a long-term injector. Because of the efficiency of blood-to-blood transmission and the high prevalence of infection among injectors, anyone who has ever injected drugs, even if he or she may have experimented only once in the past, is at risk for infection. Due to common modes of transmission, a large proportion of injection drug users infected with HCV are also infected with hepatitis B virus and/or HIV.

Natural History of Hepatitis C

Following exposure to the virus, most people with acute infection display no symptoms and continue to feel well. However, some develop jaundice, and some people experience nonspecific symptoms such as anorexia (lack of appetite), malaise, and/or abdominal pain. Because specific symptoms are uncommon, the only way to determine whether infection is present is with a blood test for antibodies to the virus. The average incubation period for the virus is 6 to 7 weeks and antibodies to HCV can be detected in 80 percent of those infected by 15 weeks after exposure.

A small proportion of those with acute infection are able to clear the virus naturally from the bloodstream. However, 75 to 85 percent of those infected develop chronic infection. While most people with chronic infection do not have any symptoms, complications can occur after 10 to 20 years of unapparent infection. As liver cells die, scar tissue forms in the liver (fibrosis), preventing normal blood flow. This leads to a condition called cirrhosis, which can be life threatening. It is estimated that cirrhosis occurs in 10 to 20 percent of people with chronic infection, and 1 to 5 percent develop primary liver cancer (hepatocellular carcinoma).

It is not yet known why some people are able to clear the virus, why disease severity varies from person to person, or how to predict who will develop disease. Unlike HIV, the amount of virus in a person's blood is not a good predictor of disease progression. Recent data show that alcohol consumption can increase the risk of progression, and studies indicate that persons infected with both HCV and HIV tend to have a more rapid decline in health.

Treatment

Individuals found to be infected with HCV need to be assessed and monitored by a specialist for the presence and severity of chronic liver disease and for treatment eligibility. Infected persons should be advised to reduce alcohol intake and to abstain from using illicit drugs. Those using illicit drugs should be referred to drug treatment programs.

Screening and Prevention of Hepatitis C

Persons who have injected illicit drugs, including those who injected only once or occasionally many years ago and who may not consider themselves to be drug users, should be tested for hepatitis C infection. Because of similar risk factors for infection, drug users should also be tested for HIV and hepatitis B. Those at risk should receive immunization for hepatitis A and B. Persons with known HIV infection should be screened for HCV as well.

Regardless of test results, persons who use illicit drugs should be counseled to reduce their risk for acquiring infection or of potentially transmitting infection to others. Persons with multiple sex partners should be advised to use latex condoms.

Persons who test positive for HCV should be given information regarding the need for preventing further harm to the liver, reducing risks for transmitting HCV to others, and obtaining medical evaluation and follow-up for chronic liver disease and possible treatment. It is important that physicians know if a person is infected with HCV so that medications that

210

may have side effects involving the liver can be avoided. To protect the liver from further harm, HCV-infected persons should be vaccinated against hepatitis A and B, if susceptible, and should be strongly advised that even moderate alcohol consumption may adversely affect disease progression. All persons should be advised not to use illicit drugs.

Medical Condition Treatment Plan (DeGood, Crawford and Jongsma, 1999).

A medical condition for which the client is under a physician's care. A positive test for HIV, a medical condition secondary to chemical dependency, a history of neglecting ones physical and medical health.

Long-Term Goals

1. Accept chronic medical condition with proper medical attention.

2. Establish chemical dependency recovery that leads to improved physical health.

Short-Term Goal #1

1. Comply totally with Doctors orders for tests, limitations, and/or treatments.

Short-Term Intervention #1

1. Make any necessary arrangements required for client to obtain the medical services needed.

2. Refer client to physician for complete physical

3. Help the client understand his medical problem and the need to cooperate with physician's recommendations.

4. Monitor treatment effectiveness and follow through on physician's orders, redirect client when he is failing to comply.

Short-Term Goal #2

1. Verbalize an increased understanding of medical condition.

Short-Term Intervention #2

1. Consult with physician and review Doctors orders with client.

2.   Provide to client any appropriate literature that will increase understanding of his medical condition.

3.   Assign client to attend a support group related to his physical condition and to report the positive aspects of attending to counselor.

Short-Term Goal #3

1.   Acknowledge any high risk behaviors associated with sexually transmitted diseases (STD's).

Short-Term Intervention #3

1.   Assess clients activity for the presence of high-risk behaviors (such as unprotected sex, gay lifestyle, promiscuity, etc.) related to STD and HIV.

2.   Refer client to public health facility or physician for STD and/or HIV testing, education, or treatment.

Short-Term Goal #4

1.   List changes in nutrition and lifestyle that will be implemented to support medical recovery.

Short-Term Intervention #4

1.   Arrange a consultation with dietitian to explain the proper nutrition that will enhance medical recovery.

2.   Explore and assess the role of chemical abuse on medical condition

3.   Assign client to make a list of things he could do to help maintain physical health; process list in counseling.

4.   Refer client to a physical therapist for assessment and recommendations for an exercise program that is appropriate for client's age and medical condition.

Psychosocial and Environmental Problems

Psychosocial and environmental problems that may affect the diagnosis, treatment, and prognosis of mental disorders need to be addressed in assessment. A psychosocial and environmental problem may be a negative life event, an environmental difficulty or deficiency, a familial or other interpersonal stress, an inadequacy of social support or personal resources, or other problem relating to the context in which a person's difficulties have developed. The following is a list of problems grouped together in their categories:

1. Problems with primary support group (e.g., death of a family member, health problems in family, disruption of family by divorce, or estrangement, removal from the home, remarriage of parent, sexual or physical abuse).

Family Conflict Treatment Plan (Jongsma and Peterson, 1999).

Is usually involves a family that is not a stable source of positive influence or support. It can also imply little or no contact with other family members. Parental conflict appears ongoing and fosters dependency. The client can feel that parents are overly involved in the client's life or there are long periods of no communication with parents. Finally, the client feels that he/she is the negative person in the family structure.

Long Term Goals

1. Resolve the fear of rejection, low self-esteem, and/or oppositional defiance by resolving the conflict developed in the family of origin.

2. Decrease the level of present conflict with parents while beginning to let go of resolving pass conflicts with them.

3. Achieve a reasonable level of family connectedness and harmony where members support, help, and are concerned for each other.

Short Term Goal #1

1. Describe the conflicts and causes of conflicts between self and parents.

Short Term Intervention #1

1. Give verbal permission for client to have and express own feelings, thoughts, and perspectives in order to foster a sense of autonomy from family.

2. Explore the nature of all conflicts and their perceived causes. . (Also Goal #2)

213

Short Term Goal #2

1. Identify the client's role in the family conflicts.

Short Term Intervention #2

1. Explore the nature of all conflicts and their perceived causes. . (Also Goal #1)

2. Confront client when he/she is not taking responsibility for self in family conflict and reinforce client for taking responsibility for his her role in conflicts.

3. Ask client to read a book and select concepts from the book to begin using in conflict resolution.

Short Term Goal #3

1. Increase the number of positive family interactions by planning activities such as fishing, table tennis, bowling or doing work projects together.

Short Term Intervention #3

1. Refer family for an experiential weekend at a center for family education to build skills and confidence in working together.

2. Ask parents to read book(s) relating to their particular problem.

3. Assist client in developing a list of positive family activities that promote harmony. Schedule such activities into the family calendar.

Short Term Goal #4

1. Identify the role that chemical dependency behavior plays in triggering family conflict.

Short Term Intervention #4

1. Confront client with various activities that reflect his chemical dependency behaviors that need to change.

Short Term Goal #5

1. Report an increase in resolving conflicts with parent by talking calmly and assertively rather than aggressively and defensively.

Short Term Intervention #5

1.   Confront emotional dependence and avoidance of economic responsibility that promotes continuing pattern of living with parents

2.   Use role-playing, role reversal, modeling, and behavioral rehearsal to help client develop specific constructive ways to resolve conflict with parents.

2. Problems related to the social environment (e.g., death or loss of friend, inadequate social support, living alone, adjustment to life-cycle transition - such as retirement).

Loneliness Treatment Plan (Jongsma and Peterson, 1999).

These are individuals who frequently express sadness, pain, or resentment over passed intimate relationships. They lack energy and zest for life and believe that they have little to offer others. Generally, they overeat; overindulge in passive activity like watching TV and sleep excessively as a means of escape from the pain of loneliness.

Long Term Goals

1.   Take constructive steps to overcome loneliness by reaching out to others and becoming more socially active.

2.   Initiate weekly involvement in social activities.

3.   Act confident and appear positive in demeanor, clothing and self-care in order to attract people.

Short Term Goal #1

1.   Describe the loneliness in relation to the nature of the social contact that is desired.

Short Term Intervention #1

1.   Listen to the expression of pain surrounding the loneliness and assess what level of companionship is desired.

Short Term Goal #2

1.   Express feelings surrounding the loneliness.

Short Term Intervention #2

1. Using a depression to determine whether the real problem is depression.

Short Term Goal #3

1. Brainstorm a list of all possible ways to increase social contact.

Short Term Intervention #3

1. Ask the client to list any and all possible ways he/she could put himself/herself in a position to meet new people. Discourage filtering the list as to whether the client could see himself /herself doing these activities, but rather brainstorm and bring the list back to the counselor for review in the next session.

Short Term Goal #4

1. Make changes in personal appearance, manner of relating, and grooming to increase positive attention and social interaction.

Short Term Intervention #4

1. Recommend changes in personal appearance, manner and grooming that could increase confidence and bring positive attention to the individual. Such changes as clothing, hairstyle, smiling more, greeting people, etc.

Short Term Goal #5

1. Reduce isolation and escape behaviors and substitute more active social activities.

Short Term Intervention #5

1. Encourage attention to fitness and diet, to increase weight loss in order to increase energy and improve appearance.

2. Refer client to an in individual who would appreciate a social call.

3. Ask the client to commit to asking one person per week for a social activity; help develop a list of possible people to ask.

4. Urge increased involvement in activities such as church, AA/NA meetings, etc. Specify possible groups and ask permission to have someone contact the person for an invitation.

5. Solicit agreement to set limits one escape behaviors such as TV viewing, too much sleep and overeating. Recommend more active, less isolated activities such as exercise, visiting the library, attending a prayer group, or a hobby/recreational group.

3. Educational problems (e.g., illiteracy, inadequate school environment, discord with teachers or classmates).

Educational Deficit Treatment Plan (Jongsma and Peterson, 1999).

This deficit refers to incompletion of high school diploma or GED. It also refers to a history of difficulties in school or other academic learning situations.

Long Term Goals

1. Recognize the need for high school completion and reenroll in the necessary courses.

2. Receive a high school diploma or GED certificate.

Short Term Goal #1

1. Verbally acknowledge the need for a high school diploma.

Short Term Intervention #1

1. Support and direct client toward obtaining further academic training.

2. Reinforces and encourage client to pursue educational and important vocational training by pointing out the social, monetary, and self-esteem advantages.

Short Term Goal #2

1. Verbalize decreased anxiety and negativity associated with learning situations.

Short Term Intervention #2

1. Give encouragement and verbal affirmation when appropriate to Klein as he she works to increase his hair educational level. (Also S/T Goal #3)

2. Assist client in the development of strategies for handling his/her fears and anxieties in learning situations.

Short Term Goal #3

1. Make the necessary contacts to investigate enrollment in high school or GED classes.

Short Term Intervention #3

1. Give encouragement and verbal affirmation when appropriate to Klein as he she works to increase his hair educational level. (Also S/T Goal #2)

2. Provide client with information regarding community resources available for adult education, high school completion, and vocational skill training.

Short Term Goal #4

1. State commitment to obtain further academic or vocational training.

Short Term Intervention #4

1. Encourage client to implement the recommendations of the educational, psychological, and/or medical evaluation.

2. Get a commitment from the client to pursue further academic or vocational training.

4. Occupational problems (e.g., unemployment, threat of job loss, difficult work conditions, job change, discord with boss or coworkers).

Vocational (Occupational) Stress Treatment Plan (Jongsma and Peterson, 1999)

This type of stress is related to any rebellion against or conflict with authority figures in the employment situation. It also relates to feelings of depression or anxiety related to complaints of job dissatisfaction or stress of employment responsibilities.

Long Term Goals

1. Increase sense of confidence and competence in dealing with work responsibilities.

2. Be cooperative with and accepting of supervision or direction in the work setting.

Short Term Goal #1

1. Describe nature of conflicts with co-workers or supervisor.

Short Term Intervention #1

1. Clarify the nature of conflicts in the work setting.

2. Help client identify his/her own role in the conflict, attempting to represent the other party's point of view.

Short Term Goal #2

1. Replace projection of responsibility for conflict, feelings, or behavior with acceptance of responsibility for own behavior, feelings, and role in conflict.

Short Term Intervention #2

1. Explore the transfer of other personal problems to the employment situation.

2. Confront projection of responsibility for client's behavior and feelings onto others.

3. Reinforce acceptance of responsibility for personal feelings and behavior.

Short Term Goal #3

1. Verbalize feelings of fear, anger, and helplessness associated with the vocational stress.

Short Term Intervention #3

1. Probe and clarify emotions surrounding the vocational stress.

2. Assess the distorted cognitive messages and behaviors connected with a vocational stress.

5. Housing problems (e.g., homelessness, inadequate housing, discord with neighbors or landlord).

Homeless-Living Environment Treatment Plan. (Perkinson and Jongsma, 1998)

This treatment plan refers to one's current living environment in which there is a high risk for relapses. It usually involves individuals who live with others who are regular abusers of alcohol or other drugs. Generally friends or relatives are addicted. Many of these individuals are financially destitute, living on the street and need assistance for adequate food and shelter.

Long Term Goals

1. Maintain a program over recovery free from substance abuse and the negative impact of a high-risk environment.

2. Improve the social, occupational, financial, and living situation sufficiently to increase the probability of a successful recovery from substance dependency.

3. Develop a peer group that is supportive of recovery.

Short Term Goal #1

1. Discuss specific living environment problems as they can negatively affect recovery.

Short Term Intervention #1

1. Help the client identify problems in the living environment and explore the negative impact they will have one recovery.

2. Help the client list specific instances in which living environment problems led to negative consequences and substance abuse.

3.   Explain the importance of a support group in recovery and help the client see how his/her current environment is a high-risk situation.

Short Term Goal #2

1.   Explain how the individual's current lifestyle increases the risk for relapse.

Short Term Intervention #2

1.   Help the client list specific instances in which homelessness problems led to negative consequences and substance abuse.

Short Term Goal #3

1.   List specific living environment problems and write a plan to address each one in recovery.

Short Term Intervention #3

1.   Help the client identified each environmental problem and assist in writing a plan to address each problem in recovery.

2.   Discuss the alternatives available for moving out of current living situation that promotes ongoing substance abuse.

3.   Help the client identify needs and write a plan to meet each need in recovery.

4.   Discuss the importance of a support group and have client list ten reasons needed to maintain abstinence.

Short Term Goal #4

1.   Meet with an AA/NA contact person to discuss plans for recovery.

Short Term Intervention #4

1.   Facilitate the client meeting with Fellowship member and encourage client to discuss recovery plans.

2.   Teach the client the importance of developing a 12 Step program and encourage individual to attend meetings.

Short Term Goal #5

1. Write a plan for developing contacts with people who would tend recovery meetings.

Short Term Intervention #5

1. Help the client develop a personal recovery plan that has all the elements necessary to recover from substance dependency and the individual's deficit living environment.

6. Economic problems (e.g., extreme poverty, inadequate finances, insufficient welfare support).

Financial Stress Treatment Plan (Jongsma and Peterson, 1999).

This usually refers to a loss of income due to unemployment or a long-term lack of discipline in money management, which has led to excessive indebtedness. There is usually a pattern of impulsive spending that does not consider the financial consequences.

Long Term Goal

1.Establish a clear income and expense budget that will meet bill payment demands.

1. Gain a new sense of self-worth, one in which the substance of one's value is not attached to the capacity to do things or own thing that cost money.

2. Understand personal needs, insecurities, and anxieties that make overspending possible.

3. Achieve an inner strength to say no to one's personal impulses, which indirectly increased debt.

Short Term Goal #1

1. Describe the details of the current financial situation.

Short Term Intervention #1

1. Provide a supportive, comforting environment by being empathetic, warm, and sensitive to the fact that the topic may illicit guilt, Shame, and embarrassment.

2. Explore the client's current financial situation.

3. Assists client in compiling a complete list of financial obligations.

Short Term Goal #2

1. Verbalize feelings of depression, hopelessness, and/or Shane that are related to financial status.

Short Term Intervention #2

1. Probe feelings of hopelessness or helplessness that may be associated with the financial crisis

2. Assess the depth or seriousness of the client's financial crisis.

Short Term Goal #3

1. Identify personal traits that make undisciplined spending possible.

Short Term Intervention #3

1. Probe for evidence of low self-esteem, need to impress others, loneliness, depression that may accelerate unnecessary, on warranted spending.

Short Term Goal #4

1. Describe honestly any of the clients or family member's substance abuse   problems that contribute to financial irresponsibility.

Short Term Intervention #4

1. Explore the possibility of alcohol or drug use by family members or a significant other.

7. Problems with access to health care services (e.g., inadequate health care services, inadequate health insurance, and transportation to health care facilities unavailable).

8. Problems related to interaction with the legal system/crime (e.g., arrest, incarceration, litigation, victim of crime).

Legal System Treatment Plan (Perkinson and Jongsma, 1998)

This conflict usually involves legal charges either pending or related to

223

probation or parole status. Usually chemical dependency resulted in several arrests and involvement with the court system.

Long Term Goals

1. Accept responsibility to the mandates of the court.

2. Accept responsibilities for decisions and actions that have led to arrests and develop higher moral and ethical standards to govern future behavior.

3. Accept and adapt to the uncontrollable actions of the court.

Short Term Goal #1

1. Describe the behavior that led to parent involvement with the court system.

Short Term Intervention #1

1. Explore the client's behavior that led to legal conflicts and assess whether it fits a pattern of antisocial behavior.

Short Term Goal #2

1. Verbalize the role Alcohol/ Drug abuse has played in legal problems.

Short Term Intervention #2

1. Explore the issue of chemical dependency and how it may have contributed to legal conflicts.

2. Confront denial of chemical dependency by reviewing various negative consequences of addiction.

Short Term Goal #3

1. Verbalize and accept responsibility for the series of decisions and actions that eventually led to illegal activity.

Short Term Intervention #3

1. Assist client in clarifying values that allow illegal actions.

2. Confront denial and projection of responsibility onto others for client's illegal actions.

Short Term Goal #4

1. Verbalize how the emotional state of anger, frustration, helplessness, or depression has contributed to the illegal behavior.

Short Term Intervention #4

1. Probe negative emotional states that could contribute to illegal behavior.

2. Refer client to support group for emotional conflicts and antisocial impulses.

Short Term Goal #5

1. Identifying cognitive distortions that foster antisocial behavior.

Short Term Intervention #5

1. Assess and clarify cognitive belief structures that foster illegal behavior.

9. Other psychosocial and environmental problems (e.g., exposure to disasters, war, other hostilities, discord with non family care givers).

If any of the above problems become too overwhelming, they can create a disturbance within the individual that can lead to a mental disorder that should be reported in Axis I. For example, if death of a friend continues to be a problem for a long period of time (60-90 days), a V-code disorder can be used to elevate the problem to an Axis I diagnosis. It's best to keep in mind that normal grief and behaviors vary with individuals.

Spiritual Aspects of Mental Disorders

The DSM accomplishes its objective of providing an understanding of the complex biopsychosocial concepts of psychiatric diagnosis. It falls short of its mission by ignoring the spiritual aspects of "mental disorders". M. Scott Peck, MD in his address to the American Psychiatric Association in May of 1992 noted that:

> *The failure of American psychiatry to deal with the issue of spirituality is itself a profoundly over determined symptom rooted in multiple historical forces and other factors. American psychiatry's neglect of spirituality is the profound influence of Freud. Freud has*

had a profound influence upon American psychiatry than upon psychiatry anywhere else on the globe... [Freud] was deeply threatened by the issues of spirituality so much as to terminate his relationship with his most beloved disciple, Jung.

This historical break between science and religion has filtered into the substance abuse treatment programs and also into the fabric of how one financially survives in the medically driven model of reimbursement. This model has also had an effect on the kind of information we allow in our offices. Many psychotherapists refuse to listen to the client's spiritual life and at times make a concerted effort to divert the client's attention to more secular minded discussions. Peck (1993) has referred to this problem as mistreatment, believing that psychotherapists (psychiatrists, psychologists, and clinical social workers) have failed to encourage healthy spirituality, failed to combat unhealthy spirituality or false theology and failed to comprehend important aspects of the patient's life (Peck 1993, p.246). Fromm (1973), a Neo-Freudian, believed that evil exists in the world and that a there is a type of person he called the necrophilous personality or lover of death. These are individuals whose passion in life is to destroy life for the sake of destruction. These individuals appear to have a passionate attraction to all that is dead. Fromm believed that such individuals like Hitler, Stalin, Jim Jones, Charles Manson, etc. are not confused, misled, sick people but fully conscious of their acts of evil.

As a way to remedy this neglect Peck suggesting two (2) new diagnostic revisions to the DSM:

1. Virulent Personality Disorder - a category for people who have been labeled evil.

2. Possession - a category, which needs to be distinguished from Dissociative Disorders.

Peck concluded his discussion by suggesting a Spiritual Axis to our diagnostic nomenclature along with a patient's Stages of Spiritual Development. (Peck, 1993 p. 253). Although Peck makes sense too many holistic thinkers one suspect that much of spiritual psychiatry will never become main-stream and only a few traditionalists will give him serious consideration. This profound neglect of spirituality by American psychiatry and its entrenchment in secularism, suggests that the future of psychotherapy will be guided more by non-medical health professionals and self-help groups like Alcoholics Anonymous, than from medical practitioners (psychiatrists) who appear to be struggling with their own survival in the managed health care system.

Finally, there is a glimmer of spiritual hope in the DSM under *Other Conditions that may be a Focus of Clinical Attention,* there is a V code called *Religious or Spiritual Problems.* This category describes impaired religious or spiritual difficulty, such as that associated with lost or questioned faith. Although the category isn't considered a disorder, it does begin a dialogue that could take us down a path that brings spiritual issues into the mainstream of the assessment system known as the DSM.

Spiritual Relationship Treatment Plan (Kok and Jongsma, 1998).

This treatment plan is related to individuals who struggle with understanding and accepting Alcoholics Anonymous Steps 2 and 3 and have difficulty in believing in a higher power. These individuals usually verbalize feeling of emptiness in their lives, as if something was missing. The idea of a closer relationship to a higher power is considered to be important in the individual's recovery process.

Long Term Goals

1. Clarify spiritual concepts and instill a freedom to approach a higher power as a resource for support.

2. Increase belief in the development of a relationship with a higher power.

3. Begin to have faith in a higher power and incorporate this idea into a support system.

Short Term Goal #1

1. Summarize the highlights of the spiritual quest or journey to this date.

Short Term Intervention #1

1. Ask client to write a story of his/her spiritual quest or journey and process material with counselor.

Short Term Goal #2

1. Describe beliefs about the idea of a higher power.

Short Term Intervention #2

1. Assist in processing and clarifying ideas and feelings regarding a higher power.

227

2. Assign client to list all beliefs related to a higher power and then process the beliefs.

Short Term Goal #3

1. Verbalize an increase of knowledge and understanding of a concept of a higher power.

Short Term Intervention #3

1. Ask client to talk with a spiritual leader regarding spiritual struggles, issues, or questions he/she has and record their discussion for the next counseling session.

2. Assign client to read a book that builds knowledge and concept of a higher power.

Short Term Goal #4

1. Identify specific blocks to believing in a higher power.

Short Term Intervention #4

1. Explore religious distortions and judgments that client was subjected to buy others throughout his life.

2. Assist client in identifying specific issues or blocks that prevent the development of a belief in a spiritual force.

Short Term Goal #5

1. Read books that detail the experience of others who had spiritual awakenings or spiritual struggles.

Short Term Intervention #5

1. Encourage client to read self-help books dealing with spirituality and changes in personality.

Short Term Goal #6

1. Implement daily attempts to be in contact with higher power.

Short Term Intervention #6

1. Recommend implementation of daily meditations and/or prayer. Process the experience in counseling.

2. Assign client to write a daily note to his/her Higher Power.

3. Assist client in the development and encourage implementation of a daily devotional time or other rituals that fosters his/her spiritual growth.

Short Term Goal #7

1. Ask client to find a respected person who has apparent spiritual depth to serve as a sponsor/mentor.

Short Term Intervention #7

1. Help client connect to 12 Step fellowships and find a sponsor or Mentor.

Chapter Eight
Case Management in Recovery

The term case management has appeared in social services literature more than 600 times in the last 30 years, referring to everything from the routing of court dockets through the judicial system to the medical management of a hospitalized patient's care. This document uses the term to refer to interventions designed to help substance abusers access needed social services.

Support for the use of case management in this setting developed from both clinical practice and empirical observation suggesting that substance abusers who seek treatment have significant problems in addition to using psychoactive substances. Alcohol or other drug use often damages many aspects of an individual's life, including housing, employment, and relationships (Oppenheimer et al., 1988; Westermeyer, 1989). Clients in substance abuse treatment programs, particularly publicly funded treatment programs, present a variety of associated problems. Many use multiple substances and may be poly addicted. Many suffer from related health disorders, either caused by their substance abuse such as liver disease and organic brain disorders-or exacerbated by neglect of health and lack of preventive health care. In addition, some diseases including HIV/AIDS, tuberculosis, and some strains of hepatitis are transmitted by substance abuse, either directly or indirectly.

Substance abusers also have a higher incidence of mental health disorders than the general population. Up to seventy percent (70%) of individuals treated for substance abuse have a lifetime history of depression (Mirin et al., 1988). Between twenty and fifty-six percent of individuals with diagnosable Axis I mental disorders also have a substance abuse or dependence disorder (Regier et al., 1990).

Substance abuse clients often arrive in treatment programs with numerous social problems as well. Many are unemployed or under- employed, lacking job skills or work experience. Many in publicly funded treatment programs do not have a high school diploma. Some are homeless, and those who have been incarcerated may face significant barriers in accessing safe and affordable housing. Many substance abuse clients have alienated their families and friends or have peer affiliations only with other substance abusers. Women in treatment have often been victims of domestic violence, including sexual abuse; some women in treatment may be living with an abuser. Achieving and maintaining abstinence and recovery nearly always requires forming new, healthy peer associations.

230

A significant number of clients in treatment are also under some form of control by the criminal justice system. Criminal justice substance abuse clients represent more than half of all clients in treatment in many state and local jurisdictions. Although those afflicted by chemical addiction are found among all socioeconomic groups, persons already plagued by poverty, disease, and unemployment are over represented (CSAT, 1994). Particularly in publicly funded treatment programs, substance abuse clients have limited resources and may lack health insurance. Many are eligible for publicly supported health and social benefits, including Medicare, food stamps, or welfare.

Data suggest that substance abusers who receive professional attention for these additional problems will see improvements in occupational and family functioning and a lessening of psychiatric symptoms (McLellan et al., 1982; Moos et al., 1990; Siegal et al., 1995).

Case Management - A Brief History

One of the first legislative embodiments of case management occurred in the 1963 Federal Community Mental Health Center Act (Intagliata, 1982) in anticipation of the deinstitutionalization, in which persons in long term psychiatric care were moved into community settings. The expectation that these individuals would need services previously provided in the institution led to the rapid expansion of community-based social services. Unfortunately, these services were often created independently of one another and, coupled with the categorical nature of the eligibility for services, led to difficulties for persons used to having these services provided in institutions. The Community Support System developed by the National Institutes of Mental Health in 1977 envisioned case management as a mechanism for helping clients navigate this fragmented social service system. Accessing these resources would thus enable them to live and function adequately in their communities (Intagliata, 1981; Stein and Test, 1980; Test, 1981; Turner and TenHoor, 1978).

Substance abusers historically were never institutionalized as often as were persons with chronic mental illness and so were not directly impacted by deinstitutionalization legislation. Substance abusers were not generally targeted for the development of categorical systems of service delivery and were not generally recipients of case management services. However, case management like services were provided to substance abusers under other titles, such as "mission work," and frequently delivered by the clergy or others in skid row missions, detoxification centers, and ad hoc halfway houses. Jails and county work farms were generally the institutions of choice in dealing with this population. Only after substance abuse began to be decriminalized and defined as a disease were substance abusers referred to various social services.

231

Canadian's were among the first to translate many generic case management functions into the field of substance abuse treatment, outlining the essential elements of a union of case management and substance abuse treatment (Graham and Birchmore-Timney, 1990; Ogborne and Rush, 1983; Rush and Ekdahl, 1990). Case management for substance abusers initially gained attention in the United States through the Treatment Alternatives for Safe Communities (TASC) program (formerly known as Treatment Alternatives to Street Crime). TASC began linking the criminal justice system with the drug abuse treatment system in 1972 and has grown to over 185 programs today. (Cook, 1992)

A 1987 National Institute of Mental Health initiative funded thirteen demonstration projects targeted at young adults with coexisting mental health and substance use problems. Of these 13 projects, 10 identified some form of case management as a primary service and provided a general description of the case management intervention (Teague et al., 1990). Initiatives undertaken by both the National Institute on Drug Abuse (NIDA) and National Institute on Alcohol Abuse and Alcoholism (NIAAA) resulted in numerous projects that used case management to enhance treatment (Bonham et al., 1990; Conrad et al., 1993; Cox et al., 1993; Inciardi et al., 1993; Fletcher et al., 1994; Mejta et al., 1994). Case management in these projects was designed to increase retention in the treatment continuum and to improve treatment outcomes.

Definitions and Functions

Any definition of case management today is inevitably contextual, based on the needs of a particular organizational structure, environmental reality, and prior training of the individuals who are implementing it, whether they are social workers, nurses, or case management specialists. Nonetheless, there is relatively widespread agreement on the basic definition.

While definitions are useful in guiding general discussions, functions are a more helpful way to approach case management as it is actually practiced. As with definitions, there is a high degree of consensus about a core group of functions. One widely accepted set of functions comprises (1) assessment, (2) planning, (3) linkage, (4) monitoring, and (5) advocacy (Joint Commission on Accreditation of Healthcare Organizations, 1979). The National Association of Social Workers' standards for social work case management include assessing, arranging, coordinating, monitoring, evaluating, and advocacy (National Association of Social Workers, 1992).

There is also general agreement about case management functions in the specific context of substance abuse treatment. Case management is one of eight counseling skills identified by the National Association of Alcoholism and Drug Abuse Counselors (National Association of Alcoholism and Drug

Abuse Counselors, 1986) and one of five performance domains developed in the Role Delineation Study (International Certification and Reciprocity Consortium, 1993).

Models of Case Management

Case management models, like the definitions of case management, vary with the context. Some models focus on delivering social services, others on coordinating the delivery of services by other providers. Some provide both. The models result, as much from the needs of specific client populations and service settings as they do from distinct theoretical differences about what case management should be. Four models from the mental health field have been adapted for the field of substance abuse treatment. Each of these models broker/ generalist, strengths-based, assertive community treatment, and clinical/ rehabilitation-has proved valuable in treating substance abusers in a particular setting.

For example, the strengths based approach was adapted to work with crack cocaine users. This approach was chosen not only for its focus on resource acquisition but also because it helps clients see their own assets as a valuable part of recovery (Siegal et. al, 1996). Assertive community treatment was implemented to provide parolees a wide range of integrated services, including drug treatment, skills building, and resource acquisition.

1. Brokerage/Generalist

Brokerage/ generalist models seek to identify clients' needs and help clients access identified resources. Planning may be limited to the client's early contacts with the case manager rather than an intensive long-term relationship. Ongoing monitoring, if provided at all, is relatively brief and does not include active advocacy.

Brokerage /Generalist models are sometimes disparaged in discussions of case management because of the limited nature of the client case manager relationship and the absence of advocacy. Nonetheless, this approach shares the basic foundations of case management and has proved useful in selected situations. The relatively limited nature of the relationship in this model allows the case manager to provide services to more clients. This approach is also appropriate in instances where treatment and social services in a particular area are relatively integrated and the need for monitoring and advocacy is minimal. The model works best with clients who are not economically deprived, who have significant intent and sufficient resources, or who are not in late stage addiction. Small agencies or agencies that offer narrowly defined services may be in an ideal position to offer brokerage - only services.

233

Two creative uses of a brokerage model involved clients who were infected with the human immunodeficiency virus (HIV) or who were at significant risk of acquiring HIV. In one program, case managers also served as educators, delivering cognitive, behaviorally oriented, educational sessions focusing on substance abuse and high-risk behaviors (Falck et al., 1992). The mixing of the educator and case manager roles was intended to increase clients' receptivity to HIV prevention messages by reducing barriers to services that would address problems that might divert attention from those messages. In another variation of the brokerage model, case managers in a large metropolitan area conducted extensive assessments with HIV infected clients, generally making at least two referrals during the initial session. This "quick response" approach was intended to provide immediate results to clients and to link them with agencies or services that would provide ongoing services (Lidz et al., 1992).

Generalist approaches to working with substance abusing clients have taken several forms. Case managers in the central intake facility of a large metropolitan area performed the core functions of case management, linking clients with area substance abuse treatment and other human service providers. These case managers had access to funds for purchasing treatment services, thereby drastically reducing waiting periods for these services (Bokos et al., 1993).

Willenbring and his colleagues were among the first to adapt a mental health model for persons with substance abuse problems, specifically chronic public inebriates (Willenbring et al., 1990). The model deviated from the usual approach to dealing with substance abuse clients in two ways. First, instead of expecting clients to come to services when they "hit bottom," case managers sought out clients through a process known as "enforced contact." Second, case managers and the services team acknowledged the chronic nature of the client's condition and sought to modify the course of the condition and to alleviate suffering. The clients were not required to pledge a goal of abstinence.

2. Clinical/Rehabilitation

Clinical/ Rehabilitation approaches to case management are those in which clinical (therapy) and resource acquisition (case management) activities are joined together and addressed by the case manager. It has been suggested that the separation of these two activities is not feasible over an extended period of time and that the case manager must be trained to respond to client focused, as opposed to solely environmental issues (Kanter, 1996). Client focused services could include providing psychotherapy to clients, teaching specific skills, and family therapy. Beyond the usual repertoire of case management functions (e.g., monitoring), the case manager should be aware of numerous issues including transference, counter transference, how clients

234

internalize what they observe, and theories of ego functioning (Harris and Bergman, 1987; Kanter, 1996).

Many substance abuse treatment programs use a clinical model in which the same treatment professional provides, or at least coordinates, both therapy and case management activities. Staffing considerations frequently drives such an approach: It is more economical to have one treatment professional provide all services than to have separate clinical and case managers deliver them.

One example of combining clinical and case management activities is found in a program for women who have substance abuse problems (Markoff and Cawley, 1996). In Project Second Beginning, an emphasis on relationships and empowerment is used both to secure needed resources and to guide implementation of therapy activities. This approach is based on the belief that women have special needs in the treatment setting needs that can most appropriately be addressed through a therapeutic relationship with a single caregiver. The Clinical /Rehabilitation approach has been widely used in the treatment of persons with diagnoses of both substance abuse and psychiatric problems (Drake et al., 1993; Drake and Noordsey, 1994; Lehman et al., 1993; Shilony et al., 1993).

3. Strengths Based Perspective

The Strengths Based perspective of case management was originally developed at the University Of Kansas School Of Social Welfare to help a population of persons with persistent mental illness make the transition from institutionalized care to independent living (Rapp and Chamberlain, 1985). The foremost two principles on which the model rests are (1) providing clients support for asserting direct control over their search for resources, such as housing and employment, and (2) examining clients' own strengths and assets as the vehicle for resource acquisition. To help clients take control and find their strengths, this model of case management encourages use of informal helping networks (as opposed to institutional networks); promotes the primacy of the client case manager relationship; and provides an active, aggressive form of outreach to clients.

A Strengths-Based perspective of case management has been selected for work with substance abusers for three reasons. First is case management's usefulness in helping them access the resources they need to support recovery. Second, the strong advocacy component that characterizes the strengths approach counters the widespread belief that substance abusers are in denial or morally deficient perhaps unworthy of needed services (Bander et al., 1987; Ross and Darke, 1992). Last, the emphasis on helping clients identify their strengths, assets, and abilities supplements treatment models that focus on pathology and disease. Strengths based case management has been implemented with both female (Brindis and Theidon, 1997) and male substance abusers (Siegal et al., 1995).

Because of the advocacy component and client driven goal planning, a strengths based approach can at times cause stress between a case manager and other members of the treatment team (Rapp et al., 1992). Despite this, there is evidence that the approach can be integrated with the disease model of treatment and that its presence leads to improved outcomes for clients. The improved outcomes include employability, retention in treatment, and (through retention in treatment) reduced drug use (Siegal et al., 1996; Siegal et al., 1997).

The American Society of Addiction Medicine (ASAM) Criteria

ASAM's criteria, formerly known as the ASAM patient placement criteria, is the result of a collaboration that began in the 1980s to define one national set of criteria for providing outcome-oriented and results-based care in the treatment of addiction. Today the criteria have become the most widely used and comprehensive set of guidelines for placement, continued stay and transfer/discharge of patients with addiction and co-occurring conditions. ASAM's criteria are required in over 30 states.

ASAM's criteria is an indispensable resource that addiction professionals rely on to provide a nomenclature for describing the continuum of addiction services.

How ASAM's Criteria Works?

ASAM's treatment criteria provide separate placement criteria for adolescents and adults to create comprehensive and individualized treatment plans. Adolescent and adult treatment plans are developed through a multidimensional patient assessment over five broad levels of treatment that are based on the degree of direct medical management provided, the structure, safety and security provided, and the intensity of treatment services provided.

236

https://www.asam.org/resources/the-asam-criteria/about

The six dimensions reviewed are:

1. Acute Intoxication and/or Withdrawal Potential. This dimension addresses the severity of the client's presenting substance use disorder. The interviewer attempts to assess the severity of the client's addiction and the degree of impairment in everyday functioning. Of particular concern is the risk of severe withdrawal syndrome. A client who is experiencing symptoms of withdrawal (or who is at great risk of doing so) may require treatment in an intensive type of service.

Dimension 1: They are the substance- induced disorders of intoxication and withdrawal as defined in the DSM. The system criteria for the 10 substances and all symptoms must not be due to a general medical condition and cannot be better explained by another medical condition.

237

2. Biomedical Conditions and Complications. This dimension investigates the client's overall physiological condition to determine whether there are any medical problems or concerns. If a client is suffering from a medical problem that is complicated by the use of alcohol or drugs, or he or she has a health problem of such severity that medical care is immediately necessary, then the inclusion of medical management in the treatment setting becomes critically important.

Dimension 2: This dimension relates to Axis III of the DSM, general medical conditions that are potentially relevant to the understanding and management of individual substance dependency orders.

3. Emotional/Behavioral or Cognitive Conditions and Complications. This dimension addresses the client's mental status, in terms of the effects of any emotional or behavioral problems on the presenting substance use disorder. The client is evaluated in terms of his or her emotional stability, and the interviewer attempts to assess the degree to which the client could present a danger to self or others. The goal of this dimension is to identify any psychological disorders which could complicate drug and alcohol treatment, and which may need to be treated concurrently. This dimension also identifies any unpredictable or self-defeating behaviors in response to emotional or environmental stressors.

Dimension 3: relates to many different parts of the DSM, such as, mood disturbances, anxiety, thought and perception disturbances, phobias, hallucinations, obsessions, etc. Dimension III also impacts on some Axis IV psychosocial stressors

4. Readiness to Change. This dimension examines the client's attitude towards treatment. The degree, to which the client understands the nature and consequences of his or her addiction, as well as his or her motivation to engage in recovery, are vital considerations to be made when deciding upon an appropriate setting for treatment.

Dimension 4: the DSM does not address this dimension in any meaningful way. Except for suicidal or comorbidity concerns most interviewers pay little attention to the client's motivation in relation to his or her readiness to engage in the recovery process.

5. Relapse, Continued Use or Continued Problem Potential. This dimension's focus is the client's ability to maintain abstinence from alcohol and other drugs. It examines how the client deals with triggers and cravings and attempts to assess what changes in behavior are needed for him or her to maintain abstinence. Like the treatment acceptance dimension, this is a critical gauge of the degree of structure the client needs in his or her treatment program.

238

Dimension 5: This dimension in the DSM is more a response to issues of prognosis in evaluation. There is little attention given to ones relapse potential. The closest clinical thought has to do with issues of remission, which are projected over a one-year period.

6. Recovery/Living Environment. This dimension evaluates the client's social and living environment in terms of how it promotes or denigrates the client's recovery efforts. Its main concern is whether the client's peers, family, and/or significant others are supportive of his or her recovery, either directly or indirectly. Severe conditions can require relief from the social environment in a structured setting, and information about the client's coping patterns can be valuable in developing his or her treatment plan.

Dimension 6: This dimension in the DSM is a part of Axis IV-psychosocial stressors. Concerns about family, housing, legal, etc. should be reflected in decisions related to the recovering individual's environment.

Through the above strength-based multidimensional assessment the ASAM criteria addresses the patient's needs, obstacles and liabilities, as well as the patient's strengths, assets, resources and support structure.

Six Guiding Principles in Treating Clients with COD

The guiding principles are derived from a variety of sources: conceptual writings, well-articulated program models, a growing understanding of the essential features of COD, elements common to separate treatment modalities, clinical experience and available to curable evidence. Principles identified by Drake and colleagues (1993) and by the Center for Mental Health Services Managed Care Initiative Panel (1998), as well as the assumptions that underlie the model Comprehensive Continuous Integrated Systems of Care described in the TIP protocols. The principles suggested below are consistent with these protocols but reflect the specific focus of the consensus panel on how best to provide COD treatment in substance abuse treatment agencies. The following section discusses each of the six principles in turn.

The Six Guiding Principles are:

1. Employ a recovery perspective. Recovery is a long-term process of internal change and recognizes that these initial changes proceed through a variety of stages.

2. Adopt a multi-problem viewpoint. Treatment should address immediate and long-term needs for housing, work, health care and supportive and network services. All services should be comprehensive to meet the multidimensional problems typically presented by clients with COD.

3. ***Develop a phased approach to treatment.*** Many clinicians view clients as progressing through a variety of phases. Generally, three to five are identified, including engagement, stabilization, treatment, and aftercare or continuing care. These phases are consistent with, and parallel to, stages identified in the recovery perspective.

4. ***Address specific real-life problems early in treatment.*** All treatment approaches must incorporate case management, and intensive case management services to help clients find housing or handle legal and financial matters. Psychosocial rehabilitation helps the client develop the specific skills and approaches needed to perform a variety of roles, such as student, employee, community member, etc. Often it is the most important component of the person's treatment strategy.

5. ***Plan for the client's cognitive and functional impairments.*** Client impairments frequently call for relatively short, restructured treatment sessions that are focused on practical life problem. Gradual pacing, visual aids, and repetition often are very helpful.

6. ***Use support systems to maintain and expand treatment effectiveness.*** The use of self-help groups, the family, the faith community, and other resources that exist within the client's life can play an invaluable in recovery. Mutual self-help principles, highly valued in the substance abuse treatment field, are now widely recognized as important components in the treatment of COD. Mutual self-help groups must be used as an adjunct to primary treatment. These self-help groups, not only provide a vital means of support during outpatient treatment, but also are used commonly in residential program such as therapeutic community.

Comprehensive Treatment Model

✓ Assessment, to include a medical examination, drug use history, psychosocial evaluation, and where warranted, a psychiatric evaluation, as well as a review of socioeconomic factors and eligibility for public health, welfare, employment, and educational assistance programs.

✓ Same-day intake, to retain the patient's involvement and interest in treatment.

240

- ✓ Documenting findings and treatment, to enhance clinical case supervision.

- ✓ Preventive and primary medical care, provided on site.

- ✓ Testing for infectious diseases, at intake and at intervals throughout treatment, for infectious diseases, such as hepatitis, retrovirus, tuberculosis, HIV/AIDS, syphilis, gonorrhea, and other sexually transmitted diseases.

- ✓ Weekly random drug testing, to ensure abstinence and compliance with treatment.

- ✓ Pharmacotherapeutic interventions, by qualified medical practitioners, as appropriate for patients having mental health disorders, addiction to opiates, and HIV-seropositive.

- ✓ Group counseling interventions, to address the unique emotional, physical, and social problems of HIV/AIDS patients.

- ✓ Basic substance abuse counseling, including psychological counseling, psychiatric counseling, and family or collateral counseling provided by persons certified by State authorities to provide such services. Staff training and education are integral to successful treatment programs.

- ✓ Practical life skills counseling, including vocational and educational counseling and training, frequently available through linkages with specialized programs.

- ✓ General health education, including nutrition, sex and family planning, and HIV/AIDS counseling, with an emphasis on contraception counseling for adolescents and women.

- ✓ Peer/support groups, particularly for those who are HIV-positive or who have been victims of rape or sexual abuse.

- ✓ Liaison services with immigration, legal aid, and criminal justice system authorities.

✓ Social and athletic activities, to retrain patients' perceptions of social interaction.

✓ Alternative housing for homeless patients or for those whose living situations are conducive to maintaining the addicted lifestyle.

✓ Relapse prevention, which combines aftercare and support programs, such as Alcoholics Anonymous and Narcotics Anonymous, within an individualized plan to identify, stabilize, and control the stressors which trigger and promote relapse to substance abuse.

✓ Outcome evaluation, to enable refinement and improvement of service delivery.

Chapter Nine
Social Model of Recovery

Self-directed health care is emerging as a critical element in the transformation of America's health care system. Two of the factors that are driving this trend are the recent increases in the cost of health insurance and health services and the inconsistent quality of health care. Both private and public health care delivery systems are responding by developing new consumer-directed products. The President's New Freedom Commission on Mental Health has called for the development of consumer-driven models of care and system changes to support community-based services in behavioral health care. All components of the health care system urgently need to become more consumer-centered; behavioral health services are no exception (DHHS, 2005)

This consumer-centered model of *"recovery"* began in the addictions field, referring to a person recovering from a substance use disorder. Originating from the 12-Step Program of Alcoholics Anonymous and the Civil Rights Movement, the broadening of the social model of recovery to include not only drug and alcohol but also mental health emerged due to a perceived failure of the medical model of services delivery and the evolving belief by that the medical model did not adequately support social inclusion. (http://en.wikipedia.org/wiki/Recovery_model 2012).

The term recovery services has more recently been adopted in the mental health field as people realize that, similar to recovery from an addiction, recovery from a mental illness is also possible. The Substance Abuse and Mental Health Services Administration (SAMHSA) and the Interagency Committee on Disability Research (ICDR) began an effort in 2004 to develop a consensus statement on a definition of *"recovery"* in the mental health field. *"The expert panelists agreed that recovery is an individual's journey of healing and transformation to live a meaningful life in a community of his or her choice while striving to achieve maximum human potential"* (U.S. Department of Health and Human Services, 2005b, p. 4, as cited in NASW, 2005).

For many, *"recovery"* has become a political as well as a medical challenge. The social model of recovery can thus be viewed as one manifestation of empowerment. An empowerment model of recovery which emphasizes that conditions are not necessarily permanent, that other people have recovered who can be role models and share experiences, and *"symptoms"* can be understood as expressions of distress related to emotions and other people. One such model from the US National Empowerment Center proposes a number of principles of how people recover and identifies the characteristics of people in recovery. (Fisher, 2005) Some individuals working in the field believe that recovery should be seen as more of a philosophy or attitude than a specific model, requiring that *"we regain personal power and a valued place in our communities. Sometimes we need services to support us to get there".* (Davidson, et, al, 2006)

Elements of a Social Model of Recovery

Each individual's journey of recovery and transformation is a deeply personal process, as well as being related to an individual's community and society (Repper & Perkins, 2006). This personal process of recovery is seen by many as a journey that involves developing hope, a secure base and sense of self, supportive relationships, empowerment, social inclusion, coping skills, and meaning. The social model of recovery has now been explicitly adopted as the guiding principle of many behavioral health systems.

As mentioned above, a number of core elements have been identified with a social model of recovery:*

Hope-Finding and nurturing hope has been described as a key to recovery. It is said to include not just optimism but a sustainable belief in oneself and a willingness to persevere through uncertainty and setbacks. Hope may start at a certain turning point, or emerge gradually as a small and fragile feeling, and may fluctuate with despair. It is said to involve trusting and risking disappointment, failure and further hurt. (Repper & Perkins, 2006)

Secure base-Appropriate housing, a sufficient income, freedom from violence, and adequate access to health care has also been proposed. It has been suggested that home is where recovery may begin but that housing services and the *"continuum of care concept"* have failed to flexibly involve people and build on their personal visions and strengths, instead *"placing"* and *"reinstitutionalizing"* them. (Lori, Anthony & Chris, 2008).

Self-Recovery of a durable sense of self (if it had been lost or taken away) has been proposed as an important element. A research review suggested that people sometimes achieve this by *"positive withdrawal"*—regulating social involvement and negotiating public space in order to move towards others in a way that feels safe yet meaningful; and nurturing personal psychological space that allows room for developing understanding and a broad sense of self, interests, spirituality, etc. It was suggested that the

---

*To perform an assessment of agencies activities, values, and practices in relation to a social model of recovery go to Recovery Self-Assessment Provider Scale. The Recovery Provider Scale can be accessed through the following web site:
ttps://sites.google.com/site/pascalscolesccp/

Supportive relationships-A common aspect of recovery is said to be the presence of others who believe in the person's potential to recover, and who stand by them. While mental health professionals can offer a particular limited kind of relationship and help foster hope, relationships with friends, family and the community are said to often the significant long-term benefits. Others who have experienced similar difficulties, who may be on a journey of recovery can be of particular importance. Those who share the same values and outlooks more generally (not just in the area of mental health) may also be particularly important. It is said that one-way relationships based on being helped can actually be devaluing, and that reciprocal relationships and mutual support networks can be of more value to self-esteem and long-term recovery. (Repper & Perkins, 2006).

Empowerment and Inclusion -Empowerment and self-determination are important to recovery. This can mean developing the confidence for independent assertive decision making and help-seeking. Achieving social inclusion requires support and a willingness to challenge stigma and prejudice about the community's perception of behavioral health concerns. It may also require recovering unpracticed social skills or making up for gaps in work history. (Repper & Perkins, 2006).

Coping strategies- The development of personal coping strategies (including self-management or self-help) is an important element. This can involve making use of medication or psychotherapy if the consumer is fully informed and listened to, including about adverse effects and about which methods fit with the consumer's life and their journey of recovery. Developing coping and problem solving skills to manage individual traits and problem issues (which may or may not be seen as symptoms of a mental disorder) may require a person becoming their own expert, in order to identify key stress points and possible crisis points, and to understand and develop personal ways of responding and coping. (Repper & Perkins, 2006)

Meaning-Developing a sense of meaning and overall purpose is important for sustaining the recovery process. This may involve recovering or developing a social or work role. It may also involve renewing, finding or developing a guiding philosophy, religion, politics or culture. (Repper & Perkins, 2006) From a postmodern perspective, this can be seen as developing a life narrative. (Gold, 2007).

Finally, the social model of recovery is based on the concepts of strengths and empowerment, indicating that if individuals with behavioral health challenges have greater control and **choice** in their process of recovery, they will be able to take increased control and initiative in their lives.

Choice is the hallmark of a strength-based strategy (social model of recovery) that gets interpreted in a person-first assessment and planning process of recovery. The emphasis on **choice** implies that a variety of community resources are available to help people effectively manage their behavioral health challenges and arrange their lives in accordance with their own preferences (NASW, 1996).

The Flow of Recovery

The healing process from a person's trauma of addiction is not just related to an individual's past explanations of their trauma, but also the direct experience of their emotional thoughts and feelings, and the remnants of those emotions that we continue to revisit (Epstein, 1995, p. 192).

The ability to change and to some extent heal from the trauma of addiction is often related to an individual's capacity to manage, adapt and integrate new knowledge, that facilitates a more positive productive view of one's past and how that past influences a person's recovery in the present and future. If one stops old behaviors, such as substance use, without new behaviors, he/she is doomed to failure. Therefore, the absence of alcohol or other drugs from one's body is only the beginning of recovery. To have a responsible life in recovery a person must engage in new-found resilience, with a life process known as flow. (Seligman and Csikszentmihalyi, 2000).

According to Becvar (1997), it appears that finding resilience through flow involves the integration and awareness of the following into one's daily living and sense of well-being:

1. There must be a continuous interplay between our thoughts, emotions, and our physical and emotional state of health and well-being (Becvar, p.20).

2. Individuals are primarily responsible for our life and thus for our health (Becvar, p.20).

3. Emotions and the mind play a large part in the creation of "disease," they also can be employed in the healing process (Becvar, p.20).

4. A person's body and mind have an intelligence of its own. Each cell has the wisdom and inclination to carry out its function, which may be negatively or positively influenced consistently with the messages received.

5. The body/mind speaks to us and can be our teacher if we are willing to learn. Pain, discomfort, and disease provide information about conflict and disharmony (Becvar, p.20).

6. Symptoms of illness must be considered at a variety of levels, including the mental, the physical, the emotional and the spiritual levels (Becvar, p.20).

7. The inner self is always seeking growth (Becvar, p.20)

8. The reduction and possible elimination of conflict are facilitated by a desire, and willingness to pursue self-awareness actively (Becvar, p.20).

9. What appears to be an illness may be the necessary by-product of a deeper level of healing. As we heal holistically, we go through periods of detoxification that may be experienced as a temporary discomfort (Becvar, p.20).

10. Each of us must get to know our body/mind better than anyone else. By learning to listen "within," we also become our own greatest healers (Becvar, p.20).

Long-term health in an individual involves a body, mind and spiritual balance characterized by positive emotion, constructive thoughts, and responsible actions while supporting the notion of the physical, emotional, social and spiritual integration of the whole person (Scoles, 2015. p.167).

In recovery, individuals must create a life in which the focus is no longer on negative behavior, but instead emphasizes positive solutions that facilitate wellness in a holistic sense (Becvar, 1997, p.69). Therefore, the absence of alcohol or other drugs from one's body is only the beginning of recovery. Without the thought of having some control over life events, it is complicated to build self-esteem and find a positive flow process that reflects resilience and transformation. To sustain a life of positive well-being one must embrace a redistribution of energy so that our consciousness can form a new balance that encourages and to some extent creates both internal and external harmony (Scoles, 2015, p. 51). One of the ways an individual can redistribute energy is through flow. Flow often refers to a sense of timelessness or living in the moment, or a state of absorption characterized by intense concentration, with a feeling of being correctly challenged by the moment. Anyone can experience flow, in different areas of his or her life, such as play, creativity, work, recovery. The energy or "fuel of flow" appears to be related to (1) a viable philosophy of life, (2) a relationship with a "higher power", (3) a developing sense of Self, (4) a feeling of being connected, (belonging) to the universe and (5) a connection with a community that nurtures spiritual growth (Clinebell 1995, p.82).

In the flow process, the emotions are not just contained (as in early recovery) and channeled, but positive, energized, and aligned with current activity (as in full long-term recovery). Feelings of spontaneous joy, even rapture while performing a task is the flow experience. Words used to describe flow have been "to be in the moment," "in the zone," "on a roll," "wired in," "in the groove," "centered," or "singularly focused." (Csikszentmihalyi & Nakamura, 2002). Flow is achieved when the challenge of a given life event is aligned with one's ability to cope and manage a given life event.

The traditional linear thought of relapse that one starts over again and loses all *"their clean time"* is counterproductive to the concept of flow and gives no credibility to the circularity of energy and its relationship to the flow of recovery. Circularity of flow refers to the fact that energy is never lost, it is always with us and at times resurfaces in conscious and unconscious activity (Jung, 1964;1980). This Jungian concept gives credibility to the thought that one never is recovered from their trauma but always in a state of recovery. The challenge of relapse for an individual with one month of recovery is not the same as the relapse experienced by an individual with many years of recovery. The latter event can be more traumatic, since the loss appears to not recognize the person's *"clean time"* (the positive experience) but only concentrates on the relapse (the negative experience). What is more important is not the relapse but how one manages their relapse and strengthens their positive flow of resilience. Relapse behaviors (future challenges) are significant not because they occur but because it gives one the opportunity to build resiliency for future events.

The challenge for someone, early in recovery can result in a state of anxiety, stress and possible relapse. Insufficient life challenges for someone in long-term recovery can result in boredom and make one more vulnerable to a disruption in ones' flow of positive recovery. Zoya (1989), reflecting on drug use and the avoidance of life challenges states that,

> *We often come across people who say that they have turned to drugs with a desire of dying little by little. Even when the physical death of the individual is not an issue, psychic death is still constellated. One often turns to drugs because of the insignificance, senselessness, and flatness of one's present life. A dead and senseless thing fueled by solely reflex action (p.63).*

The impact of challenging situations in recovery means that flow is often temporarily exciting and variously stressful, but this is considered "positive" flow and should never be confused with "negative" or debilitating stress. Disruptions in flow (relapses) occur when the body, due to anxiety, depression, anger, is challenged by the inability to align with the mind. Flow is difficult to achieve when one's body and mind are not in harmony. The lack of body-mind synchronicity is considered a major impediment to recovery and a high-risk factor for relapse. This disequilibrium is one of the

248

main reasons why the thread to a person's spiritual life is difficult to harness. This disequilibrium makes it more difficult to "cross over the bridge" and find your spirituality in everyday life. This disruption is partly related to social determinants of health such as, a body that is poorly nourished, or lacking a consistent place to live, or a mind devoid of positive thoughts (Scoles and DiRosa, 2018).

A significant volume of scientific research has developed to support a positive flow model of human development which is in fundamental disagreement with many of the psychological tenants of Western medicine (Seligman and Csikszentmihalyi, 2000; Seligman, 2007). A person's ability to shift the focus away from individual blame and towards a more positive personal acceptance and respect for the dignity of others means that one must move away from diagnostic labels and acknowledge a person's participation in their own lives and the potential to change their lives so that he or she may more fully empower themselves to challenge life more holistically. (Becvar, 1997, p. 106). In the process of suspending personal judgment, we move from linearity to circularity and create what C.G. Jung referred to as a reality that is more participatory and less causal therefore allowing for a more empowering model of behavior devoid of negative values (Jung, 1966, p.118). People in their recovery from substance abuse are regularly engaged in the management of events that trigger past experiences. These survivor past experiences are circular in nature simply because trauma and its effects do not follow a linear path of experience. Re-emergence of flooding memories even after the survivor thought he/she thoroughly addressed the trauma of addiction is a common behavioral health challenge. (Herman, 1992). Energy flows circularly and is never lost in our personal, cultural or collective experiences. It should be noted that the circularity of energy flow should not be confused with stagnation, despair or helplessness, which can generate a sense of purposelessness, boredom or depression.

The Flow and Developmental Fixation

Early recovery is a health challenge because the individuals' psychological, developmental curve is out of sync with one's biological rhythm (Jung, 1972, p. 588). Many individuals who are struggling in their recovery appear to be emotionally fixated at the age they started drinking or doing drugs which is usually around late adolescence. In general, the psychology of youth is in the biological body of a middle-aged person. (Erickson, 1968). This developmental fixation has to do with concrete perceptions of the world and is at times lacking abstract reasoning. Due to this developmental lag, creativity about life was limited because their teenage years were interrupted by their addiction. If a created expression is a path to adulthood, substance abuse represents one of the most clear-cut examples of social and psychological atrophy. Erickson (1963) in Childhood and Society, clearly

249

articulates many of the problems of adolescence that resonate with people in recovery:

1. **Identity Disillusion.** Looking at others to find out who they are as a person. This projection during one's addiction allows the individual to pick the least socially acceptable friends.

2. **Egocentric Needs and Desires.** Focusing on their own experience with a little, if any, regard for others. Many individuals in addiction believe that their conceptualization of the world is more important than the rest of society.

3. **The Lack of Peer Pressure Experience**. This identity crisis of early recovery is related to an individual 's non-existent testing of new and different roles of adolescents and young adulthood. Self-help groups, such as Alcoholics Anonymous, is for many recovering individuals the first meaningful attempt to "grow up" and engage in the possible variations of decisions and situations of adulthood.

The great tragedy of modern life is the loss of supportive communities that foster active healing communities by building passion and managing frustration and confusion which are necessary for success. Many self-help groups exist to give encouragement, support, and understanding to individuals who face lifelong adversities from various traumas. Many support groups have borrowed heavily from the Twelve Steps of Alcoholics Anonymous. Many support groups outline a way of living that is not just related to issues of substance use and abuse but provide a spiritual path to a more positive life worth living. The Steps are more than just a flow of recovery but a flow about a life of perseverance, meaning, and transcendence. The perseverance experience is the steadfast pursuit of a task, mission, or journey despite obstacles, discouragement, or distractions. Duckworth (2016), argues that the flow of perseverance is a trait known as grit. Grit enables an individual to persevere in accomplishing a goal despite obstacles over an extended period (: https://afineparent.com/building-character/what-is-grit.html). One's grit leads to a transcendence experience when an individual identifies with a group of people who have a collective experience of transformation (Jung, 1968, p. 451).

The practice of the Twelve Steps is reflective of the flow of recovery and encourages the use of positive meaning beyond our daily life struggles. The Serenity Prayer is a call to action. It encourages the best of our thoughts and behaviors. By asking, "What can I change and what can't I change?" one begins to devise a plan of action. For things we cannot change, our task is to work on accepting them. For things we can change, we must determine what action is necessary to support such change and then to find the courage to act. The process sounds simple but isn't. That is why it requires serenity, courage, and the "wisdom to know the difference." The Serenity Prayer offers guidance and wisdom for all of life's problems. The initial part of the serenity prayer is the most widely known, but there is more to it than just the first few lines

> *God, grant me the serenity to accept the things I cannot change, courage to change the things I can, and the wisdom to know the difference. Living one day at a time, enjoying one moment at a time, accepting hardship as the pathway to peace; taking, as He did, this sinful world as it is, not as I would have it; trusting that He will make all things right if I surrender to His will; that I may be reasonably happy in this life, and supremely happy with Him forever in the next (www.winternet.com/~terrym/serenity).*

To *"accepting the things, I cannot change"* one needs to review life events that brought the individual to seek recovery. Exploration involves (1) Examining the pros and cons of a healthy lifestyle (2) Dealing with discrepancies between the individual's perception of their challenges and others' perceptions of their challenges (3) Receiving information about behavioral health risks and (4) Providing feedback about their recovery journey. The most difficult thing to do in recovery, as in life, is to act in accordance with one's positive thoughts. Even more difficult is accepting what can't be controlled. Effective individuals spend a significant amount of positive intellectual activity bringing harmony to what they believe they can bring into a supportive recovery reality. In that reality process, Individuals need the knowledge and skills to not control others or project one's wishes and desires on others. In general, recovering individuals need to avoid negative feelings of anger, rage, anxiety, depression, and extreme frustration.

"Courage to change the things I can" is being able to identify what can be under your influence and to some extent control. Individuals need the helping skills to focus on the here and now, to act, and work on themselves. As a result, people in recovery must develop positive affirmations, that lead to long-term positive behaviors, and develop a stronger sense of Self. These positive affirmations must (1) Engage the individual in programs and community activities that reinforce the importance of remaining in a recovery/resilience-oriented system of care that supports a realistic view of change through incremental small steps, (2) Acknowledges change processes difficulties in the early stages of healing, (3) Provides assistance to individuals in finding new self-identified reinforcers of positive change, (4) Helps people in early recovery identify useful coping skills in high-risk situations and (5) Helps the person assess whether he or she has a healthy community, family and/or social support network.

"Wisdom to know the difference" is learning to differentiate between the impossible and the possible. Individuals need the skills to talk about feelings, accept limits, and ask themselves the most fundamental question in recovery *"do I have the capacity to change."* The ability to change is related to an individual's capacity to: (1) identify new friends, new social outlets and new ways in which to use leisure time productively, (2) Make lifestyle changes, (3) Affirm ones resolve and self-efficacy, (4) Practice and use new coping strategies to avoid a return to old patterns, (5) Develop a recovery management plan to inhibit returning to past negative behaviors and (6) Review and manage long-term goals.

As a result, of the above practice principles people in recovery can achieve a balanced lifestyle, the ability to deal with urges and cravings, and avoid impulsive, destructive decisions and negative interactions (www.winternet.com/~terrym/serenity).

True transformative learning in support of a person's flow in recovery tends to involve the following four steps:

1. Creation-thoughts and feelings that formulate new interactions with symbols felt to be personally relevant to the individual.

2. Reflection-Intellectual thinking and intelligent analysis of previously incorporated attitudes about the meaning of life events.

3. Integration-the evolution of a conscious attitude that is expansive, integrated and differentiated from prior attitudes.

4. Action-changing ones' daily life activities to reflect this renewed perspective. (Dobson, p.150)

In the above transformative model of recovery, it is essential that the individual understand the relationship between the mind, body and spirit and best practices for partnering with people in the quest to achieve health and wellness. It is imperative that individuals understand the value of inclusion of faith, spirituality and the honoring of ways in which people, families, and communities heal. Finally, understanding holistic care principles enhances the chances for long-term recovery for the individual, the family, and the community.

Extended Recovery Support*

The need to incorporate extended recovery support services are based on at least two ideas:

(1) without such support services, the severity, duration, and consequences of an individual's recovery will worsen over time for many people. This could result in repeated outbreaks of symptoms and innumerable episodes of crisis interventions without the achievement of long-term recovery-sustained symptom reduction/remission, a movement toward global health, and enhanced quality of life.

(2) with extended support, many people with severe behavioral health challenges could completely eliminate or drastically reduce episodes of active illness and achieve personally fulfilling and socially contributing lives in the community

The interest in recovery support and sustained professional- and peer-based support services has grown out of several developmental models of recovery based on long-term studies of mental illness and addiction. These models share several key propositions:

❖ Recovery is often characterized by predictable stages and milestones

❖ The movement through the stages of recovery is a time-dependent process; some aspects of recovery cannot be hurried; some aspects of the recovery process are enduring—requiring vigilance and active management throughout one's life.

❖ Each stage of recovery is marked by developmental tasks that must be completed before movement to the next stage can occur.

❖ These stages and tasks may vary from individual/family to individual/family.

❖ These developmental tasks are shaped by the interaction of problem severity/complexity and personal, family, social, and community recovery capital (assets).

---

*Tools for Transformation Series: Extended Recovery Support (2006) This Extended Recovery Support packet was authored by: William L. White M.A.; Joan Kennerson King, R.N., M.S.N., CS; Seble M. Menkir M.A; Ellen Faynberg, Psy.D. This material is in the public domain and is being reproduced with minor editorial Changes.

❖ Treatment and support interventions appropriate to one stage of recovery may be ineffective or even harmful when misapplied to another stage of recovery.

Such interest has also grown out of research confirming the positive role of sustained support in the recovery process. The following factors can play crucial roles in strengthening and extending long-term recovery:

> Recovery support from family and friends,

> Participation in peer-based recovery support groups,

> Access to recovery-focused professional treatment,

> Participation in professionally-directed continuing care services,

> Participation in treatment Alumni Association activities,

> Access to peer-based recovery support services,

> A recovery-conducive living environment,

> Recovery conducive education/employment, and

> A local culture that celebrates recovery and eliminates barriers to full community participation.

One of the primary lessons learned from listening to the stories of recovered and recovering people is that recovery initiation and recovery maintenance are different processes. The former is a process of *recovering from*—escape from painful and often debilitating conditions. The latter is a *process of recovering to*—the discovery of new aspects of self and family and the exploration of new opportunities.

Behavioral health professionals (psychiatrists, psychologists, social workers, addictions counselors, etc.) can enhance extended recovery support for each people through six broad categories of activity:

• Assessing the recovery capital of each person to determine the level of family, social, and community resources that will need to be mobilized to sustain long-term recovery, a discussion of Recovery capital can also build resiliency in managing future challenges.

• Increasing personal knowledge of recovery support alternatives both locally and nationally (e.g., Internet-based recovery support meetings),

254

• Educating each person/family on the importance of post-treatment and on-going recovery support and recovery support alternatives,

• Assertively linking each person to local communities including communities of recovery and, when indicated, to indigenous recovery support institutions (e.g., peer recovery support centers, recovery homes, recovery schools, recovery industries, and recovery ministries/churches). Discussing with the Person in Recovery which community or communities they identify with and then facilitating linking with these communities.

• Delivering or advocating the development of post-treatment recovery support services that include sustained monitoring, stage appropriate recovery education, active recovery coaching, and, when needed, early re-intervention, and

• Working to sustain and expand recovery support alternatives within the local community.

Extended Recovery Support*

The concept of Extended Recovery Support was developed in the addiction community and refers to the availability of resources and relationships to bolster the ongoing recovery process following the stabilization of a behavioral health challenge. Such initial periods of stabilization may be self- or family-initiated and/or professionally-directed. For people with a primary mental health challenge extended recovery support refers to the availability of resources and relationships to support their long-term recovery and the achievement of their hopes and dreams.

The term extended means that these resources and relationships are available and present over a period of months or years rather than days or weeks. Where traditional models of treatment for behavioral health disorders often involve relationships that are hierarchical and short-term, recovery support term resolution of behavioral health problems. Recovery specific support can range from specialized treatment by service professionals knowledgeable about the long-term recovery process to peer-support offered through recovery support groups whose members share their experience,

---

*Tools for Transformation Series: Extended Recovery Support (2006) This Extended Recovery Support packet was authored by: William L. White M.A.; Joan Kennerson King R.N., M.S.N., CS; Seble M. Menkir M.A; Ellen Faynberg, Psy.D. Important guidance, input and review time was provided by Sade Ali M.A., Michelle Khan M. Ed, Margaret Minehart M.D.; Andrew J. DeVos M.Ed.; Hikmah Gardiner, Jeff Shair, Bryce McLaulin, M.D. This material is in the public domain and is being reproduced with minor editorial Changes.

strength, and hope through the extended process of recovery. Together, these general and specific supports can be thought of as a form of recovery capital.

Recovery capital is the total quantity of internal and external resources that can be mobilized to initiate and sustain recovery from a behavioral health disorder (Granfield & Cloud, 1999). This recovery capital can exist in individuals, families, neighborhoods, and whole communities. One of the primary goals of behavioral health systems transformation in Philadelphia is to increase recovery capital at all of these levels.

The meaning of *support* in the phrase *"extended recovery supports"* spans very different types of assistance. For example, peer-based recovery support services have often encompassed five types of support (Solomon, 2004):

> **1) Emotional Support**: expressions of empathy, care, concern, reassurance, and encouragement; sharing "experience, strength, and hope" in the context of exchanging personal life stories.

> **2) Informational Support**: enhancement of knowledge about the recovery process and recovery support resources; advice and other problem-solving assistance; linkage to resources for recovery skills development.

> **3) Instrumental Support**: assistance in the logistics of constructing a recovery lifestyle, e.g., safe and/or sober housing, transportation to recovery support group meetings, child care, development of social and leisure activities or recovery-conducive employment and education.

> **4) Companionship**: helping people get connected to local communities of recovery as well as to the larger community.

> **5) Validation**: Helping people normalize the recovery experience through comparison and feedback with others in recovery. Sharing that *"I have been there and gotten through it, you can too."*

Chapter Ten
Community Empowerment and Models of Recovery

The Behavioral Health profession is engaged in a movement away from the conventional disease-treatment model of care, with its emphasis on diagnosis and subsequent treatment, to a more holistic approach to recovery and resilience. This approach addresses the mind/body/spirit in its entirety and reflects an understanding of the power that faith, spirituality, personal empowerment and community have in the healing process. However, as revolutionary as this model may be for many practitioners within the helping professions, the holistic approach to healing human suffering traces its practices throughout the Abrahamic religions of Judaism, Christianity and Islam, the Eastern religions of Hinduism, Buddhism and Taoism, and the first Earth-Based religions.

From a psychosocial perspective, religion and spiritual practices have helped individuals and their cultures create meaning to their existence and offer explanation for disease, violence, natural disaster and death. The Mayans believed that violent storms and earthquakes were a direct result of the anger of the gods. The Black Plague that swept Europe in the 1300s generated a profound interest in the afterlife and a belief that sickness was the result of human sin.

While there are still theologians who preach that natural disasters are God's wrath against human frailties, many present-day religions have adopted a more complex view of disease, war and famine. Faith and spiritual leaders in the post-modern era emphasize a human race fallen out of harmony with the natural earth and living in isolation from family and community. Through the excessive and careless misuse of resources the human race has set the globe on an unsustainable course. Although technological advances have empowered humans to travel across a continent in a day, or communicate by internet with a business associate on the other side of the globe, the pace of human experience moves at such a rapid rate, isolation and dehumanization are at epidemic proportions.

Religious and Spiritual Community as a Form of Healing

Buddhist practice encourages a return to a more ecologically balanced way of being in the world in order to preserve our natural resources, sustain the entire population and engage in community as a sacred experience. Doctrines from all the major religious faiths urge the act of giving to others. The Third Pillar of Islam is almsgiving. Buddhist practice underscores giving to those in need as the beginning of the path to Nirvana. Judaism teaches the mitzvah, the act of doing a good deed for another as a path to inclusion in the book of life. In Hinduism,

Vedic theology promotes sharing of personal wealth with neighbors in one's community who are less fortunate (www.hinduism.iscon.com). A basic tenet of Christianity is to give to those in great need and bring relief to others who are suffering. These deeds may pay homage to one's faith, but the act itself is also a form of building and strengthening one's community. These deeds are recognition that the human condition is a shared cultural and collective experience and honors the mutual relationship between individuals, families and their communities (Germain, & Gitterman, 1996).

Beyond the search for an explanation of suffering, human beings have always been in search of a path to transcend physical calamity, disease and death of the body. While human suffering and the human condition in general predisposes us to existential crisis and feelings of disempowerment at both the individual and communal level, the practice of rites, ritual and ceremony traditionally acted as a path to recovery, resilience and transformation. Rites and rituals that constituted religious practices empowered believers, gave them a structure for creating meaning out of their suffering and offered a path to spiritual healing.

A Cree Indian word, *Oenikika*, translated as breath of life, was the traditional purification ceremony practiced by First Nation people in the Americas. A sweat lodge was built from branches, covered with tarps and blankets, and contained lava rocks and a fire to emit steam. Specific ceremonies varied from tribe to tribe, but for all Native people, who use this tradition, the ceremonial lodge was constructed for sacred space, time for prayer, transformation, and healing of the spirit (Null, 1998).

Historically, these practices of religion through rites, ritual and ceremony not only created meaning to human existence they fostered a culture of community and group cohesion and identity. During the Oenikika Ceremony as many as thirty tribal members sat in circle at one time offering prayers of thanks and praise for the Great Spirit. After prayer, the participants brought in food and gifts for the medicine man or woman leading Oenikika; this practice of gathering together for thanksgiving, prayer and healing solidified social values and fortified communal bonds (Null, 1998).

The historical shift of one's collective identity which had solidified social and communal bonds, at least for Native and African people who endured holocausts, the destruction of kinship models, the tearing of the fabric of their very cultures was not a simple matter of free choice. Humans now experience the self in isolation, rather than in community where the immediacy of human contact once gave accurate feedback of how people connect to one another. Instead, community and cultural experiences were being defined by mass media and technologically based social networks. Large portions of society prefer to tune into reality television shows such as Survivor to watch human beings creating a false community. Internet-based social networks such as Face Book and Twitter have become the alternative meeting places for connecting with friends, family and acquaintances. These artificial constructs continue to create a discrepancy between one's authentic self and creates a psychic dissonance that erodes emotional health (Fromm, 1941).

Social Determinants of Health*

Studies have found that increases in income, educational opportunities, and accessible housing have the largest positive effect on population health (Frieden, 2004, 2010), and that social spending, not health care spending, is significantly associated with improvement in mortality rates (Healthy People.gov, 2020). As a result, the behavioral health field is currently engaged in a movement to expand the conventional medical treatment model of care, which emphasizes diagnosis and subsequent treatment, to the more comprehensive and inclusive model of population health. The goal is to redirect the focus on the social determinants of health (SDOH) as the means to reducing health inequities and disparities among different population groups.

Therapeutic healing can be found in addressing those social determinants that influence many lifestyle choices. Therefore, from a behavioral health perspective, a population health focus would best be defined by the clinician's advocacy effects to intervene upon and influence these complex social, behavioral, and environmental factors affecting the individual members of diverse populations within the communities they serve. This shift to a holistic model of healing is successful by creating a transformed system of care for adults with behavioral health challenges. The realization that the old entrenched methods of behavioral health care delivery are not working has provided an impetus for this new movement. The new model is a shift from a professionally driven care approach to a system of care that provides lifetime supports while recognizing the many pathways to health (Lamb, Evans, and White, 2009).

The behavioral health field is engaged in a movement to expand the conventional medical treatment model of care that emphasizes diagnosis and subsequent treatment to the more comprehensive and inclusive model of population health. Improving *"the health outcomes of a group of individuals, including the distribution of such outcomes within the group"* (Kindig and Stoddard, 2003, p.1) is the critical focus of the Population Health Model. The goal is to redirect the focus on the social determinants of health (SDOH) as the means to reducing health inequities and disparities among different population groups.

---

*Scoles, Pascal and Francesco DiRosa. Social Determinants of Health and Behavioral Health Challenges. **Counselor**, June 2018. pp. 28-31.

Research indicates a high correlation among these social inequalities and health disparities (Orsi, et al., 2010); thus, in primary care and public health, the lack of improvement in social determinants (SDOH) confounds our ability to improve the health of a community (Practical Playbook, 2016). What studies have found is that increases in income, educational opportunities, and accessible housing have the largest positive effect on population health (Frieden, 2004, 2010), and that social spending, not health care spending, is significantly associated with improvement in mortality rates (Healthy People.gov, 2020).

The social determinants of health (SDOH) focus on the social, environmental, and cultural concerns impacting children, adolescents, and adults who are members of diverse populations within our society (Healthy People, 2020). "Where we live, work, learn and play is as significant as our genetic code" (Practical Playbook, 2016, p.24). The current behavioral health system with its focus on acute disorders continues to be inadequate in helping our communities and its members to develop healthy lifestyles. Thus, professionals in varied disciplines, education, psychology, social work, nursing, etc., are seeing greater evidence that a person's individual health cannot be separated from an individual's community health (Koh, et al., 2011). Moreover, we believe a lack of attention to these social determinants contributes to the overall "community pathology" and low rates of therapeutic success. (Scoles, 2016, p.21). Educational therapeutic healing catalyst can be found in addressing those social determinants that influence many lifestyle choices. Thus, from a community health perspective, healing the community heals the individual, understanding that one inherently does not exist without the other.

Environmental and social exposures to factors such as high-crime and drug infested areas, domestic violence, as well as lack of access to parks or playgrounds, transportation, quality education, social services, and mental health care create a significant impact on lifestyle choices and trajectories. Therefore, from a behavioral health educational perspective, a college-based population health focus would best be defined by the advocacy effects to intervene upon and influence these complex social, behavioral, and environmental factors by actively working to engage, community organizations, families, schools and individuals in efforts to create and shape positive and healthy environments in which all members can thrive. Clinical practitioners have been moderately successful in the treatment of individual disorders, but most often are ignorant to and neglectful of the interplay between one's "pathology" and the community within which he or she resides. The recognition that an individual's health is linked to a community's overall health is the missing link to consistent and efficient treatment. Without practitioners engaging in a comprehensive evaluation of the concomitant social determinants of health (SDOH) to which communities and its members are exposed, a long-term successful solution to the individual's behavioral health challenges can be nearly impossible. Incumbent upon the field of behavioral health is the obligation not only to influence an individual's therapeutic choices toward making healthy life style changes, but also to remain active in their communities. Professionals must simultaneously help shape the community perspective of what changes need to occur within and among their existing micro and meso systems to foster more positive and healthy lifestyle factors for all residents whom reside within.

Each of the below five social determinant areas in Figure 1 reflect a critical component or significant issue that makes up an underlying factor in the arena of population health. (Social Determinants of Health | Healthy People 2020: www.healthypeople.gov/2020/topics-objectives/topic/social-determinant).

Figure 1: Social Determinants of Health (SDOH)

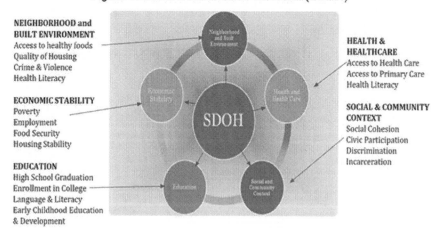

NEIGHBORHOOD and
BUILT ENVIRONMENT
Access to healthy foods
Quality of Housing
Crime & Violence
Health Literacy

ECONOMIC STABILITY
Poverty
Employment
Food Security
Housing Stability

EDUCATION
High School Graduation
Enrollment in College
Language & Literacy
Early Childhood Education
& Development

HEALTH &
HEALTHCARE
Access to Health Care
Access to Primary Care
Health Literacy

SOCIAL & COMMUNITY
CONTEXT
Social Cohesion
Civic Participation
Discrimination
Incarceration

The above organizing framework is used to establish a set of objectives for the five topic areas. It also identifies existing "Healthy People" objectives in other subject areas that are complementary and highly relevant to social determinants. This organizing framework has been used to determine an initial set of resources and other examples of how a social determinant approach to health is implemented at a state and local level. (Social Determinants of Health/Healthy People 2020. www.healthypeople.gov/2020/topics-objectives/topic/social-determinants).

Historically, the lack of a comprehensive vision of health that includes a focus on the influencing social determinants of health (SDOH) is traced partly to the bio-medical movement of the helping professions that sought to replicate the three top elements in the medical model of health care: assessment, diagnosis, and treatment. The cultural and ethnic sensitivity to community processes involved in determining health and pathology in our communities were factors that were lacking in all three of these elements of instituted healthcare as well as behavior health and social services.

The Road to a Population Health Model

Certainly, behavioral health challenges exist that require diagnosis and medical and psychosocial interventions. Surely, to survive in the behavioral health field, clinicians must know and contribute to the diagnostically driven payment system of healthcare. The DSM does accomplish its objective of providing an understanding of the complex bio psychosocial concepts of psychiatric diagnosis.

While the etiology of these disorders may be the imprint of a person's DNA, they are frequently the result of, or compounded by, psychosocial, environmental and cultural factors. The degree to which these factors play in the overall health of an individual has been a subject of controversy among clinicians. What is known is that deterioration of social determinants of health in neighborhoods is a predictive factor in a person's chances for recovery from addiction, trauma, and other behavioral health challenges (The Practical Playbook, 2016). If a community is dysfunctional, that is, lacking necessary supports for economic and social sustainability of its members, the individual's chances for resilience, health and wellness decline; therefore, a vulnerable community will just as likely drown its members in poverty, violence, and isolation. When we refer to the individual in this holistic approach to recovery, resilience, health and wellness, we are not only referring to the person or the family but the community and the neighborhood (Scoles, 2015, p. 48-64).

Throughout most of the history of behavioral health care, community involvement and neighborhood connection were viewed as something that happened near the end of treatment (if at all) depending on adherence and symptom remission and control (DBHIDS, Practice Guidelines 2009). Systems did not view the community as capable of promoting people's health, but as a place to which people might be released when they were "healthier." People were told to wait until they had achieved abstinence or stability before pursuing any workforce activity or educational studies. The treatment community simply did not view the neighborhood in which clients lived as a possible contributing factor to either the problem or the solution. Finally, the person receiving services along with his or her supporters had very little input into these decisions. The individual's immediate eco-community (e.g., family, key allies, spiritual resources) were seldom invited into assessment, planning or service-delivery processes. Community connections were considered the purview of social workers—and even then, were done as referrals rather than intentional connections to these resources. (http://dbhids Practice-Guidelines, 2009).

262

Culture, Ethnicity, and Assessment

To help remedy aspects of the above situation and begin to transform health care delivery, stakeholders in the behavioral health community had to re-evaluate the way they assess individuals regarding diagnosis and treatment. The purpose of diagnosis is to identify areas of disruption in a person's life that have a negative impact on current behavior and lifestyle trajectories. However, the danger in this restrictive perspective is that the clinician will often fail to consider ethnic, and other cultural and environment issues. The need for a more environmentally sensitive classification system, one that acknowledges the role that cultural, community, and intergenerational factors play in behavioral health issues and clinical judgments about them is a topic in need of serious consideration. Historically, this lack of holistic assessment has led too labeling (stigmatizing) individuals with inappropriate disorders. Certain behaviors and personality styles, when not understood within ethnic or cultural context, could be viewed as deviant or dysfunctional, when in fact, they were culturally congruent. There is increasing pressure for practitioners to become more knowledgeable, comfortable and skilled in working with individuals from different cultures, ethnic backgrounds, sexual orientations, genders, gender identities and religious/spiritual orientations. This multi-dimensional framework provides a more dynamic and realistic therapeutic approach that focuses on assessing the person's physical, behavioral, emotional and psychological health within various and diverse environmental and cultural contexts. Moreover, this direct multidimensional practice of direct engagement with clients and community shifts the Behavioral Health practitioners away from the historical treatment emphasis on psychopathology, disease, and disorder and simultaneously accents resilience, strengths, gifts, and capacities of both communities at-large and its residing members (Scoles, 2016, pp. 117-121).

The strengths perspective is primarily a philosophy of interpreting information about our body, mind, and community that reinterprets self-defeating behavior, guilt feelings, and dysfunctional relationships. The strengths approach is a more positive framework. The goal of all interactions and to some extent assessment is to assist with the identification and augmentation of the individual's strengths and resources. There is a perception that powers exist both in the person and in their larger environment and that, the individual and his or her supporters know best how to utilize these resources (Saleeby, 1997). Many social scientists believe that ethnic and community identity is a significant cultural variable that affects a person's s concept of belonging to other members of a subgroup and defines the individual's relationship to the dominant culture. These shared influences can influence a person's willingness to seek help concerning a behavioral health challenge. Additionally, a person's cultural perspective affects the way in which he/she may describe his/her problems to a professional worker (Olandi, 1992).

263

A transformed health care system must embrace the concept that "the health of individuals is affected by the health of the overall community. Provider agencies exist within the community. They are members of the community and therefore have a responsibility to participate in and assist in improving the overall health of the community" (http://dbhids.org/2015/01/Practice-Guidelines)

A comprehensive behavioral health management approach must embrace a holistic approach that focuses on (1) the elimination of stress in the overall community; (2) be attentive toward environmental factors such as, divorce, death and illness; and (3) support and provide opportunities for better housing, increased employment opportunities and active family activities. Without attention to these social determinants of health, one will continue to live in a static environment or a neighborhood in decline that becomes a toxic wasteland for individuals, their families and community (White & Sanders, 2008).

The behavioral health advocacy movement rose in reaction to the continued stigmatization, medicalization and criminalization, and penalization of behavioral health challenges in the 1980s and 1990s. White and Kurtz, (2006) believe that this consumer-driven social movement includes reaffirming the reality of long-term behavioral health recovery, celebrating the legitimacy of multiple pathways of healing, enhancing the variety, availability and quality of local/regional treatment and community support services, and transforming existing treatment businesses into *"recovery-oriented systems of care"*.

Over 15 years ago, JL Geller indicated that the great challenge for community mental health in the 21st century was our continued concerns about the locus of care, and our confusion with the humaneness, effectiveness, and quality of care. Geller felt that success would be more reflected in a public health response that addresses issues of individuals who became destitute and marginalized and not in treatment. Geller concludes that even after 50 years of moving "patients" out of state hospitals and putting them somewhere else, behavioral health policymakers and practitioners remain too myopic in their ability to create a system of comprehensive care (Geller, 2000)

The failure of the medical model of community service delivery to consider any evolving advocacy groups in its concept of community care contributed to a standard of care that for years continued to support the underlying dehumanization and stigmatization of people with behavioral health challenges. To bring parity and balance to the healing process population health seeks to build on and complement the classic efforts of the first three paradigms: (1) medical diagnosis, (2) behavioral health counseling and (3) public health.

Within the field of public health transformation, there are nine guiding principles that support the development of a comprehensive community support network perspective that can impact on an individual's negative environment and exposure to behavioral health challenges which create an atmosphere of change for the person their family and the community (www.samsha.gov-Recovery Support Strategic Initiatives).

1. Healing should be person-driven

Self-determination and self-direction are the foundations for transformation as individuals define their life goals and design their unique path(s) towards those aims.

2. Healing occurs via many pathways

Healing builds on the multiple capacities, strengths, talents, coping abilities, resources, and the inherent value of each.

3. Healing is holistic

Healing from life's traumas is a lifelong process, which includes one's mind, body, spirit, and neighborhood.

4. Healing must be supported by peers and allies

Peers encourage and engage other peers and provide each other with a vital sense of belonging, supportive relationships, valued roles, and community. are critical for children with behavioral health challenges.

5. Healing must be supported through relationship and social networks.

Family members, peers, providers, faith groups, community members, and other allies form vital support networks. These positive healing processes have led to a greater sense of belonging, empowerment, autonomy, social inclusion, and community participation.

6. Healing must be culturally-based and influenced

All services should be culturally grounded, attuned, sensitive, congruent, and competent, as well as personalized to meet each need.

7. Healing must be supported by addressing trauma

The experience of trauma is associated with behavioral health challenges. Services and supports should be trauma-informed to foster both physical and emotional safety and trust.

8. Healing involves the family, and community strengths and responsibilities

Individuals have a personal responsibility for their self-care. People must have an opportunity to speak for themselves and families, and significant others have responsibilities to support their loved ones.

9. Healing must be based on respect

An appreciation and societal acceptance for people affected by behavioral health challenges must include protecting their rights and eliminating discrimination and is crucial in achieving positive outcomes.

The nine challenges facing a comprehensive community support network can be enhanced when human service workers, educators and policy makers embrace a paradigm shift that will facilitate change toward a holistic model of healing that embraces an approach that brings balance to an individual their family and community.

Healing from Trauma: Recovery as it Applies to the Community Model

Judith Herman's work on trauma and recovery states that, "The core experiences of psychological trauma are disempowerment and disconnection from others. Recovery and resilience, therefore, is based upon the empowerment of the survivor and the creation of new connections. Recovery and resilience can take place only within the context of relationships; it cannot occur in isolation" (Herman, 1992, p.134). Additionally, the survivor's sense of emotional and physical safety, autonomy, and the ability to make crucial decisions that impact his or her future is principal for recovery. Therefore, to achieve empowerment, new relationships forged between the survivor and others should reflect an equal balance of power where a healthy self may emerge.

In the Community Empowerment and Transformation Model of Recovery, the behavioral health worker's role shifts from director of care to an ally to the survivor in making his/her own therapeutic decisions for recovery. This shift in power is a salient factor in successful recovery because it encourages the survivor to take greater control of his/her outcome, which is the very concept that had been stolen during the traumatic event(s).

Herman outlines three stages of recovery for trauma survivors that the community empowerment and transformation model incorporate: (1) establishment of safety, (2) remembrance and mourning, and (3) reconnection with ordinary life. Establishment of safety requires that the survivor regain power and control over his or her surroundings, emotions and body. In the second stage of recovery, remembrance and mourning, the survivor works to reconstruct his/her narrative of the traumatic event in an effort to transform the traumatic memory in order to integrate it into the survivor's life story (Herman, 1992). In the third stage of recovery, which is reconnection, the trauma survivor is tasked with creating a new life. "Her relationships have been tested and forever changed by the trauma; now she must develop new relationships.

The old beliefs that gave meaning to her life have been challenged; now she must find anew a sustaining faith" (Herman, 1992, p. 196).
It is important to note that these stages are not linear. The survivor experiences these stages in a cyclic manner simply because the nature of trauma and its effects do not follow a linear path of experience. Re-emergence of flooding memories even after the survivor thought she thoroughly addressed them is common in this disorder (Herman, 1992).

Sabotaging Incarceration and the Process of Recovery

While we live in a community and repeatedly meet one another by way of geography, many of our intentional relationships are frequently eroded and in need of revitalization. Those members of our community who are survivors of trauma and struggling with behavioral health issues often get caught in a system of criminalization and dehumanization. This pattern does not interrupt the cycle of violence. In fact, it perpetuates it. For trauma and recovery survivors, safety is hardly achieved behind the bars of a prison cell. Nor does prison offer the therapeutic support necessary to complete the emotional work of reconstruction of the self during the stage of remembrance, mourning and or recovery.

According to a study released by the Pew Foundation in 2008, one in 100 adults in the United States is incarcerated. One in 31 adults are either in jail, prison, on probation, or on parole. 7.3 million people comprise the correctional population. Most of them are living in the community. However, 90 percent of funding allocated for this population is spent on prisons, while only ten percent of funding is allocated for services to ex-offenders. Prison costs twenty-two times more than community-based corrections. It is also important to note that the United States encompasses five percent of the globe's population, but twenty-five percent of the globe's prison inmates (Pew Center on the States, 2008).

The connection between drug abuse, crime and incarceration is well known. Drug abuse is implicated in at least three types of drug related offenses: (1) offenses defined by drug possession or sales, (2) offenses directly related to drug abuse (e.g., stealing to get money for drugs), and (3) offenses related to a lifestyle that predisposes the drug abuser to engage in illegal activity (e.g., through association with other offenders or with illicit markets). If one connects incarceration with drug use arrests, the patterns of violence overlaps significantly with substance abuse patterns and a case could be made that prisons have become our hidden asylums for "treating" behavioral health challenges by warehousing individuals that are in desperate need of care and rehabilitation. In its 1997 survey, the Bureau of Justice Statistics (BJS) estimated that about 70 percent of State and 57 percent of Federal prisoners used drugs regularly prior to incarceration (Mumola, 1999). A 2002 survey of jails found that 52 percent of incarcerated women and 44 percent of men met the criteria for alcohol or drug dependence (Karberg & James, 2005). In 2003, nearly 6.9 million adults were involved with the criminal justice system, including 4.8 million who were under probation or parole supervision (Glaze & Palla, 2004).

Restorative Justice as a principle of the Community Empowerment and Recovery/Resilience

The prevailing criminal justice system violates many of the principles of recovery and resilience simply because it doesn't address the needs of the person who has been victimized. Restorative justice practices must be mainstreamed into our community in order to interrupt the cycle of victimization. Restorative justice focuses more on the harm that has been done to an individual who has been victimized rather than the law that was broken. Meeting the needs of the person who has been victimized and seeking to repair the harm that was done requires a new model of action that enlists community members to take part in the process (Zehr, 2002).

This process may include victim/offender conferencing where the person who offended is required to take responsibility for the offense and make reparations to the person victimized for his or her crime. This is a more intimate and authentic process that seeks to re-humanize both the person victimized and the person who offended and encourage the latter to understand the gravity of the harm done. It also provides a significant audience for the person victimized in aiding him or her to reconstruct his or her trauma narrative. Finally, it offers community support and connection for the person victimized who might otherwise become a nameless, faceless statistic. While victimized persons are frequently not ready to face their attacker and should never be pressured to participate in such a conference, restorative justice gives victimized persons more choices in the process, which ultimately aids in their re-empowerment.

Creating a transformed system of care for adults with behavioral health challenges is a top priority in several urban centers in the United States. The realization that the old entrenched methods of behavioral health care delivery are not working has provided impetus for this new movement. The new model represents a shift from a professionally driven acute care approach to an approach that provides long-term supports while recognizing the many pathways to recovery and resilience (Lamb, Evans and White, 2009). Community advocates, behavioral health clinicians and educators, faith-based organizations, and local government agencies are developing blue prints for this model of holistic behavioral healthcare. In this uniquely Philadelphia story, professional treatment is one aspect among many that support people in managing their own conditions to the greatest extent possible.

Transformation to an orientation of recovery and resilience in behavioral health service delivery becomes possible by focusing on the central role of individuals and families in responding to, managing, and overcoming these challenges. This focus must be used as an organizing principle for the entire system (www.dbhmrs.org/conceptual-framework/#Conceptual Framework documents).

This transformation to a new behavioral health paradigm consists of four primary strategies: 1) Building community capacity; 2) Enhancing treatment quality; 3) Changing administrative structures; and 4) Mobilizing people in recovery and their families (www.dbhmrs.org/technical-papers-on-recovery-transformation).

1.Building Community Capacity

This refers to a macro approach to improving social conditions by promoting comprehensive strategies to reduce crime and revitalize communities. Building community capacity means encouraging communities to help themselves by empowering them to a) reduce violent and drug crime; b) strengthen community resources to increase the quality of life; c) promote long-term community health and resilience through education. To build community capacity, stakeholders representing various cultural, faith/spiritual based groups and geographic sectors must be included in a continuous dialogue for assessing the community's health needs.

2.Enhancing Treatment Quality

Success can be measured through a broad range of improvements for people receiving services, increased length of stay, a better-educated workforce, and clear expectations of performance measurements. These measures are referred to as best practices. Best practices are defined as the most efficient (least amount of effort) and effective (best results) way of accomplishing a task based on repeatable procedures that have proven themselves over time for large numbers of people.

3.Changing Administrative Structures

Agency employees are the heart of an institutional environment. They are a major factor of social system change. Staff and administrators are key to organizational operations, vision, and purpose in the organization's highly interdependent environment. Staff behaviors are governed by the following: Professional orientations, ethical codes and standards, licensing and regulatory boards, union contracts, funding sources, the media and the public.

All of these represent powerful constituents in the transformation paradigm. In order for administrative structures to change, a planned and transparent paradigm shift must occur that prioritizes the needs of the community over the need of maintaining the system (www.dbhmrs.org/conceptualfrwk)

Champions of recovery assert that the greatest impact of a recovery-oriented system of care will be on behavioral health providers and the future design of the service delivery system. They envision services being structured to be recovery-oriented to ensure that recovery takes place. They envision behavioral health professionals believing in and supporting people in their quest to recover. William A. Anthony described recovery as a guiding vision that *"A vision is not reflective of what we are currently achieving, but of what we hope for and dream of achieving. Visionary thinking does not raise unrealistic expectations. A vision begets no promises but a passion for what needs to be accomplished".*
(www.surgeongeneral.gov/library/mentalhealth/chapter2/sec7.html, 2015)

4.Mobilizing People and their Families in Recovery

Organizing to develop or supplement resources is indicated when a significant number of people within given ecological boundaries (e.g., neighborhoods, communities, institutions) or populations who share certain characteristics have needs for which matching resources are unavailable. Moreover, as physical environments, technological advances, and political and social circumstances relentlessly change, communities are constantly confronted with the need to organize resources in response to both old and evolving needs.

The above four strategies of Transformation specifically refer to healing addictions, trauma, mental health and psychosocial issues. It is the process of pursuing a contributing and fulfilling life, regardless of the difficulties one has faced. It involves not only the restoration, but also continued enhancement of a positive identity as well as personally meaningful connections and roles in one's community. It is facilitated by relationships and environments that promote hope, empowerment, choices, and opportunities that support people in reaching their full potential as individuals and community members (Philadelphia Department of Behavioral Health and Mental Retardation Services, Recovery Advisory Committee, 2006).

The Guiding Principles of the Philadelphia Community Model

The guiding principles of the Philadelphia Community Model are recovery, resilience and self-determination, with transformation being the overarching goal which includes children, adult services, as well as work with intellectual disabilities

Resiliency refers to the protective process, which enables individuals to reach good outcomes even though they have endured significant adversities. This model seeks to build upon recovering persons' core strengths and natural resilience as opposed to underscoring problems.

Self-determination refers to the ability to influence one's own future, and make choices regarding one's own social, economic and cultural development.

Finally, transformation means disbanding structures and reforming for radical change. The community empowerment model is a model of transformation because it works to dismantle the structures of oppression and rebuild them under the co-direction of the empowered recovering person and the health professional. (www.dbhidrs.org/technical-papers-on-recovery-transformation).

Chapter Eleven
Self-Help Movement, and The
Healing Process

The healing process of addicted individuals begins with one stopping the use of alcohol or drugs. No successful attempt at recovery could begin if an individual is not detoxified from ones alcohol or drug use. One cannot find their spiritual space if an individual is active in his/her use of alcohol or drugs. Abstinence is considered a prerequisite for any successful recovery management. The author is aware that some researchers believe that one can treat an individual's problems in living and minimally address the chemical use of the individual while in treatment (Denning, 2000). In my opinion, this recovery strategy ignores the significance of the addiction process. Central to all stories of recovery is the theme of personal empowerment and transformation. All self-help programs are based on a voluntary commitment to change. The greatest weakness of the 12 Step Program-its dogmatism-is possibly also its greatest strength. The 12 Step Program gives people who are highly vulnerable and clutching for support something concrete, something more faith based than scientific to embrace. One is hard put to fault the kind of personal support that so many recovering alcoholics and other drug addicts have derived from what is commonly referred to as the Fellowship.

This positive 12 Step model is not without its skeptics. Major criticisms include the large percentage of alcoholics/drug addicts who drop out of 12 Step programs (according to AA's own survey, 50% after 3 months) (Chappel, 1993; Galaif & Sussman, 1995). There are contradictory studies that indicate AA works no better than other approaches, including no treatment (W. R. Miller & Hester, 1986; Peele, 1992), and findings that indicate no significant relationship between AA attendance and outcomes (McLatchie & Lomp, 1988; W. R. Miller, Leckman, Delaney, & Tinkcorn, 1992). In addition, methodological problems endemic to research on AA lead some researchers to dismiss such attempts as mere exercises in speculation (Harvard Mental Health Letter, 1996). For example, despite years of research, a definitive picture of a person's characteristics that can predict a positive or negative outcome with AA has not emerged (Tonigan & Hiller-Sturmhofel, 1994). White (1998) and others indicate that A.A.'s reliance on a Higher Power undermines personal responsibility and the development of internal strengths, ignores environmental factors that contribute to alcohol problems, and A.A.'s political influence has had a deleterious effect the scientific advancement of the alcoholism treatment field and contributed to clinical rigidity.

How consumers/survivors of recovery can transform the substance abuse system to embrace the culture of self-determination and community participation that is inclusive of care that responds to the individual needs of people that reflects the diversity of addiction transformation is the major challenge to the concept of multiple paths to recovery. Changing the addiction system to one that is based on the principles of recovery transformation will require a concerted effort of consumers and traditional professional allies working to bring about changes in beliefs and practices at every level of the system. The building of these alliances will require the trust, understanding and respect by all parties involved. Distinguishing "recovery," which is a personal, individual process, from "wellness," which involves families and the whole community involves a process of trust and understanding from the 12 Step community and those individuals promoting practice guidelines that emphasize the person-family-community paradigm.

A significant part of the community of recovery must buy into wellness for appropriate policy to be adopted. Our collective recovery consciousness needs to think strategically about the use and impact of language and conceptualize in terms of three simultaneous levels of impact—individual, family, and community/society (White, and Ali, 2010). The future of addiction treatment and recovery in America appears to be more of a struggle between two competing yet related activities. The **first** is a treatment renewal movement. Led by front line service providers from across the country, the goals of this movement include reconnecting treatment to the process of long-term recovery and rebuilding relationships between treatment organizations, local communities and local recovery support groups. A **second** movement, the new recovery advocacy movement, rose in reaction to the restigmatization, demedicalization and recriminalization penalization of AOD problems in the 1980s and 1990s. This movement has been led organizationally by a coalition of the Faces and Voices of Recovery, the National Council on Alcoholism and Drug Dependence, the Johnson Institute, the Legal Action Center, and (until recently) the Center for Substance Abuse Treatment's Recovery Community Support Program. The goals of this second movement include reaffirming the reality of long-term addiction recovery, celebrating the legitimacy of multiple pathways of recovery, enhancing the variety, availability and quality of local/regional treatment and recovery support services, and transforming existing treatment businesses into "recovery-oriented systems of care" (White,2000; White & Kurtz, 2006).

Professionals and consumers who are committed to recovery transformation will find that the history of the 12 Step recovery model must coexist and evolve as one successful aspect of a multidimensional perspective on the paths to recovery. Their parallel evolutionary streams, their confluence, and points of departure and integration all reflect a successful path to recovery transformation for individuals' families and the community.

273

Despite the scientific attempt to evaluate the 12 Step programs there is adequate evidence to suggest that many recovering individuals who become involved in 12 Step programs will find skills they can use to improve their lives on a long-term basis (Chappel, 1993). L. F. Kurtz and Fisher (2003), in their interviews with 33 individuals actively involved in 12 Step programs and community activity, demonstrated that through the 12 Step fellowships, they developed the skills and confidence to seek out and engage in community service. Emrick (1987), after his extensive review of findings from the empirical literature, concludes that although AA is not for everyone (particularly those who just want to reduce their drinking or those with co-occurring disorders). *"Nevertheless, AA has been demonstrated to be associated with abstinence for many alcohol-dependent individuals and thus the professional who comes in contact with alcoholics should become familiar with AA and utilize this self-help resource whenever possible"* (p.421).

This chapter on the Healing Process is one that builds bridges between the traditions of 12 Steps, the faith and spiritual communities and the evolving recovery transformation movement. A logical extension of this integrated model will be to embrace various professional disciplines, individuals, families and the larger community of recovery empowerment in a process that the author's believe is revolutionary in its intent and comprehensive in its approach.

The management of an individual's recovery must be a personal disciplined experience that is one's own responsibility and not contingent or dependent on our day-to-day conscious world. The path of recovery to resilience and transformation appears to be grounded in: (1) the Analytical Psychology of Carl Gustav Jung, who saw all life as a balance between spirit and matter (Harris, 1996, p.175) and (2) the 20th century self-help movement of Alcoholics Anonymous and other 12 Step Programs.

Carl Gustav Jung and Alcoholics Anonymous

All self-help programs, like the fellowship of Alcoholics Anonymous, engage the individual in a process of discovery between their personal conscious experiences and their unconscious archetypal configuration. This connection allows the archetype to be humanized.

A person feels less isolated and lonely if he realizes that his individual trials illustrate a universal problem. Such recognition helps to relativize the ego; the client can learn to see himself as an appropriately tiny but still integral part of an enormous universe, rather than (say) as the target of persecution by a destructive Fate (Harris 1996, p. 150)

The central issue to positive mental health, and the resolution of life problems, such as, alcohol or drug addiction, gambling, abuse, etc., is partly vested in a strong recovery management system that impacts on an individual's cultural and social support system. The loss of supportive communities is one of the great losses of modern life. Since the 1930's recovery groups have provided peer support and understand of the particular dangers individuals face on a daily basis. Support group members are willing to confront each other and give encouragement when needed. Many support groups borrow heavily from the A.A. model of Twelve Steps. The slogans and traditions and the concept of spirituality are related but differ from the organized practice of religion.

Alcoholics Anonymous dates back to June 10, 1935, when Bill W., a 39-year-old compulsive alcoholic with four "drying out" periods at a Manhattan hospital, began to recognize his powerlessness over alcohol. During his treatment by Dr. William Silkworth, a New York specialist in alcoholism, Bill W. heard of the Oxford Group, a popular non-denominational movement of recovering alcoholics who recognized and admitted their powerlessness over alcohol. It took a failed business trip in May of 1935, in Akron, Ohio for Bill W. to reach out and contact Dr. Bob a member of the Oxford Group. Both of these men met and gained support from each other by sharing experiences about the devastation of alcohol in their lives. It was this seemingly chance meeting that led to one of the founding principles of the spiritual movement that was to develop into Alcoholics Anonymous. Bill W. returned to New York and established a second group in addition to Dr. Bob's group in Akron, Ohio. By 1939, *"the group"* had reached about 100 members. (A.A. Comes of Age, 1985) At that time the **Big Book** was published and the new fellowship took its name from the title of the book, Alcoholics Anonymous. (A.A.1976). Today the writings, philosophy and the fellowship of A.A have influenced millions of individuals. Questionnaires and studies show that 40 to 50% of alcoholics who join A. A. become long-term members and about two-thirds of those members achieve total abstinence or a substantial decrease in drinking. At any given meeting about 70% of the participants have been sober from one to five years and the remaining 30% have over five years sobriety (Galanter, 1993, p.126). A. A. meetings typically have a speaker who "tells a story" which strikes a familiar chord to all the listeners. Members can speak if they want or they can listen to a variety of topics or discussions, which develop from the Twelve Steps, Twelve Traditions, or from a variety of helpful slogans, such as,

"God never closes a door without also opening a window",

"Ninety meeting in ninety days",

"Fake it till you make it",

"For an alcoholic, one drink is one too many - one thousand not enough",

"If you don't do anything to make it better it will get worse".

The use of A. A. sponsors encourages individuals to identify and draw strength, hope, and support from individuals with similar problems. Through the sharing of A. A. members' experiences of how they learn to overcome craving and compulsive behavior in their own disease, new members develop a sense of solidarity and identity that leads to cohesion and universality, a sense that, at last, they are not alone and have found a place of fraternal fellowship. A. A. experience, although not a formal therapy group, usually provides a significant amount of therapeutic exposure and is regarded by many clinician's as a significant part of an individual's recovery management plan. Many mental health professionals recognize that the A. A. approach can be a strong incentive to produce maximum support and healing. Gorski (1989) refers to the Twelve Steps Plus approach of therapy and attendance at A.A. as one of the significant contributors to high retention rates at meetings. Gorski believes that higher relapse rates occur when alcoholics only attend A.A meetings (Gorski, 1989, p. 18).

For many years, traditional A. A. members have been, at times, less than friendly to the professional mental health community and continued to see Twelve Step work in conflict with the treatment community. This thought is partly justifiable since mental health professionals seem to be ignorant of recovering issues and antagonistic toward the spiritual aspects of recovery. With the exception of Jung's analytical psychology and the transpersonal or existential movement, the field of psychiatry and psychology has traditionally been at odds with the Twelve Steps of Alcoholics Anonymous.

Many individuals believe that the art of psychotherapy should maintain not only a psychological but also spiritual focus. Instead it is oriented towards a psychopathologic perspective, or a stimulus response learning relationship (non-strength based perspective). Interestingly, the word *"psycho"* comes from the Greek psyche, meaning spirit, soul, or being. The word *"therapy"* comes from the Greek word, *therapeutikos*, which means one who takes care of another. Therefore, psychotherapy means to take care of another person's soul, spirit, or being (Kleinke 1994, p. 1). If American clinicians would practice the art as it is defined, one suspects that the recovery community, as reflected in the spirituality of Alcoholics Anonymous would not be so antagonistic. It is a well-established truth that some of the Fellowship questions the relationship between psychotherapist and the recovery process. One can partly blame the single mindedness of some recovering people, who think at times that sobriety is everything. It is a truism that if one can't maintain sobriety one will never be able to effectively resolve underlying problems and develop healthier coping skills. What is striking at A. A.

meetings is how many individuals are *"sober"* but still living out their own version of hell on earth, *"one day at a time"*.

Many recovering professionals who believe it is only through the spirit of life that one can chart a path, which provides the positive energy to overcome our mental health and/or addiction challenges. Jung talking about the soul of man said,

> *What we call civilized consciousness has steadily separated itself from the basic instincts. But these instincts have not disappeared. They have merely lost their contact with our consciousness and are thus forced to assert themselves in an indirect fashion. This may be by means of physical symptoms in the case of neurosis...or unacceptable moods, unexpected forgetfulness, or mistakes in speech (Jung, 1964, p.83).*

Surrender

The first three Steps have sometimes been referred to as the *"surrender"* Steps or the *"God"* Steps partly due to issues of powerlessness and turning one's will over to a Higher Power. Surrender in recovery is critical to an individual's trust in the spiritual process of the 12 Steps. Without trust through surrender it is almost impossible to move into the confessional Steps of Four and Five.

One spiritual value related to trust is surrender. Paradoxically, most people in recovery spend much of their time gaining personal control over some of the ups and downs of their lives, and yet, surrender requires relinquishing control over situations in which there really is none. What needs to be understood is that there are two basic types of control. The first is an attempt to change the world and external circumstances so that it is compatible with our needs (Rothbaum, Weisz, & Snyder, 1982). The second is to be willing to change oneself to accept the direction life takes (Cole & Pargament, 1999). Either of these approaches may be adopted during times of severe stress but the second path appears more consistent with recovery management.

Pargament, Smith, Koenig, & Perez (1998) studied the relationship between a persons' belief in God and their approach to managing stress and reported five different coping strategies: (1) *deferring*, *(2) pleading*, *(3) self-direction*, *(4) collaboration*, and *(5) spiritual surrender*. The strategy of *deferring* involves the person not being actively involved in dealing with the stressor but, rather, turning it over to God. The *pleading* strategy involves bargaining with God to intervene and improve the situation or to perform a miracle. Recovering individuals employing the *self-directing* approach take responsibility for making decisions about how to respond to stress without God's help. Those who opt for *collaboration* manage stressful situations by making themselves partners with God. Those who choose *spiritual*

277

surrender take control of what they can do and leave the rest to God. Research results revealed that the collaborative approaches tend to be more effective than deferring (Pargament, Kennell, Hathaway, Grevengoed, Newman, & Jones, 1998), pleading, and self-direction strategies (Pargament 1997) especially in situations where personal control is at a minimum (Bickel, Ciarrocchi, Sheers, Estadt, Powell, & Pargament, 1998).

When individuals are faced with situations in which there is little personal control, such as chronic or terminal illness, death, or accidents, surrender might be appropriate for one to consider. This spiritual strategy involves having the person acknowledge that under certain negative circumstances there could be a greater good than personal control. Moreover, surrender involves not only a cognitive shift, but an experiential one as well in which one is in touch with self-transcendence that leads to serenity. This strategy seems to have positive associations with psychological and spiritual well-being for persons in crisis (Cole & Pargament, 1999).

Before one approaches the notion of surrender, it is important that the recovering person be committed to their spiritual perspective and determine for themselves, hopefully with the help of a sponsor, if surrender would be a helpful intervention. Cole and Pargament (1999) caution against presenting the concept of surrender as a means of gaining control of a stressful situation. They emphasize the paradoxical reality that a secondary sense of control (accepting life's circumstances as they come) may result from surrender, but that it is certainly not a goal or an expected outcome. In addition, Cole and Pargament suggested that at its best, surrender is an appropriate response to human limitations. However, they warn practitioners that what looks like surrender could really be some form of learned helplessness.

What is important about the first three Steps of surrender is the recovery person's ability to know what aspects of a person's problem is within their control and what aspect of their problem is outside of their control and needs to be surrendered to a Higher Power. This exercise helps make cognitive errors visible because people both think they can control situations that they cannot and think they cannot control circumstances that are clearly within their control (Cole & Pargament, 1999). The AA Serenity Prayer of change becomes relevant in early recovery and will continue to guide one's decisions throughout all of the Steps.

In admitting powerlessness over the disease, people in recovery are in effect gaining power, through enlisting the support of their higher power and the fellowship itself, to be responsible for their own recovery. A misunderstanding of this process can lead to an interpretation that people in self-help are somehow "copping out" from personal responsibility. The point is that while the addict may not be responsible for having a disease

278

that involves physiological and possibly genetic, psychological, and overwhelming environmental components, in 12-Step fellowships the addict is most certainly responsible for his or her own recovery' (Retrieved January 2, 2010 http://www.cnsproductions.com/pdf/12step)

The Self Help Movement and the Twelve Steps

The 12 Steps present such a positive path. What is deceptive about the 12 Steps is that they seem so simple and easy to understand.

1. We admit we were powerless over alcohol, that our lives had become unmanageable.

The concept in recovery that one's life has become unmanageable and that one cannot control his/her life is a significant factor in the therapeutic process of positive growth. One of the major decisions in early recovery is that one must face their denial and stop making excuses for his/her behavior. Repeated failures at abstinence, outbursts of rage and anger, major family disruptions, job loss, symptoms of helplessness and drinking or drug taking for relief of anger, insomnia, fatigue or social discomfort, are what people often mean by the "insanity of addiction." What is insane is the belief that these events are "normal" or by doing the same thing over and over, one is expecting different results. It is during the early stages of recovery, usually the first 60 to 90 days of abstinence that one needs to examine their denial, projection, rationalizations, hopelessness and acting out behaviors. Sobriety or a drug free state is not an end in itself but only the beginning of a long search for meaning in one's life. The majority of recovering people have significant long-standing emotional problems that need to be addressed in their recovery. Sober/drug free people, although "sane", in the recovery sense, still go through a painful life of anger, despair, and anxiety. The fact that one is abstinent or drug free does not necessarily equate with emotional health. An individual could demonstrate little change except sobriety, yet be in recovery. What is important is does ones recovery make a transition into resilience and transformation. *"Powerless over our lives"* is not only a difficult idea for one to believe but also an unpleasant thought to accept. However, many addicted individuals are powerless, and must accept their addiction in order to improve their lives. Denial only leaves one less able to avoid danger or pain. Step One helps individuals see the world around them more realistically. Powerlessness, or an inability to feel or believe that one is in control of his/her life, doesn't have to be a constant a part of one's consciousness, the event only has to enter our consciousness once in a while to make our lives unmanageable.

Many people in recovery have experiences of loss and demonstrated powerlessness in their health, career, relationships, or other important life events. Feelings of Powerlessness appear to always be associated with individual's lack of responsibility. If one has no power over life events then he/she can't be responsible for their consequences. When an individual denies powerlessness, he/she feels responsible for things he/she doesn't control. The question a person in recovery must ask himself/herself is "What are things I feel responsible for that I don't have any control over?" and "How have these feelings/experiences affected my life?

A 12 Step recovery model of mutual sharing by members provides solutions to some alcohol and drug related problems. Regular meetings help members maintain and work towards continued abstinence and give support for emotional, behavioral, and spiritual life. Twelve Step programs have been and continue to be a positive beneficial source of inspiration and hope for millions of recovering people, but it is a Fellowship, not psychotherapy. It is in this difference that one can find strength and positive energy to gain self-control and self-discipline about life. Clinical relationships are unilateral because the focus is on the client. The therapist's problems are secondary and insignificant to the recovering client. Mutual sharing is done only in the context of helping the client understand his or her emotional life. The interaction between helper and helpee is directed toward the individual in pain, hoping to resolve certain problems and achieve certain goals. The therapeutic relationship is formal because the interaction occurs at a specific place and within a limited time function. The therapist is not a sponsor or constant friend of the recovering client. He or she has no other roles, duties, or obligations than those defined in the context of the therapeutic relationship. Therapeutic relationships are temporal in nature, they end when an agreed upon objective or goals have been accomplished. Finally, psychotherapy offers more than support; it gives recovering people an opportunity to take risks, challenge old behaviors, generalize what they have learned in therapy and apply it to the outside world (Kleinke, 1994, P.88).

During the first three steps of recovery .the recovering individual must begin to develop a value system that honors:

- Sensitivity to feelings by being open, honest, and genuine with others.
- Responsibility for their actions.
- Effective strategies to cope with stress.
- Becoming aware of spiritual potential and one's ability to grow.
- An ability to give and receive affection and respect for human values.
- Practicing habits of good physical health.
- Seeking spiritual understanding of one's place in the universe and the strength to seek communication with a higher spiritual power (Jensen & Bergin, 1988, pp.290-297).

2. Came to believe that a power greater than ourselves could restore us to sanity.

3. Made a decision to turn our will and our lives over to the care of God as we understand him.

Past failure is never a reason to give up hope everyone can be helped despite repeated failures. As long as we accept the fact that others know more and have specialized skills to guide and help one reshape our lives. Problem solving has never been an experience that one accomplishes alone The recovering person must believe that part of his/her disease is the inability to develop attitudes that people care about them and want to help him/her through this life crisis. Through trust and awareness the recovering person can move from self-centeredness toward acceptance and humility. The difficulty in Steps Two and Three is that one must recognize the clear limitations of an individual's power and the need to acknowledge other resources outside of themselves that will help them eventually deal with life on life's terms.

Powerlessness and irresponsibility are difficult concepts to understand and accept in Step One. Step Two gives one the thought that one is "insane". Most chemically dependent individuals already know inside that they are out of control *"that our lives had become unmanageable"* and this may have caused a significant amount of despair, depression, anxiety and anger.

The lesson to be learned in Step Two, it is hope. Being powerless doesn't mean one's life has to stay out of control, individuals in recovery can find happiness and peace through *"*a Power greater than ourselves" taking control. Many individuals want to argue the issue of a Higher Power. The question one should be debating is what would one have to gain, or lose, by accepting the idea of a Higher Power that could create the order in one's life that many have wanted but have been unable to find?

No real action is called for in Steps One and Two. Step Three asks an individual to make a decision to turn his/her will and one's life over to God. For many people, this idea seems irrational. We grow up with the belief that one should be in control of his/her life. The idea of turning over control to someone else sounds insane. Many addicted individuals have done their best to solve their own problems in the past and have continually fallen short of their expectations.

Some people recommend breaking Step Three down into phrases and examining them one by one. To start with, the first phrase is *"Made a decision."* This first phase sounds like a shift from thinking to action. The question is how ready is a person to decide on strong action to change some things in their life? Many individuals need to think about it for a while longer, before they decide to change. The Step doesn't say that once we make this decision we have to *"turn our will and our lives over"* today. Turning something over sounds like a good idea but it needs to be handled carefully. This concept involves a lot of trust. A big part of trust is learning how much trust we can give other people. If we trust them to do something they can't do, the recovering person will be disappointed and maybe hurt.

The last part of Step Three is *"to the care of God as we understood Him."* This Step doesn't ask us to trust anyone else's version of God. It asks one to set aside whatever he/she has been taught about God and start over. It requires an individual to have a personal view of God and tries to understand what kind of God or Higher Power makes sense to one in recovery. Since the idea that God is a being whose powers are mainly to provide support and guidance, what would *"turning it over mean?"* Will we be hurt again by trusting God to do things He wouldn't be able to do?

The second and third Steps are very much influenced by Alfred Adler's view of addiction as striving for power, which compensates for feelings of inferiority and C. G. Jung's concept of individuation and the movement toward wholeness. The Adlerian view emphasizes the idea that an addicted individual has an enhanced need for power but cannot discover how to achieve his /her goal. He/she resorts to alcohol or drugs to gain a sense of power or a sense of relief, and in turn gives the false impression that the individual has achieved something in his/her life. Much of the power fantasies of addicts are a result of overindulgent or neglectful parents who did not allow their child the opportunity to cope with everyday problems of growing up, therefore allowing feelings of inferiority and frustration to dominate their developmental life. With the introduction of alcohol or drugs into their life, power and superiority returned and the individual felt in charge of his/her life.

The Jungian view of spirituality is best described in Bill W.'s extraordinary exchange of letters with Carl Jung in 1961 (Letters, 1963). In this correspondence Bill W. talks about a patient of Dr. Jung's named Roland H. whom he treated in 1931. Following treatment, the patient, Roland H. relapsed and returned to Dr. Jung for treatment. Jung informed him that the only hope he had for recovery was to *"become the subject of a spiritual or religious experience"*. Roland H. joined the Oxford Group, which strongly stressed meditation and prayer. The original six tenets of the Oxford movement were:

- ✓ Admitted we were powerless over alcohol.
- ✓ Got honest with ourselves as never before: made an examination of conscience.
- ✓ We made a rigorous confession of our personal defects.

✓ We surveyed our distorted relations with people, visiting them to make restitution.
✓ We resolved to devote ourselves to helping others in need.
✓ By meditation we sought God's direction for his life and help to practice these principles at all times (A.A., 1985)

Roland H., through Dr. Jung's advice and counsel along with the practicing of the six tenets, found a spiritual experience. Roland H. influenced "Ebby", a schoolmate of Bill W. In November of 1934, Bill W. met with "Ebby" and noted in his letter to Dr. Jung that:

> *Because he was a kindred sufferer (Ebby) he could unquestionably communicate with me at great depth. I knew at once I must find an experience like his or die. (Bill W. goes on to note) Because of your conviction (Dr. Jung's) that man is something more than intellect, emotion, and two dollars' worth of chemicals you have especially endeared yourself to us. (A. A.)*

Dr. Jung's response to Bill W's. letter clearly demonstrates his support for a *"spiritual thirst"* for wholeness and the need to consider recovery as more than just physical or psychological changes. Later in his life, just before his death, Jung indicated that man; in order to sustain his creed…pays the price in a remarkable lack of introspection. He is blind to the fact that, with all his rationality and efficiency, he is possessed by powers that are beyond his control. His gods and demons have not disappeared at all; they merely got new names. They keep him on the run with restlessness, vague apprehensions, psychological complications, and an insatiable need for pills, alcohol, tobacco, and food and, above all, a large array of neurosis (Jung, 1964, p.83).

On June 10, 1935, Bill W. and Dr. Bob convened the first Alcoholics Anonymous meeting in Akron, Ohio. It began the integration of science and spirituality as a way to treat alcoholics. Through the fellowship, one finds support to act more responsibly and to change his /her life situation. The Fellowship also establishes a social system that responsibly addresses a human problem. Through Alcoholics Anonymous purpose and function, it gives direction to a full range of client needs. It is that empowerment that has allowed members to take charge of their lives and chart a spiritual pathway to recovery.

The Recovery Paradigm Shift in the first 3 Steps

Finally, there needs to be a paradigm shift that will facilitate change by the individual toward a holistic model of health that integrates the spiritual dimension. O'Hara (1998) has suggested that many of the principals underlying gestalt therapy may be useful as a transformational psychology for contemporary shifts in human consciousness. For example, she suggests that in a postmodern world we need "creative pluralism, mutual recognition, diversity with tolerance, dynamic stability, contained competition, and collaboration" (p. 158). This shift in consciousness by the recovering person must: (1) Affirm the importance of a spiritual/religious path even before an individual discerns whether this path is helpful or harmful to ones recovery, (2) In order to strengthen this new recovery alliance, one must understanding the importance of religious/spiritual paths, embrace a worldview through use of congruent vocabulary and imagery, and (3) attempt to discern cognitive, moral, and faith-oriented developmental models of a commitment to truth.

Steps Four and Five, sometimes called the *"confessional"* Steps, are meant to help individuals overcome shame and guilt.

4. We make a searching and fearless moral inventory of ourselves.

5. We admitted to God, to ourselves, and to another human being, the exact nature of our wrongs.

The Fourth Step is the first introspective step, in that it requires a spiritual commitment to exploring oneself and understanding the relationship between addiction and mental health. It requires an honest and open recognition of strengths and weaknesses. In a Jungian conceptualization, these two steps are the first encounter with the unconscious Shadow or the negative side of the personality. Most of an addict's life is centered on hiding the unpleasant qualities or inferiority feelings of our primitive nature. In many ways the Shadow possesses the ego personality even though its power resides in the unconscious psyche. A powerful Shadow deprives one of choice and the individual is powerless to dispose of his/her will, therefore, consciousness loses its freedom and creates disequilibrium that seeks compensation through alcohol and drug use. The self-inventory of Step Four enables an individual a conscious way to begin exploring the unconscious control of the ego by the Shadow.

> ..and so in the psyche we cannot dispose of dangerous or destructive aspects of ourselves. We can only know of their presence and how they tend to function. If we work at it, we may be able to transform these dark elements from something virulent to something manageable. This is part of the greatness of Jung's concept of the self-regulating nature of the psyche. He never supposed evil could be done away with, but thought to expose and understand the potentiality for evil in our own souls as well as that for good (Singer, 1994, p. 164).

284

Rollo May, (1969) in describing the transformative, power of the diamonic:

> ...the diamonic pushes us toward the logos (the underlying meaning or significance).The more I come to terms with my diamonic tendencies, the more I will find myself conceding and living by a universal structure of reality. This movement toward the logos is transpersonal. Thus we move from an impersonal through a personal to a transpersonal dimension of consciousness. (p. 176)

Steps 4 and 5 are usually presented together, because many recovering people experience them as a single process even though they are separate Steps. The writing and sharing of a personal inventory is the first introspective experience in recovery. Generally, Steps 4 and 5 are anxiety-producing experiences for many recovering people; many recovering individuals feel a great peace of mind, a strong sense of connection to other people and a better feeling about their Higher Power by completing a *"Searching and Fearless Moral Inventory"* and *"Share It with Another Person"*.

Many individuals in recovery approach these Steps by focusing on events that cause them to feel resentment. These feelings usually have a relationship to something one wants or needs such as: self-esteem, relationships with other people, emotional comfort, and physical and material security or sex. It is important that one acknowledges his/her faults in situations where one has resentments. For many individuals resentments are related to selfishness, dishonesty, fear or inconsideration.

The Fifth Step is frightening for many people. Recovering individuals fear that the people who hear their inventories will reject them and they will lose respect and friendship. The Fifth Step generates a fear that people will tell our secrets to others. All of these fears are reasonable, and to keep these things from happening, it is important to choose the right kind of person to hear the inventory. Some people who might be trusted with this Step could include a sponsor or another person from a Twelve-Step program, a close friend, a doctor or therapist, a priest or minister, or a trusted relative.

In general, the person chosen to hear the inventory will not only continue to accept and respect you, he or she will share some of the same problems you felt the most fear and shame about revealing. Once the Fifth Step is completed, the individual should take a few minutes to sit quietly and notice how one's feelings have changed. Most people find that they feel a huge sense of relief and a new peace of mind, as if a great burden has been lifted from them. Many individuals feel less isolated and more connected with others, and many even say they feel a strong sense of the presence of their Higher Power.

Some recovering individuals struggle with the Fourth and Fifth Steps because they require a knowledgeable and experienced person to assist them. In the absence of a strong working relationship with a skilled helper (sponsor and/or therapist), most recovering individuals fail to make progress in other aspects of their Twelve Step recovery program. Steps Four and Five insist that an individual begin to open his or her life to evaluation and scrutiny. Most people in pain only venture into this area of difficulty if there is a strong empathic supportive person available to help him understand his deepest thoughts, beliefs, and feelings. During this phase of recovery, a helper must move from confronter of denial to support motivator and from structured listener to active teacher of new coping behaviors. Individuals will pass through Steps Four and Five if the helper or sponsor values the following issues:

- ✓ Sensitivity to feelings
- ✓ Builds autonomy, freedom and responsibility
- ✓ Develops effective strategies to cope with stress
- ✓ Becomes aware of inner potential and ability to grow
- ✓ Develops an ability to give and receive affection (Jensen & Bergin, 1988, pp. 290-297).

The confessional Steps (four and five) have particular meaning and influence in the Hindu traditions. The Hindu philosophy of Karma that we create our lives through our actions and ultimately we accept the consequences of our behavior, the belief in a self-regulation process to ones path and the need to change from external interpersonal issues to a concern for spiritual values and turning away from social and individual success is a significant evolutionary process on the road to finding spirituality and healing ones soul.

Soul Healing: Finding our spiritual path in Steps Four and Five

Soul-healing includes the awareness of a transcendent dimension of existence that is embodied in all relational interactions. Its goal is not only the growth and development of persons but of the "soul of the world" (Becvar, 1997, p. 5).It involves the "creation of contexts in which the focus is no longer primarily on problems, but rather emphasizes solutions and the facilitation of wellness in a holistic sense" (Becvar, 1997, p. 4).

A soul healing perspective involves five principles: acknowledging connectedness, suspending judgment, trusting the universe, creating realities, and walking with heart (Becvar, 1997). Acknowledging connectedness means underscoring the interdependence between persons, and persons and the world. Suspending judgment means shifting the focus away from blame toward acceptance and respect for the dignity and worth of persons. It means to "work to bring about a change in context rather than seeing a problem as

286

residing within a particular person" (Becvar, 1997, p. 7). Trusting the universe involves adopting a life-stance of mystery and awe with a basic faith in ourselves and a power beyond ourselves. Creating realities suggests we are participants in forming the realities we experience and that we have the capacity for awareness of ourselves as co-creators of our experiences. Walking with heart means living and working in such a way that human potential is more fully developed and that the goals of compassion and peace are integrated into our daily lives.

It is important that the recovering individual pass through Steps four and five with a soul healing perspective. Like the last two Steps, Steps Six and Seven are presented as a single process.

6. Were entirely ready to have God remove all these defects of character.

7. Humbly asked Him to remove our shortcomings.

Step Six asks an individual to be *"entirely ready"* to have God remove one's defects of character. Reflecting on Step Four, one must reflect on the meaning of *"defects of character"*. Looking at Step Four one thinks about what defects of character led to various actions and situations in your life. Many of the same underlying patterns of thinking and feeling connected to the inventory list are one's *"defects of character"*. Step Six involves giving up the effort to control and make things happen ourselves, and trusting our Higher Power that one will be better following problem resolutions.

Step Seven, dealing with shortcomings is another way of *"humanizing the Shadow"*. Sometimes shortcomings vanish instantly. Others say they go through a more gradual change, not noticing a difference right away but seeing it over days, weeks, months or years. Often others notice before the addicted individual does that they have changed in small ways, such as finding oneself, being more considerate of other drivers in traffic, laughing about situations that used to cause anger or anxiety, being more patient with children, etc.

> *(our)...underlying wound, rage, and emptiness doesn't need*
> \ *to be rejected. It needs to be seen, understood, and released*
> *from the images and misunderstandings and delusions that*
> *bind it. (Davis, 1999. P. 133)*

One needs to acknowledge the Shadow aspects of their personality and deal with inferiorities, unacceptable impulses, and shameful acts which are painful to admit. Jealousy, insecurity and outrage at life's inequities must be accepted and understood, as a part of our consciousness and individuals must commit themselves to positive life style changes. During this phase of recovery, the person must work successfully to alter behavior such as selfishness, narcissism and blaming of others for their current life situation. Blame is particularly relevant to Step Seven since it begins with anger.

Anger is related to our lack of submission to a higher power (Peck, 1993, p.36).

Anger and Anxiety in Steps Six and Seven

An individual's recovery is restricted by the addictive person's inability to manage his anger, despair (hopelessness), or anxiety. Relapse is almost always related to poor coping strategies. If there is a universal truth about addictive life style client it is that:

- ✓ They make poor appraisals of problems.
- ✓ They are inflexible and have little creative, alternative plans and
- ✓ They have no appreciation for the long-term effects of their actions.

Anger or hostility, although a common human response, can hinder one from reaching their goals or objectives. There are several conclusions researchers agree on in relation to a person's anger:

- ✓ Anger is often a result of our desire to get what we want from someone.
- ✓ Anger is usually expressed to someone we love or toward friends because they fail to live up to our desires or wishes
- ✓ The expression of anger is almost always interpreted as negative and not helpful.
- ✓ The satisfaction after expressing anger does not achieve our goals in the long run. (Kleinke, 1994, p.100)

Assessing anger

Coping with anger in everyday life and managing stress without the use of alcohol and drugs is a necessity, if one is to ever redirect their life process and find spiritual wellbeing. Understanding the difference between aggression and assertiveness is an essential beginning to disarming anger. To be aggressive involves taking advantage of others by standing up for our rights in a hostile manner. Aggressiveness is generally a way an individual overpowers, humiliates, degrades or belittles another individual. Aggressive individuals are more concerned about their rights, needs and desires with no appreciation for the other person. Generally, aggression alienates us from others and turns us into suspicious, fearful, hostile individuals. On the other hand, assertive people stand up for their rights by direct, honest and appropriate expression of their thoughts and feelings. They relate to others in a tactful manner, being sensitive to their demands but do not allow people to take advantage of them. An assertive person is flexible and understands he/she will not always get everything they want. In many ways, an assertive person demonstrates many of the skills of an effective helper. They are empathic, they own their feelings and they act in a responsible manner. In a Jungian sense they demonstrate the compensatory function. If the recovering person can act in a fair and impartial manner he/she will demonstrate self-respect. Generally, addictive individuals lack negotiation and compensatory skills. A significant number of clinicians believe that anger can be transformed and integrated into consciousness. Once anger is expressed, experienced and understood it can be managed by the ego (Fenichel, 1945, p. 92).

Anger is sometimes referred to as anxiety turned inward. Many of the techniques to help control anxiety are similar to those used to manage anger. Anxiety is usually a result of emotional states of tenseness and distress that at times can result in anger. When inappropriate anger turns inside, the body reacts by heart palpitations, shortness of breath, loss of appetite, rapid breathing, sweating, trouble speaking, restlessness, etc. One's thoughts become confused, the individual has difficulty concentrating, and one has a fear of losing control, and an individual becomes self-conscious, hyper-vigilant and memory function is impaired. One's sense of well-being is depressed, tense, jumpy, impatient, alarmed, edgy, etc. (Siegel, 1986, pp. 191-200). Although anxiety is also related to fear, the end result, a sense of vulnerability or helplessness leaves the person unable to cope with stressful situations without resorting to alcohol or drugs.

Steps Six and Seven demand that we own our feelings of blame, anger, prejudices and we develop tactful ways that enhance relationships.
The more that consciousness is influenced by prejudice, errors, fantasies, and infantile wishes, the more the already existing gap will widen into a neurotic dissociation and lead to a more or less artificial life, far removed from healthy instincts, nature and truth (Jung, 1964, p. 49)

Change appears to follow a series of stages, which is more spiral or circular in progression than linear. Most people in early recovery progress from sobriety to relapse and back to sobriety with progression being related to guilt, embarrassment and shame regarding regression to earlier stages of addiction.

The research of Prochaska, DiClemente and Norcross (1986), indicates that most individuals go through different stages related to changing their addictive behaviors and that change has a cyclical process as opposed to a linear perspective. Most addictive people typically recycle (relapse) through various stages several times before termination of their maladaptive behavior. Relapse is a key to recovery if individuals learn from their mistakes and try something different the next time the "triggered" event

289

resurfaces in the environment. In general, the more action one takes following the relapse, the higher the probability of future success. The stages of change are:

Precontemplation - During this stage most individuals are still in some denial and appear to be unaware of their problems. The thought of changing is related more to job or family pressure and once the pressure is off, many of them quickly return to their addictive patterns.

Contemplation - During this stage people are aware that a problem exists and give serious thought to overcoming the addiction but have not taken their thoughts to an action stage. Many individuals can be in this phase of their recovery for up to two years. An important aspect of this stage is weighing the pros and cons of one's addiction and beginning to think about solutions to the problem.

Preparation for change - This activity is the beginning of serious action and some behavioral change. A full commitment to a total lifestyle change is beginning to occur, most individuals developing criterion for effective management of a different and new life style.

Action and *Maintenance*, avoidance of relapse through consciousness raising and self-liberation appear to have their foundation in the Eighth, Ninth and Tenth Steps.

8. Made a list of all persons we had harmed and became willing to make amends to them all.

9. Made direct amends to such people wherever possible, except when to do so would injure them or others.

10. Continued to take personal inventory and when we were wrong promptly admitted it.

The social inventory of Step Eight has its foundation in the personal inventory of Step Four. It allows the individual to bring his personal moral inventory into social consciousness and recognizes that we are social beings who must live with our fellow human beings in harmony and responsibility. Although we are not responsible for our addiction, we are responsible for our recovery and we must face up to the truth of what we have done to others and take actions to make amends. Step Eight is very much involved with the theological principal of forgiveness, a concept conspicuously absent from the literature of psychotherapy. When a person forgives his/her self or another human being it does not mean that the negative experience is forgotten, it only means that the individual has taken responsibility for his/her actions and acknowledge that bad or undesirable acts do not make the individual a bad or undesirable person (Ellis,1962). It is through forgiveness that recovering people find their sanity. "The reason to forgive is for our own sake, for our health. Because beyond that point needed for healing, if we hold onto our anger, we stop growing and our souls begin to shrivel (Peck, 1993, p. 46)

Steps Eight and Nine help an individual make the changes in one's recovery clear to the people in their lives who have been affected by an individual's addictive behaviors. Steps Eight and Nine are complicated for most people and may raise some difficult questions. The first thing Step Eight asks one to do is to make "a list of all persons we had harmed," we need to identify who we've hurt, and what we've done to hurt them. Most people find that the lists of people and institutions they resented and feared, which they created in Step Four, make a good starting point for Step Eight. Step Eight and Nine if handled properly can result in removing perfectionism and false pride and begin to allow reality based humility to appear as a function of a recovering person's new personal identity.

The next phrase is *"and became willing to make amends to them all."* The recovering person must be willing to do this activity. The word willing is the key. It doesn't say one has to want to, or that we have to like doing so, only that the individual must be willing to make amends. If a person has had trouble understanding how failure to make amends might lead to relapse, sponsors must help the recovering individual think about how having these things unresolved affects his/her self-esteem and level of anxiety. A sponsor can be very helpful during this time in a person's recovery.

If an individual is willing to make amends, it's time to move on to Step Nine. The first part says we should make *"direct amends to such people wherever possible."* The individual must now take action regarding *"the willingness to make amends"*. Remember the words *"direct amends"*. This means that if given the choice between personally talking to the individual and writing a letter, a person must do it face to face. It may be more uncomfortable this way, but most individuals appear to get a greater benefit by talking directly to the person. When one talks directly to another individual about how he/she harmed them it is not uncommon for the person to express anger at ones "willingness to make amends". It is during this time that one's recovery and commitment to change will be truly challenged. In that challenge the person in recovery must:

(1) Listen to the angry person until they have said everything they have to say. Confirm with the person you are making amends to that you have covered all areas of their anger towards you,

(2) make sure that the angry person has been heard by reviewing with the individual their main points. This second point can be very difficult because most people in recovery have a difficult time admitting to their indiscretions,

291

(3) tell the angry person you would like time to think carefully about what they said to you. Set up a second time to talk with them within twenty-four hours. Generally, if you wait for more than a day the emotion is usually too diluted to be of any immediate help in bringing resolution to the anger. Spend the day between meetings talking to a friend or sponsor about the experience,

(4) When you meet the person for the second time you should review the main points covered and that you agree with his/her assessment,

(5) ask the person if there is any specific thing or activity you could do to bring some resolution of this situation, if not, just thank the person for giving you the time to meet and leave the door open for any future discussions,

(6) if the person wants to work on the relationship try to develop a specific plan of action and implement it immediately, and finally

(7) set aside another date within a week to review your progress. This process can be repeated in order to continually work on problems.

Before taking any action, we need to consider the second part of Step Nine: *"except when to do so would injure them or others"*. An individual doesn't need to let him/her be victimized in this process. Keep in mind that Step Nine is about personal recovery, and how others react is less important than how one feels afterward. Some people may be rude or ungrateful.

The Ninth Step brings us to action and creates enormous pain for the recovering person since it takes courage to accept personal responsibility to change one's attitude and behavior towards others. During the Tenth Step the individual needs to continually review their life and maintain a sense of emotional maturity and emotional honesty. The Tenth Step promotes a sense of thinking first and acting second.

Step Ten begins the maintenance phase of recovery. In many was Step Ten is a partial repetition of Step Four. It has been referred to as the "working through" step. Steps Ten through Twelve are the ones that help an individual avoid old habits and convoluted thinking. Unlike the first nine Steps, which the client can start, carry out, and finish, Step Ten begins a lifetime process. Step Ten says one should continue to take personal inventory. The next phrase is *"and when we were wrong promptly admitted it."*

During Steps Eight, Nine, and Ten action is most important. Action is when individuals change their behavior and experience their environment in order to overcome their addiction. Reviewing certain addictive behavior and subsequent commitment to change requires time and energy. The transition from the action stage to maintenance is demonstrated by no relapses and consolidation of gains attained through the action oriented approach to one's recovery. Through consciousness raising and self-reevaluation, individuals solidify the process of recovery. Self-evaluation relates to how one feels and thinks about his/her problems with respect to personal responsibility. It usually leads to corrective emotional experiences and clarification of beliefs and values. On the other hand, consciousness raising increases information to an individual through reading, confrontation, interpretation and observation of an individual's behavior in the environment.

Our spiritual awakenings are meaningless if not expressed in real actions within the context of our real lives…to try and fill your emptiness with meaning from outside yourself is like pouring water into the ocean to make it wet (Ash, 1993)

These two important interventions for change usually occur in the context of a caring, supportive environment. In the addiction field, they tend to be found in therapeutic relationships and/or self-help groups.

11. Sought through prayer and meditation to improve our conscious contact with God as we understood Him, praying only for knowledge of His will for us and the power to carry that out.

12. Having had a spiritual awakening as the result of these steps, we tried to carry this message to alcoholics, and to practice these principles in all our affairs.

During these last two steps the individual seeks a spiritual path that requires contemplation and a new vision of the world and his/her position in this new reality. This *"spiritual awakening"* is more an internal search for power and knowledge that gives purpose and meaning to life. Step Eleven asks one to seek through prayer and meditation to improve our *"conscious contact with God as we understand him"*. The second part of Step Eleven indicates that one is *"praying only for knowledge of God's will for us and the power to carry that out"*.

Prayer

Prayer is one of the most universal and personal aspects of almost every world religion and is central to spirituality that is not expressed in religious dogmas, doctrines, or denominations. Prayer is *"thoughts, attitudes, and actions designed to express or experience connection to the sacred"* (McCullough & Larson, 1999, p. 86). Prayer is a way of accessing a richer, more intense life, and is a means by which people experience transcendent and super empirical reality (McCullough & Larson, 1999).

Research results have indicated that 90% of Americans pray, 97% believe that prayer is heard, and 86% believe that prayer makes them better people (Gallup, 1993). In addition, several researchers have shown that women pray more frequently than men do (Husaini, Moore, & Cain, 1994) and that they pray in a more meditative manner with deeper religious experiences than men (Gallup, 1993; Poloma & Gallup, 1991). African Americans have been shown to pray more often than Whites and reported greater satisfaction with their prayer life than did Whites (Gallup, 1993). Older persons have been shown to be more religious than younger ones and to engage in prayers more frequently than younger people do (Gallup, 1993; Poloma & Gallup, 1991).

Researchers investigating prayer have discovered that it is often used as a coping mechanism for serious problems (Neighbors, Jackson, Bowman, & Gurin, 1983); that it is positively correlated with life satisfaction, well-being, and religious satisfaction (Markides, 1983; Poloma & Pendleton, 1989, 1991); and that it acts as a buffer for stress (Pargament, 1997). It is impossible to explain what happens during prayer and what makes it helpful. Dossey (1993) proposed that the effects could be explained by the placebo effect, the mind-body connection, or perhaps transcendent healing.

Some types of prayer include contemplative/meditative, ritual, petitionary, colloquial, and intercessory (McCullough & Larson, 1999). Contemplative/ meditative prayer involves a receptivity in which one experiences oneself in God's presence. This involves a transcendence of words and images in which one focuses attention of the experience of the sacred. This type of prayer has been shown to be positively related to recovery from a stressful event (Pargament, Koenig, & Perez, 1998). Ritual prayer involves reciting prayers either from written materials or from memory (Poloma & Pendleton, 1989). Although there is little research conducted in this area, some studies suggest that this type of prayer could be associated with lower well-being (McCullough & Larson, 1999). Petitionary prayer means going to God or one's Higher Power asking for the particular needs of others to be met (Poloma & Pendleton, 1989). This form of prayer is not uniquely associated with measures of well-being and, used exclusively could be an indicator of psychosocial distress resulting from negative life events (Pargament, Smith, Koenig, & Perez, 1998). Colloquial prayer is a conversation with God that might include elements of petition, adoration, and simply sharing feelings with God (Scarlett & Periello, 1991). This type of prayer could be a form of religious coping that is positively related to health and well-being (McCullough & Larson, 1999). Intercessory prayer involves praying for others and has been subjected to many attempts at empirical study. Investigators have raised methodological and interpretive challenges; however, one assumption has been that intercessory prayer may be therapeutic for the agent of prayer as well as for persons for whom prayer has been offered (McCullough & Larson, 1999).

In the therapeutic arena, prayer may be used in three major ways: (a) by recovering individuals to facilitate recovery management as well as mental health treatment; (b) by Fellowship members and practitioners who pray about or for their friends outside of meetings or counseling session; and (c) by Fellowship members and practitioners who pray with their clients in the counseling session. People who choose to pray for insight, guidance, healing, or change for other individuals in recovery may find that prayer is a means of collaborating with God (a Higher Power) to bring about change not just for themselves but for other people in recovery. In a sense, these individuals are using their religious or spiritual beliefs to support the effectiveness of the therapeutic process. Although the efficacy of such a process can be debated on both metaphysical and psychological grounds, it is certainly plausible that the mere act of trusting in the power of prayer could bring about significant cognitive transformation (Propst, Ostrom, Watkins, Dean, & Mashburn, 1992). Because of cognitive shifts, individuals might find themselves more open to the influence of others such as family members and community leaders. In addition, meditative/contemplative prayer as an adjunct to recovery management might be able to use the data suggesting that this form of prayer is positively associated with well-being (Carlson, Bacaseta, & Simanton, 1988; Finney & Malony, 1985).

Meditation

Meditation is a form of contemplation *"that involves concentrated practice"* (Miller, 1994, pp. 2-3) and involves training the attention (Goleman, 1988). Marlatt and Kristeller (1999) noted that there are two basic types of meditation. The first is concentrative, in which one focuses on something such as a candle, a mandala, or one's own breathing. The second type of meditation is referred to as *mindfulness,* in which one opens up the self, surrender's control, and awaits insight. In practicing mindfulness, one engages in self-observation or self-monitoring of one's stream of consciousness. Persons who practice mindfulness adopt an accepting and nonjudgmental attitude toward the self (Marlatt & Kristeller, 1999).

Meditation is often associated with Eastern religions, such as Hinduism and Buddhism, and spiritualities that exist outside of religious structures. For this reason, some Christian clients may not be comfortable practicing meditation (McLemore, 1982) despite its similarities with Western practices such as contemplation, imagery, and centering prayer (Carlson et al., 1988; Finney & Malony, 1985).

Meditation has been shown to be effective in managing stress, anxiety, depression, post-traumatic stress disorder (PTSD), health problems (Benson, 1996), and is useful for the prevention and treatment of addictive behaviors (O'Connell & Alexander, 1994). When attempting to integrate meditation into one's recovery, it might be necessary to be trained by a person familiar with the basics of the meditative process.

The true meaning of Steps Eleven and Twelve is reflected in the Jungian struggle of individuation which leads one on the path toward wholeness and a personal commitment to manage life, dominated by grateful living and gratitude. This new life is guided by our capacity for self-awareness, our ability to find more meaningful relationships with ourselves and others and our search for meaning and direction in life. The search for meaning and direction in life was articulated well by Victor Frankl who believed that the three most distinctive human qualities are: spirituality, freedom and responsibility (Frankl, 1984). The recovering person must see himself as a unique spirit, capable of making decisions and possessing the ability to act responsibly about life events.

The recovering individual enhances at this point the recovering individual has worked his/her way through all the Twelve Steps and, if he/she is continuing to practice Steps Ten through Twelve, the individual is using a system that has helped many millions of people avoid relapse and continue to grow in peace of mind and ability to handle life's difficulties. If the recovering person actively practices the program, the individual now has a support group of people, who know him/her, accepts him/her, and cares what happens to him/her. Finally, the individual has also become a support to others in recovery by helping other addicts; therefore the newcomer: or the potential newcomer; is what in the end gives the program meaning. Just as the individual in recovery brings his or her story to other addicts, clarifying and helping them toward wholeness, the fellowships bear their own witness in bringing their story in a process of attraction, placing principles before personalities, to those in cultures who feel themselves, for whatever reason, to be outside the support of 12-Step recovery (http://www.cnsproductions.com/pdf/12step).

Mel Ash expresses the paradox of being alone together when he states: Standing alone on our own two feet with our arms around the people next to us, we close our meetings in a very physical demonstration of being alone together. Squeezing each other's hands at the close of prayer, we affirm our great need and love for one another. Alone together we save each other from our active diseases. Alone and together, we can befriend this lonely, splintered world. Like separate chapters in the same book, we need each other to see how the story turns out (Ash, p.162)

The 12-Step self-help movement is a universal spiritually which embraces more than just Christian spiritual values (www.cnsproductions.com/pdf/12step).

Within the recovering persons desire to stop drinking and/or using drugs,

296

there are many spiritual paths that support recovery management and transformation.

The autonomy of individual groups is upheld by the Twelve Traditions. These form the by-laws of 12-Step recovery and differ as little as the Twelve Steps do between fellowships. The traditional so ensure that AA-based fellowships have no opinion on outside issues, and religion is an outside issue. The core of the Twelve Steps is spiritual and relative. The truth of this is borne out by the variety of cultures, including those in Eastern Europe and Asia, embodying a wide variety of religions and religious beliefs as well as degrees of atheism and agnosticism, wherein the 12-Step movement has taken root and begun to flourish (Braxton, Smith & Seymour, 1987, p.280).

Spirituality of Ordinary People

There are many definitions of spirituality and recovery. It generally refers to something that is transcendent, ultimate and becomes known to an individual in an extrasensory manner (Myers et al 1991, p.4). It is sometimes referred to as the *"life force"* or the *"essence of life"*. An organized way of expressing ones' spirituality can be observed in Western culture as practicing one's faith within a structured religion. Artress (1995), suggested that religion is the container and spirituality the essences held within it (p.5). Although religion and spirituality are interconnected, religion tends to define a more concrete cultural specific expression, while spirituality represents a more universal concept (Fukuyaman and Sevig 1999, p.7). Some individuals appear to be resistant to an organized religious state probably based on their early childhood experiences. As adults these individuals appear more receptive to the concept of a spiritual space on earth devoid of an organized perspective (religion). In both cases, one's commitment to a higher power is not diminished by how one organizes their process of finding a spiritual process. What is significant is that both groups share a worldview that believes in:

- ❖ The goodness of human beings.
- ❖ The unconditional love from the creator of life.
- ❖ The concept of *"free will"*, that human beings are responsible for their actions. (Fukuyama and Sevig 1999, p.26).

These three universal beliefs are shared by the Hebrew, Christian and Islamic traditions as expressed by their respective prophets Abraham, Moses, Jesus, and Mohammed. The highest expression of an individual's spiritual awakening is communicated through acts of compassion, understanding, and peacefulness. Clinebell (1995) suggests several areas of healthy spiritual needs:

- ❖ The need for a viable philosophy of life.

297

- ❖ The need for a relationship with a *"higher power"*.
- ❖ The need to develop a sense of Self.
- ❖ The need to feel connected, (belonging) to the universe.
- ❖ The need for a community that nurtures spiritual growth (p.82).

A true believer in the 12 Steps helps other individuals and they cope with the human condition and foster love, compassion and understanding. If one believes that humans have souls (spirits) that continue after the biological death of their body one is forced to value their deeds and worship their ancestors. The common themes of Judaism, Islam, and Christianity, is that judgment day and external existence is based upon both good and bad thoughts and actions recorded in our memory. In the Eastern religions (e.g. Buddhism, Hinduism, etc.) this life cycle belief (judgment day) finds expression in the belief in reincarnation. The *"law of Karma"* directs biological death or the continuity between lives. One has the potential of advancing toward *"god status"* or declining toward *"animal or plant status"*. An individual is released from the birth/rebirth cycle through enlightenment. What appears to elevate one's afterlife is how one uses their resources to foster the positive elements of the human condition (Hopkins, 1992, p. 154).

Finally, one should review the promises that Twelve-Step literature indicates one can expect to come true, if a recovering person continues to work the program. From the Big Book, Alcoholics Anonymous World Services, Inc., (1976):

> *If we are painstaking about this phase of our development, we will be amazed before we are halfway through. We are going to know a new freedom and a new happiness. We will not regret the past nor wish to shut the door on it. We will comprehend the word serenity and we will know peace. No matter how far down the scale we have gone, we will see how our experience can benefit others. That feeling of uselessness and self-pity will disappear. We will lose interest in selfish things and gain interest in our fellows. Self-seeking will slip away. Our whole attitude and outlook upon life will change. Fear of people and of economic insecurity will leave us. We will intuitively know how to handle situations, which used to baffle us. We will suddenly realize that God is doing for us what we could not do for ourselves (pp. 83-84)*

298

References

Abe-Kim, J.S., and Takeuchi, D.T. (1996). Cultural competence and quality of care: Issues for mental health service delivery in managed care. **Clinical Psychology Science and Practice.** Vol.3. pp.273-295.

Ackerman, R.J. (1978). **Children of Alcoholics: A Guidebook for Educators, Therapists and Parents.** Florida: Learning Public.

Adler, A. (1979). **Superiority and Social Interest: A Collection of Later Writings.** H.L Ansbacher & R.R. Ansbacher (Eds.). New York: W.W. Norton & Co

Alcoholics Anonymous: The story of how many thousands of men and women have recovered from alcoholism. (1976) New York: Alcoholics Anonymous World Services

Alcoholics Anonymous Comes of Age: A Brief History of A.A. (1985). New York: Alcoholics Anonymous World Services.

Alcocer, A.M. (1993). Patterns of alcohol use among Hispanics. In R.S Mayers, B.L. Kail, and T.D. Watts (Eds.), **Hispanic substance abuse.** Springfield, IL: Charles C. Thomas.pp.37-49.

Ali, S. (2005) – **Developing a Bio-cultural Psychosocial Assessment.** American Psychiatric Association. (2000). **Diagnostic and statistical manual of mental disorders** (4th ed. text revision). Washington, D.C.

Allen, J.P., and Columbus, M., eds. **Assessing Alcohol Problems: A Guide for Clinicians and Researchers**, 2nd ed. NIH Publication No. 03-3745. Bethesda, MD: National Institute on Alcohol Abuse and Alcoholism, 2003.

American Psychiatric Association. **DSM-5.** (2013).

Archer, J. Sex differences in physically aggressive acts between heterosexual partners: A meta-analytic review. **Aggression and Violent Behavior** 7:313–351, 2002.

Arndt, S., Black, D.W., Schmucker, A., and Zwick, J. Association among outcomes in a naturalistic statewide assessment of substance user treatment. **Substance Use & Misuse** 39(8):1215–1234, 2004.

Artress, L. (1995). **Walking a Sacred Path: Rediscovering the Labyrinth as a Spiritual Tool**. New York: Riverhead.

Alexander, E. (1991). Sharing power among organizations: Coordination models to link theory and practice. In J. M. Bryson & R. C. Einsweiler (eds.), **Shared power, what is it? How, does it work? How can we make it work better?** Lamham, MN: University Press of America, 213-247.

Allen, D.M., Lehman, J.S., Green, T.A., Lindegren, M.L., Onorato, I.M. and Forrester, W. (1994). HIV infection among homeless adults and runaway youth, United States, 1989-1992. **AIDS.** Vol. 8 (11) pp.1593-1598,

Amaro, H. Whitaker, R., Coffman, G., and Heeren, T. (1990).
  Acculturation and marijuana and cocaine use: Findings from
  HANES 1982-84. **American Journal of Public Health**. Vol. 80
  pp. 54-60.
American Psychiatric Association. (2000).**Diagnostic and Statistical**
  Manual of Mental Disorders (4th ed.). Washington, D.C.:
  American Psychiatric Press, Inc. Brunner/Mazel Publishers.
  American Society of Addictive Medicine (1996). **Patient Placement**
Criteria for the Treatment of Psychoactive Substance Use Disorders.
  ASAM.
Amodeo, M., Robb, N. Peou, S. and Tran, H. (1996). Adapting mainstream
  substance abuse Interventions for Southeast Asian clients The **Journal**
  of Contemporary Human Services Vol. 77. pp. 403-412.
Anderson, D. and Berlant, J. (1995). Managed Mental Health and Substance
  Abuse Services. In: P. Kongetvedt (Ed). **Elements of Managed**
  Health Care. MD: Aspen Pub. Inc.
Arroyo, J.A., Westerberg, V., Tonigan, J.S. (1998). Comparison of treatment
  utilization and outcome for Hispanics and non-Hispanic Whites
  Journal of Studies on Alcohol. Vol.59. pp. 286-291.
Ansbacher, H.L. (1974). Goal Oriented Individual Psychology: Alfred
  Alder's Theory. In A. Burton (Ed). **Operational Theories of**
  Personality. New York: Brunner /Mazel.
Ash, M. (1993). **The Zen of Recovery.** New York: Putnam Books.
Austin, C. D. (1990). Case management: Myths and Realities. **Families**
  in Society, 71(7), 398-405.
Avins, A.L., Woods, W.J, Lindan, C.P.; Hudes, E.S. Clark, W. and Hulley,
  S.B. (1994). HIV infection and risk behaviors among heterosexuals
  in alcohol treatment programs. **JAMA.** Vol. 271 (7). pp.515-518.
Axelson, J. (1985). **Counseling and Development in a Multicultural**
  Society. Monterey, CA: Brooks/Cole.
Ackerknecht, EH (1959). **A Short History of Psychiatry.** New York: NY,
  USA: Hafner.
Bailey, M. B. and Stewart, S (1967). Normal Drinking by Persons Reporting
  Previous Problem Drinking. **Quart. J. Stud. Alc.,** 28: 305-31
Baker, B. and Wheelwright, J. (1982). Analysis with the Aged. In: Stein,
  M. *(Ed.).* **Jungian Analysis**. LaSalle, II.: Open Court. pp.256-
  274.
Bandura, Albert. (1961). Transmission of Aggression through Imitation of
  Aggressive Models. **Journal of Abnormal & Social Psychology**
  (63: 575-582, September).
Balch, J. and Balch, P. (1998). **Prescription for Natural Healing**. NY:
  Graphic Connections
Bander, K.W., Goldman, D.S., Schwartz, M.A., Rabinowitz, E., and English,
  J.T. (1987). Survey of attitudes among three specialties in a teaching
  hospital toward alcoholics. **Journal of Medical Education.** Vol. 62.
  (1). pp. 17-24.

300

Barker, R. L. (1995). **The social work directory**, (3rd ed.), Washington, DC: NASW Press.

Bartholomew, N.G., Hiller, M.L., Knight, K., Nucatola, D.C., and Simpson, D.D. Effectiveness of communication and relationship skills training for men in substance abuse treatment. **Journal of Substance Abuse Treatment** 18(3):217–225, 2000.

Becvar, D. (1997). **Soul Healing.** NY: Basic Books.

Beck, A., Wright, F., Newman, C. and Liese, B. (1993). **Cognitive Therapy of Substance Abuse.** New York: Guilford Press.

Beck, A. (1976) **Cognitive Therapy and Emotional Disorders.** New York: International Universities Press.

Benjamin, L.T. (2007). A Brief History of Modern Psychology. Oxford: Blackwell Publishing.

Bettelheim, B. (1982). **Reflections of Freud and The Soul.** New Yorker. March 1, 1982.

Bolen, J. (1979). **The Tao of Psychology: Synchronicity and The Self** San Francisco: Harper & Row.

Bremner, J.D. (1966). Chronic PTSD in Viet Nam Combat Veterans: Course of Illness and Substance Abuse. **American Journal of Psychiatry** (153: p.369-375).

Burgess, A.W., Hartman, C.R., McCormack, A. (1987). Abused to abuser: Antecedents of Socially Deviant Behavior. **American Journal of Psychiatry** (144:1431-1436).

Beatrice, D. F. (1990). Inter-agency coordination: A practitioner's guide to a strategic for effective social policy, **Administration in Social Work,** 14 (4), 45-60.

Breslau, N. Gender differences in trauma and posttraumatic stress disorder. **Journal of Gender Specific Medicine** 5(1):34–40, 2002.

Brodkin, E.Z. (1997). Inside the welfare contract: Discretion and accountability, in state welfare administration. **Social Service Review,** 71 (1), 1-31.

Brookins, G. K., Peterson, A. C., & Brooks, L M. (1997). Youth And families in the inner city: Influencing positive outcomes In H. J. Wilber-,0. Reyes &- R. P. Weissberg (eds.), **Children and Youth Interdisciplinary Perspectives, Thousand** Oaks, CA: Sage, 45-66

Brooks-Gunn, J & *G. J.* Duncan, (1997), The effects of poverty on children: The future of children, **Children and Poverty,** 7 (2) 55-71.

Bruner, C., (1991). **Thinking collaboration: Ten questions and answers to help policy makers improve children's' services,** Washington, DC: Education and Human Services Consortium.

Barrera, M. (1978). Mexican -American mental health service utilization. **Community Mental Health Journal.** 14:35-45.

Beauvais, F. (1996). Trends in drug use among American Indians students and dropouts, 1975-1994. **American Journal of Public Health.** Vol. 86 (l). pp.1594-1598

301

Beauvais, F. (1992). An integrated model for prevention and treatment of drug abuse among American Indian youth. **Journal of Addictive Diseases.** Vol. (3). pp. 63 –80.

Beauvais, F., and LaBoueff, S. (1985). Drug and alcohol abuse intervention in American Indian communities. **International Journal of Addictions.** Vol. 20. pp. 139-171.

Bernard, B. *(1991).* **Moving toward a just and vital culture: Multiculturalism in our schools.** Portland, OR: Northwest Regional Educational Laboratory, Western Center for Drug Free Schools and Communities.

Beutler, L.E., Zetzer, H., and Yost, E. (1997). Tailoring interventions to clients: Effects on engagement and retention. In L.S. Onken, J.D Blaine, and J.J. Boren (Eds.), **Beyond the therapeutic alliance: Keeping the drug-dependent individual in treatment.** NIDA Research Monograph 165. Rockville, MD: U.S. Department of Health and Human Services. pp .85-109.

Black, S.A., and Markides, K.S. *(1993).* Acculturation and alcohol consumption in Puerto Rican, Cuban American, and Mexican American women in the United States. **American Journal of Public Health.** Vol. 83 (6). pp. 890-893.

Blackbird, E. (1981). **Native American Church Ceremony.** Macy, NE: Omaha Indian Reservation.

Bobo, J. K. (1985). Preventing drug abuse among American Indian adolescents. In L.D. Gilchrist and S. P. Schinke (Eds.), **Preventing Social and Health Problems Through Life Skills Training.** Seattle: University of Washington.

Bokos, P., Mejta, C., Monks, R., and Mickenberg, J. (1993). Case management program: A case management model for intravenous drug users. In: Inciardi, J.A., (Ed.) **Innovative Approaches to the Treatment of Drug Abuse: Program Models and Strategies.** Westport, CT: Greenwood. pp. 87-96

Bonham, G.S., Hague, D.E., Abel, M.H., Cummings, P., and Deutsch R.S. (1990). Louisville's Project Connect for the homeless alcohol and drug abuser. In: Stahler, G.J., and Stimmel, B., (Eds.) **Alcoholism and Drug Abuse Among Homeless Men and Women.** New York: Haworth Press. pp. 57-78.

Booth, M.W., Castro, F.G., and Anglin.(1990). What do we know about Hispanic substance abuse? A review of the literature. In R. Glick & J. Moore (Eds.). **Drugs in Hispanic communities.** New Brunswick, NJ: Rutgers Press.

Brecht, M.L. and Anglin, M.D. (1990). Conditional Factors of maturing out: Legal supervision and treatment. **International Journal of the Addictions.** Vol. 25. pp. 395-407.

Brick, J. and Erickson, C. (1999). **Drugs, the Brain and Behavior.** New York: Haworth Medical Press.

302

Brindis, C.D., and Theidon, K.S. (1997). The role of case management in substance abuse treatment services for women and children. **Journal of Psychoactive Drugs.** Vol. 29 (l). pp.79-88.

Brisbane, F. L., and Womble, M. (*1992*). **Working with African Americans: The Professional Handbook, 1992.** Chicago: HRDI International Press.

Burke, L.K., and Follingstad, D.R. Violence in lesbian and gay relationships: Theory, prevalence, and correlational factors. **Clinical Psychology Review** 19(5):487–512, 1999.

Burnette, R., and Koster, J. (1974). **The Road to Wounded Knee.** New York: Bantam Books.

Bux, D.A, Iguchi, M.Y., Lidz, V., Baxter, R.C., and Platt, J.J. (1993). Participation in an outreach-based coupon distribution program for free methadone detoxification. **Hospital and Community Psychiatry.** Vol. 44 (11). pp.1066-1072.

Borkman TJ. (1998) Is recovery planning any different from treatment planning? **Journal Subst Abuse Treat.** Jan-Feb; 15 (1):37-42.

Borkman, T., Kaskutas, L.A., Room, J., Bryan, K., & Barrows, D. (1998). A historical and developmental analysis of social model programs. **Journal of Substance Abuse Treatment,** 15, 7-17.

Becvar, D. S. (1997). Soul healing and the family. **Journal of Family Social work,** 2, 1-11.

Benson, H. (1996). **Timeless healing: The power and biology of belief.** New York: Scribner.

Bickel, C. O., Ciarrocchi, J., Sheers, N. J., Estadt, B. K., Powell, D. A. & Pargament, K. (1998). Perceived stress, religious coping styles, and depressive affect. **Journal of Psychology and Christianity,** 17, 33-42.

Buxton, M.E.; Smith, D.E. & Seymour, R.B. (1987). Spirituality and other points of resistance to the 12-step process. **Journal of Psychoactive Drugs.** 19(3):275-286.

Cahalan, D. (1970). **Problem Drinkers: A National Survey.** San Francisco, Jossey-Bass, Cahalan, D., Cisin, I. H. and Crossley, H. M. (1974). **American Drinking Practices: A National Survey of Drinking Behavior and Attitudes.** New Brunswick, Rutgers Center for Alcohol Studies

Carlson, C. R., Bacaseta, P. E., & Simanton, D. A. (1988). A controlled evaluation of devotional meditation and progressive relaxation. **Journal of Psychology and Theology,** 16, 362-368.

Caetano, R. (1990). Hispanic drinking in the U.S.: Thinking in new directions. **British Journal of Addiction.** Vol. 85. pp. 1231-1236.

Caetano, R., Schafer, J., and Cunradi, C.B. (2001) Alcohol-related intimate partner violence among White, Black, and Hispanic couples in the United States. **Alcohol Research and Health** 25 (1): 58–65,

303

Center for Substance Abuse Treatment. **Brief Interventions and Brief Therapies for Substance Abuse.** Treatment Improvement Protocol (TIP) Series 34. HHS Publication No. (SMA) 993353. Rockville, MD: Substance Abuse and Mental Health Services Administration, 1999*a*.

Center for Substance Abuse Treatment. **A Provider's Introduction to Substance Abuse Treatment for Lesbian, Gay, Bisexual, and Transgender Individuals.** HHS Publication No. (SMA) 12–4104.Rockville, MD: Substance Abuse and Mental Health Services Administration, 2001b.

Center for Substance Abuse Treatment. (1999). **Enhancing Motivation for Change in Substance Abuse Treatment.** Treatment Improvement Protocol. (TIP Series, Number 35. DHHS Pub (SMA) 98-3222. Washington, D.C.: U.S. Government Printing Office. 1-37.

Center for Substance Abuse Treatment. **Understanding Evidence-Based Practices for Co-Occurring Disorders.** COCE Overview Paper 5. (2007). DHHS Publication No. (SMA) 07-4278. Rockville, MD: Substance Abuse and Mental Health Services Administration, and Center for Mental Health Services.

Chase, K.A., O'Farrell, T.J., Murphy, C.M., Stewart, W., and Murphy, M. (2003). Factors associated with partner violence among female alcoholic patients and their male partners. **Journal of Studies and Alcohol** 64(1):137–149.

Chermack, S.T., Fuller, B.E., and Blow, F.C. (2000). Predictors of expressed partner and non-partner violence among patient's in substance abuse treatment. **Drug and Alcohol Dependence.** 58(12):43–54.

Chappel, J. N. (1993). **Long-term recovery from alcoholism.** Recent Advances in Addictive Disorders, 16 (1), 177-187.

Chappel, J.N. (2003). Spiritual components of the recovery process. In: Graham A.W., and Wilford, B.B., eds. **Principles of Addiction Medicine,** 3rd ed. (pp. 969–974). Chevy Chase, MD: American Society of Addiction Medicine.

Clinebell, H. (1995). **Counseling for Spiritual Empowerment Wholeness: A Hope Centered Approach.** New York: Haworth Pastoral Press.

Cohen, J.B., Dickow, A., Horner, K., Zweben, J.E., Balabis, J., Vandersloot, D., and Reiber, C. (2003). Abuse and violence history of men and women in treatment for methamphetamine dependence. **The American Journal on Addictions** 12(5):377–385.

Colorado, P. (1986). **Native American alcoholism: An issue of survival** Doctoral dissertation. Brandeis University, The Heller Graduate School for Advanced Studies in Social Welfare.

Cole, B. S., & Paragament, K. I. (1999). Spiritual surrender: A paradoxical path to control. In W. R. Miller (Ed.), **Integrating spirituality into treatment.** Washington, DC: American Psychological Association. 179-198

Callicott, K. (2003). Culturally-sensitive collaboration within person-centered planning. **Focus on Autism and Other Developmental Disabilities,** 18 (1), 60-69.

Chinman, M. J., Allende, M., Weingarten, R., Steiner, J, Tworkowski, S., & Copeland, M. (2002). **The depression workbook: A guide for living with depression and manic depression Wellness Recovery Action Plan.** Oakland, CA: New Harbinger Publications.

Cowger, C.D. (1994). Assessing client strengths: Clinical assessment for client empowerment. *Social Work 39*(3), 262-268.

California Department of Corrections. (1998). What percentage of the California correctional population has a history of substance abuse? **California Correctional Statistics.** . July. pp.1-98.

Canda, E., & Phaobtong, T. (1992). Buddhism as a Support System for Southeast Asian refugees, Social **Work,** 37(1), 61-67.

Carlton-LaNey, I. (1999). African American social work pioneers' response to Need, **Social Work,** 44 (4), 311-321

Cnaan, R. A., & Rothman, J. (1986). Conceptualizing community intervention: An empirical test of three models of community organization, **Administration in Social Work,** 10 (3), 41-55.

Compton, B. R., & Galaway, B. (1989). **Social Work Processes** (4th ed.). Belmont, CA: Wadsworth.

Courtney, M. (1999). Challenges and opportunities posed by, the Reform era. Presented at the **Reconciling welfare reform with child welfare conference**. Center for Advanced Studies in Child Welfare, University of Minnesota, February 26.

Cross, T.L. & Bazron, B. J., Dennis, K., & Issacs, M. R. (1989). **Toward a culturally competent system of care,** Washington, D.C: Georgetown University Child Development Center.

Center for Disease Control. (1998). HIV/AIDS among American Indians and Alaskan Natives- United States, 1981-1997. **Mortality and Morbidity Weekly Review.** Vol. 47. pp. 154-160.

Center for Disease Control. (1997). **HIVIAIDS Surveillance Report.** Atlanta: CDC.

Centers for Disease Control (1996). Youth risk behavior surveillance, United States, 1995. **Mortality and Morbidity Weekly Review.** Vol. 45.

Centers for Disease Control (1997). **HIV/AIDS Surveillance Report.** Atlanta: CDC.

Centers for Disease Control and Prevention. (1987a) Antibody to human immunodeficiency virus in female prostitutes. **Morbidity and Mortality Weekly Report.** Vol. 36 (11) pp.157-161.

Centers for Disease Control and Prevention. (1993). Revised Classification System for HIV Infection and Expanded Surveillance Case Definition for AIDS Among Adolescents and Adults. **Morbidity and Mortality Weekly Report.** Vol. 41 (51) pp. 961-962.

Centers for Disease Control and Prevention. (1997a). USPHS/IDSA guidelines for the prevention of opportunistic infections in persons infected with human immunodeficiency virus: A summary. **Morbidity and Mortality Weekly Report.** Vol. 46 (RR12) pp.1-45.

Centers for Disease Control and Prevention. (1997c) **HIVIAIDS Surveillance Report.** Vol. 9 (2).

Centers for Disease Control and Prevention. (1999b) Report of the NIH panel to define principles of therapy of HIV infection. **Morbidity and Mortality Weekly Report.** Vol. 47 (RR-5) pp.1-41.

Center for Substance Abuse Treatment. (1994). **Screening and Assessment for Alcohol and Other Drug Abuse Among Adults in the Criminal Justice System.** Treatment Improvement Protocol (TIP) Series, Number 7. DHHS Pub. No.(SMA) 94-2076. Washington, DC: U.S. Government Printing.

Center for Substance Abuse Treatment. (1998). **Addiction Counseling Competencies: The Knowledge, Skills, and Attitudes of Professional Practice.** Technical Assistance Protocol (TAP) Series, Number 21. DHHS Pub. No. (SMA). 98-3171 Washington, DC: U.S. Government Printing Office.

Center for Substance Abuse Prevention. (1994.) **Following specific guidelines will help you assess cultural competence in program design, application, and management.** Rockville, MD: U.S. Department of Health and Human Services.

Chopra, Deepak (1997). **Overcoming Addictions; The Spiritual Solution.** New York: Tree Rivers Press

Churchill, W., and Larsen, D. (1981). **American Indian Substance Abuse: A Familial Solution.** Arlington, VA Center for Multicultural Awareness.

Clark, J.J. (1994). **Jung and Eastern Thought:** A Dialogue with the Orient. London: Routledge Press.

Collected Works, C.G. Jung. (1966) Vol. 8. **Synchronicity: An Acausal Connecting Principal.** pp.417-519.

Collective Works. C.G. Jung (1968). **The Archetypes and the Collective Unconscious.** Vol. 9, Part 1Princeton, N.J.: Princeton University Press.3-53.

Crowley, (2000). **Jung: A Journey of Transformation: Exploring His Life and Experiencing His Ideas.** Wheaton Illinois: Quest Books.

Collins, L.V. (1997). **Census facts for Native American.** Washington, D.C.: U. S. Census Bureau.

Collinge, W. (1996). **Alternative Medicine.** New York: Warner Books.

Colon, H.M., Robles, R.R. , Marrero, C.A., Matos, T.D.Lopez, C.M. and
Orraca, 0. (1996). Reduction, in sexual risk behaviors
among HIV seropositve drug abusers in Puerto Rico
International Conference on AIDS. Vol. 11(2). P.146.

Colorado, P. (1986). **Native American alcoholism: An issue of survival**
Doctoral dissertation. Brandeis University: The Heller Graduate
School for Advanced Studies in Social Welfare.

Conrad, K.J., Hultman, C.I., and Lyons, J.S. (1993). Treatment of the
chemically dependent homeless: A synthesis. **Alcoholism
Treatment Quarterly.** Vol.10 (3-4). pp.235-246.

Cook, F. (1992). *TASC*: Case management models linking criminal
justice and treatment. In: Ashery, R.S., (Ed.). **Progress and
Issues in Case Management**. NIDA Research Monograph
Series, Number *127*. DHHS Pub. No. (ADM) 92-1946.Rockville,
MD: National Institute on Drug Abuse .pp. 368-382.

Corcoran, K., and Vandiver, V. (1996). **Maneuvering the maze of
managed care**. NY: The Free Press.

Cory, G. (2000). **Theory and Practice of Counseling and Psychotherapy.**
New York: Brooks/Cole Publishing Co.

Crime Prevention Division. (1994). **Crime in Hawaii 1993**. Honolulu State of
Hawaii Department *of* the Attorney General.

Cross, T., Bazron, B.; Dennis, K., and Isaacs, M. (1989). **Towards a
Culturally Competent System of Care: A Monograph on
Effective Services for Minority Children Who Are Severely
Emotionally Disturbed.** Washington, DC: Child and Adolescent
Service System Program, Technical Assistance Center, Georgetown
University Child Development Center.

Cunradi, C.B., Caetano, R., and Schafer, J. Alcohol-related problems drug use,
and male intimate partner violence severity among U.S couples.
Alcoholism: Clinical and Experimental Research 26(4):493–500,
2002.

Dalai Lama. (2010). **Toward a True Kinship of Faiths**. NY: Doubleday
Religion.

Dawson, D. (1996) Correlates of past-year status among treated and untreated
person with former alcohol dependence: United States, 1992,
Alcoholism: Clinical and Experimental Research, 20, 771-779.

Delgado, M., and Delgado, D. (1982). **Natural support systems: Source of
strength in Hispanic communities. Social Work**. 27(1).

Davis, J. **The Diamond Approach: An Introduction to the Teachings of A. H.
Almaas**. Boston: Shambhala Press.

Davis, L. & Proctor, E. (1989). **Race, Gender and Class: Guidelines for
Practice.** New Jersey: Prentice Hall.

DSM-IV-TR, (2000) Arlington, Virginia: American Psychiatric Association

DSM-5, (2013). Arlington, Virginia: American Psychiatric Asco. D'Avanzo,
C.E. (1997). Southeast Asians: Asian Pacific Americans at risk for
substance misuse. **Substance Use and Misuse**. Vol. 32. pp. 829 848.

Davis, L. & Proctor, E. (1989). **Race, Gender and Class: Guidelines for Practice.** New Jersey: Prentice Hall.

Day, D. (1995). **Health emergency: The spread of drug related AIDS among African Americans and Latinos.** Princeton, NJ: The Lindesmith Center.

DeGood, D., A. Crawford and A. Jongsma. (1999). **The Behavioral Medicine Treatment Planner.** New York: John Wiley and Sons.

Delgado, M and Humm-Delgado, D. (1982). Natural support systems: Source of strength in Hispanic communities. **Social Work.** Vol. 27 (1). pp.83-89.

Delgado, M. (1997). Hispanics/Latinos. In J. Philleo, F.L. Brisbane, and L.G. Epstein (Eds.), **Cultural Competence in substance abuse prevention**. Washington, D.C.: National Association of Social Workers Press. 33-54.

Department of Health. (1994). **AIDS Surveillance Quarterly Report**. Honolulu: State of Hawaii.

Dieterich, D.T. (1997) Advances in the Pathophysiology and treatment of HIV associated wasting. **Improving the Management of HIV Disease**. Vol. 4.

Drachman, D. (1992). A stage of migration framework for services to immigrant populations. **Social Work**, 37 (1), 61-67

Drake, R.E., Bebout, R.R., and Roach, J.P.(1993). A research evaluation of social network case management for homeless persons with dual disorders. In: Harris, M., and Bergman, H.C., (Eds) **Case Management for Mentally Ill Patients: Theory and Practice**. Vol. 1. Chronic Mental Illness. Langhorne, PA: Harwood Academic Publishers. pp.83-98.

Drake, R. and Noordsey, D. (1994). Case management for people with coexisting severe mental disorder and substance abuse disorder. **Psychiatric Annals.** Vol. 24 (8). pp.427-431.

Davidson, L. (1999). On the road to collaborative treatment planning: Consumer and supporter perspectives. **Journal of Behavioral Health Services & Research,** 26(2), 211-218.

Deegan, P. E. (1992). The independent living movement and people with psychiatric disabilities: Taking back control over our own lives. **Psychosocial Rehabilitation Journal**, 15(3), 3-19.

Deegan, P.E. (1996). Recovery as a Journey of the Heart. **Psychiatric Rehabilitation Journal**, 19, 91-97.

DeJong, G. and Miller, S. (1995). How to interview for client strengths, **Social Work,** *(40),* 729-736.

Dossey, L. (1993). **Healing words.** New York: HarperCollins.

Easton, C., Swan, S., and Sinha, R. (2000). Motivation to change substance use among offenders of domestic violence. **Journal of Substance Abuse Treatment** 19(1):1–5.

Ebona, A. (1984). Federal Government Policies and India Goals of Self-government. In L. Little Bear, M., Boldt and J.A. Long (Eds.), **Pathways to Self-determination**. University of Toronto Press Toronto.

Egan, G. (2002). **The Skilled Helper.** California: Brooks/Cole. Egeland, B., Jacobvitz, D., and Sroufe, L.A. Breaking the cycle of abuse. **Child Development** 59:1080–1088, 1988

Elifson, K.W., Boles, J., and Sweat, M. (1993). Risk factors associated with HIV infection among male prostitutes. **American Journal of Public Health. Vol.** 83. pp.79-83.

Epstein, M. (1995). **Thoughts Without a Thinker.** New York: Basic Books. Inc

Estrada, A. (1991). Drug abuse and AIDS: Interventions in Hispanic American populations. In: **NIDA Conference Highlights.** Washington, DC: National Institute on Drug Abuse. p.183.

Ewalt, P. (1994). Poverty matters. **Social Work,** 39 (2), 149-151.

Erikson, E. (1963). **Childhood and Society**. (2nd Edition). New York: Norton.

Fowler, James W. (1981). **Stages of Faith**. Harper & Row.

Gary, P. (1988). **Freud: A Life for Our Times**. New York: W.W. Norton & *Co.* 197-243.

Gilligan, C. (1982). **In a different voice: Psychological theory and women's Development** Cambridge, *MA:* Harvard University Press

Goodwin, W. W., Crane, J. B., and Guze, S. B. (1971). Felons Who Drink: An Eight-Year Follow-up. **Quart. J. Stud. Alc.,** 32:136-147.

Falck, R., Siegal, H.A., and Carlson, R.G. (1992). Case management to enhance AIDS risk reduction for injection drug users and crack users: Theoretical and practical considerations. In: Ashery, R.S., (Ed.). **Progress and Issues in Case Management**. NIDA Research Monograph Series, Number 127. DHHS Pub. No. (ADM) 92-1946.Rockville, MD: National Institute on Drug Abuse pp. 167-180.

Finn, P. (1996). Cultural responsiveness of drug user treatment programs: Approaches to improvement. **Substance Use and Misuse.** Vol. 31. pp. 493-518.

Flaskerud, J. H. (1986). The effects of culture compatible intervention on the utilization of mental health services by minority patients. **Community Mental Health Journal.** 22:127-14 1.

Fletcher, B.W., Inciardi, J.A., and Horton, A.M., (Eds.). (1994). **Drug Abuse Treatment: The Implementation of Innovative Approaches to Drug Abuse Treatment**. Westport, CT: Greenwood Press.

Flynn, P.M., Joe, G.W., Broome, K.M., Simpson, D.D., and Brown, B.S. Recovery from opioid addiction in DATOS. **Journal of Substance Abuse Treatment,** 25(3):177–186, 2003.

Farmer, R., & Walsh, J. (1999). Living room assessment, **Journal of Community, Practice,** 6 (4), 79-94.

309

Freeman, E. M., & Dyers, L. (1993). High-risk children and adolescents: Families and community environments, **Families in Society**, 74 (7), 422-431.

Franklin, D. L. (1990). The cycles of social work practice: Social action vs. individual interest. **Journal of Progressive Human Services,** 1 (2), 59-80.

Frey, G. A. (1990). A Framework for promoting organizational change. **Families in Society,** 71 (3), 142-147.

Friedman, S.R., Jose, B., Deren, S., Des Jarlais, D.C., and Neaigus, A. (1995). Risk factors for human immunodeficiency virus seroconversion among out-of-treatment drug injectors in high and low seroprevalence **cities.** **American Journal of Epidemiology.** Vol. 42. pp. 864-874.

Freud, A. (1993). **The Ego and the Mechanisms of Defense.** New York: International Universities Press Inc.

Frye B.A. (1995). Use of cultural themes in promoting health among Southeast Asian refugees. Special issue: Undeserved populations. **American Journal of Health Promotion.** Vol. 9. pp. 269-280.

Frey, W., and Scommegna, P. (1997). **Black migration to the South reaches record highs in 1990s**. Washington, D.C.: Population Reference Bureau.

Fisher, D. and Ahern, L. (1999). **Personal Assistance in Community Existence. National Empowerment Center.** Downloaded from: www.cmhanipissing.on.ca/data/1/recdocs/766_pace_manual

Fisher, D. (2005). Empowerment Model of Recovery from Severe Mental Illness. **Medscape Psychiatry & Mental Health** 10 (1).

Forest, M. & Pearpoint, J. (1990). Common Sense Tools: Maps and Circles for Inclusive Education. **The Inclusion Network**. Inclusion.com.

Fromm, Erich. (1941). **Escape from Freedom** New York: Rinehart & Co.

Fenichel, O. (1945). **Psychoanalytic Theory of Neurosis.** New York.

Finney, J. R., & Malony, H. N. (1985). An empirical study of contemplative prayer as an adjunct to psychotherapy. **Journal of Psychology and Theology**, 13, 284- 290.

Fukuyama, M. and Sevig, T. (1999). **Integrating Spirituality into Multicultural Counseling**. London: Sage Publication.

Galaif, E. R., & Sussman, S. (1995). For whom does Alcoholics Anonymous work? **International Journal of the Addictions**. 30 (2),161-184.

Galanter, M. (1993**). Network Therapy for Alcohol And Drug Abuse**. New York: Basic Books.

Gallup, G. H., Jr. (1993). **Religion in America**. Princeton, NJ: Princeton Religious Research Center.

Goleman, D. (1988). **The meditative mind**. Los Angeles: Tarcher

Gorski, T. (1989). **Understanding The Twelve Steps**. New York: Simon & Schuster.

Geller J. L. (2000). "The Last Half-Century of Psychiatric Services as Reflected in Psychiatric Services." **Psychiatric Services** (51:41-67).

310

George, M.J. Invisible touch. **Aggression and Violent Behavior** 8:23–60, 2003.

Germain, C. & Gitterman, A. (1996). **The Life Model of Social Work Practice.** (2nd ed.). New York: Columbia Univ. Press.

Gold E (2007). From narrative wreckage to islands of clarity: stories of recovery from psychosis. **Canadian Family Physician 53** (8): 1271–5, August.

Gao, F., Bailes, E., Robertson, D.L., Chen, Y.; Rodenburg, CM. Michael, S.F., Cummins, L.B., Arthur, L.O., Peeters, M., Shaw G.M., Sharp, P.M., and Hahn, B.H. (1999). Origin of HIV-1 in the chimpanzee Pan troglodytes. **Nature.** Vol. 397 (6718). pp.436-441.

Garcia, M.H. (1995). An anthropological approach to multicultural diversity training. **Journal of Applied Behavioral Science** 31:490-504.

Gibson, P. A. (1999). African American Grandmothers: New mothers again, **Affilia,** 14 (3), 329-343.

Graham, J. R Barter, K. (1999). Collaboration: A social work practice method. **Families in Society,** 80 (1), 6-13.

Green, I. W. (1999). **Cultural awareness in human services: A multi-ethnic approach,** Boston: Allyn & Bacon.

Greenbaum, L., & Holmes, I. (1983). The use of folktales in social work practice. **Social Casework,** 64, 414-418.

Greenfield, P. M. (1994). Independence and interdependence as developmental scripts: Implications for theory research and practice. In P. M. Greenfield & R. R. Cocking (eds.), **Cross-cultural roots of minority child development** Hillsdale, NJ: Lawrence Erlbaum Associates. 1-24.

Gulati, P. & Guest, G. (1990). The community centered model: A garden variety approach or a radical or a radical transformation of community practice, **Social Work,** 35 (1), 63-68.

Gutierrez, I. M. (1994). Beyond coping: an empowerment Perspective on stressful life events, **Journal of Sociology and Social Welfare,** 21 (3), 201-219.

Ginzburg, H.M. (1989). **Drug abuse treatment: A national study of effectiveness.** Chapel Hill, NC: University of North Carolina Press.

Gutierrez, L. M. & Lewis, E. A. (1999). Strengthening communities through groups: A multicultural perspective. In H. Brtcher, L. F. Kurtz, & A. Lamont (eds.), **Rebuilding communities: Challenges for group work,** New York: Haworth Press, 5-16.

Gutierrez, L. M., & Ortega, R. (1991). Developing methods to Empower Latinos: The importance of groups. **Social Work with Groups,** 14 (2), 23-43.

Gloria, A.M., and Peregoy, J.J. (1996). Counseling Latino alcohol and other substance users/abusers. Cultural considerations or counselors. **Journal of Substance Abuse Treatment.** Vol. 13. pp.119-126.

311

Goddard, L. (1993). Background and scope of the alcohol and other drug problems. In L. Goddard (Ed.), **CSAP technical report 6: An African centered model of prevention for African American youth at high risk**. Rockville, MD: Department of Health and Human Services. pp.11-18

Gordon, J.U. (Ed.) (1994). **Managing multiculturalism in substance abuse services**. Thousand oaks, CA: Sage Publications.

Gorsuch, R.L., and Miller, W.R. (1999). Assessing spirituality. In: Miller, W.R., ed. **Integrating Spirituality into Treatment: Resources for Practitioners** (pp. 47–64). Washington, DC: American Psychological Association

Graham, A. W., Schultz, T. K., (Eds.) (1998). **Principles of Addiction Medicine** 2nd Edition, American Association of Addiction Medicine, Chevy Chase, MD.

Graham, K., and Birchmore-Timney, C. (1990). Case management in addictions treatment. **Journal of Substance Abuse Treatment**. Vol. 7. pp. 181-188.

Grella, C.E., Anglin, M.D., and Wugalter, S.E. (1995). Cocaine and crack use and HIV risk behaviors among high-risk methadone maintenance clients. **Drug and Alcohol Dependence**. Vol. 37. pp.15-21.

Greenfeld, L.A., Rand, M.R., Craven, D., Klaus, P.A., Perkins, C.A., Ringel, C., Warchol, G., Maston, C., and Fox, J.A. Violence by Intimates: Analysis of Data on Crimes by Current or Former Spouses, Boyfriends, and Girlfriends. **Bureau of Justice Statistics Factbook**. NCJ167237. Washington, DC: U.S. Department of Justice, 1998.

Grier, W. and Cobbs, B. (1968). **Black Rage**. New York: Bantam Books

Griffith, E.E.H., Chung, H., Foulks, E., Lu, F., Ruiz, P., Wintrob, R. and Yamamoto, J. (Eds.). (1996). **Alcoholism in the United States: Racial and ethnic considerations**. Report No.14 1.Washington, D.C.: American Psychiatric Press.

Gutierres, S., and Todd, M. (1997). The impact of childhood abuse on treatment outcomes of substance abusers. **Professional Psychology: Research and Practice**. Vol.28(4). pp. 348-354.

Hale, J and Hunter, M (1988). **From HMO Movement to Managed Care Industry. The Future of HMO's in the Volatile Health Care Market**. Inter Study Managed Care Research.

Hand, F. (1991). The role of the spiritual people in recovery. Paper presented at **American Indian Substance Abuse Conference**, Des Moines, IA,

Harris, M., and Bergman, H. (1987). Case management with the chronically mentally ill: a clinical perspective. **American Journal of Orthopsychiatry**. Vol. 57 (2) pp. 296-302.

Harris, A. (1996). **Living with Paradox: An Introduction to Jungian Psychology**. New York: Brooks/Cole Publishing.

Harvard Mental Health Letter (October 1995) Treatment of Drug Abuse and Addiction — Part III, Volume 12, Number 4.

Heyman, G. (2009). **Addiction: A Disorder of Choice**, http://. www.thecleanslate.org/wp-content/uploads/2012/08/nesarc-mature-out.png).

Hyman, SE; Malenka, RC; Nestler, EJ (2006). Neural mechanisms of
    addiction: the role of reward-related learning and memory.
    Annual review of neuroscience 29: 565–98.

Henderson, G., and Primeaux, M. (Eds.). (1981). **Transcultural Health
    Care**. Menlo Park, CA: Addison-Wesley.

Hill, T. (1990). Peyotism and the control of heavy drinking: The Nebraska
    Winnebago in the early 1900s. **Human Organization**. 49 (3).

Hisnanick, J., and Erickson, P. (1993). Hospital resource utilization by
    American Indians and Alaskan natives for alcoholism and
    alcohol abuse. **American Journal of Drug and Alcohol Abuse**.
    19:387-396.

Holmes, K.A. and Hodge, R. H. (1997). Gay and lesbian people. In J.
    Philleo, F .L. Brisbane, and L.G. Epstein (Eds.), **Cultural
    Competence in substance abuse prevention.** Washington,
    D.C.: National Association of Social Workers. pp.153-176.

Harris, A. (1996). **Living With Paradox: An Introduction to Jungian
    Psychology.** New York: Brooks/Cole.

Hackman, J. & Oldham, G. R. (1976). Motivation through the design of
    work: Test of a theory, **Organizational Behavior**.

Hackman, J. R., & Oldham, G. R. (1980). **Work design.** Reading, MA:
    Addison-Wesley.

Haight, W. L. (1998). Gathering the spirit at First Baptist Church:
    Spirituality as a protective factor in the lives of African American
    children. **Social Work**, 43 (3), 213-221.

Halpern, R. (1990). Poverty and early, childhood parenting: Toward a
    framework for intervention American **Journal of Orthopsychiatry,**
    60 (1), 6-18.

Haynes, K. S., & Mickelson, J. S. (2000). **Affecting change: Social
    Workers in the political arena,** (4th.ed.). Boston: Allyn and Bacon.

Homan, M. S. (1999). **Promoting community change: Making it happen in
    the real world.** (2nd ed.). Brooks/Cole.

Hand, F. (1991). The role of the spiritual people in recovery. Paper presented at
    American Indian Substance Abuse Conference Des Moines, IA.

Harris, A. (1996). **Living with Paradox: An Introduction to Jungian
    Psychology**. New York: Brooks/Cole.

Hazelden Foundation. **Twelve Step Recovery is Spirituality at Its Best:
    Alive & Free.** Center City, MN: Hazelden, 2003.

Hill, T. (1990). Peyotism and the control of heavy drinking: The Nebraska
    Winnebago in the early 1900s. **Human Organization**. Vol. 49 (3).

Hopkins, T. (1992). **Hindu Views of Death And Afterlife**. In: H. Obayaski
    (Ed) **Death and Afterlife. Perspectives of World Religions**
    New York: Praeger Press.

Husaini, B. A., Moore, S. T., & Cain, V. A. (1994). Psychiatric symptoms and
    help-seeking behavior among the elderly: An analysis of racial and
    gender differences. **Journal of Gerontological Social Work**, *21,* 177-
    195.

313

Hirayama, H., & Cetingok, M. (1993). Mental health promotion for South East Asian refugees in Horesji, C., Heavy, Runner B., & Hirayama, K. K., the USA. **International Social Work,** 36 (2), 119-129.

Hubbard, R.L., Marsden, M.E., Rachal, J.V., Harwood, H.J., Cavanaugh, E.R., & Herman, J. (1992). **Trauma and Recovery: The Aftermath of Violence from Domestic Abuse to Political Terror,** NY., NY.: Basic Books.

Icard, D., Longres, J. F., & Spenser, M. (1999). Racial minority status and distress among children and adolescents. **Journal of Social Service Research,** 25 (1/2), 19-40.

Ichiho, H., DeLisio, G., Sakai, T., and Maritsugu, S. (1990). The Hawaii State Department of Corrections substance abuse strategy. **Hawaii Medical Journal** 49: 200-204.

Kohlberg, L. (1987). **The Measurement of Moral Judgment.** Cambridge University Press.

Kreek, M., Nielsen, D., LaForge, KS. (2004). Genes Associated with Addiction: Alcoholism, Opiate, and Cocaine Addiction **NeuroMolecular Medicine** 5 (1): 085–108.

Imber, S., Schultz, E., Funderburk, F., Allen, R. and Flamer, R. (1976). The Fate of the Untreated Alcoholic. **J. Nerv. and Ment. Dis.** 162:238-247.

Inciardi, J.A., Tims, F.M., and Fletcher, B.W., (Eds.). (1993). **Innovative Approaches in the Treatment of Drug Abuse: Program Models and Strategies.** Westport, CN: Greenwood Press.

Indian Health Service. (1993). **Trends in Indian health.** Rockville, MD: U.S. Department of Health and Human Services.

Indian Health Service. (1995). **Trends in Indian health.** Rockville, MD: U. S. Department of Health and Human Services.

Indian Health Service. (1996). **Trends in Indian health.** Rockville, MD: U.S. Department of Health and Human Services.

Intagliata, J. (1982). Improving the quality of Community care for the chronically mentally disabled: The role of case management. **Schizophrenia Bulletin.** Vol. 8(4). pp. 655-674.

Intagliata, J. (1981). Operationalizing a case management system: A multilevel approach. **National Conference on Social Welfare: Case Management: State of the Art.** Washington, DC: U.S. Department of Health and Human Services.

Jackson, J. (Ed) (1991). **Life in Black America.** Newbury Park, CA: Sage

Jeff, M. (1994). Afrocentrism and Afro-American Male Youths. In R. Mincy (Ed). **Nurturing Young Black Males.** Washington, DC: Urban Institute Press. . pp. 99-118.

Jenkins, J. (1991). Cross-cultural Studies in Depression. In J. Becker & A. Kleinman Ed). **Psychosocial Aspects of Depression.** Hillesdale, NJ: Lawrence Erlbraum

Ja, D.Y., and Aoki, B. (1993). Substance abuse treatment: Cultural barriers in the Asian American community. **Journal of Psychoactive Drugs.** Vol. 25. pp.61-71.

314

Jackson, J. (Ed) (1991). **Life in Black America.** Newbury Park, CA: Sage

Jacobs, J. (1993). **Black America, 1992: An overview.** In Tidwell (Ed.). **The state of black America.** New York: National Urban League. pp.1-10.

Jacobson, N. and Greenley, D (2001). What is Recovery? A Conceptual Model and Explication. **Psychiatric Services**52, 482-485

Joint Commission on Accreditation of Healthcare Organizations. (2004). **Spiritual Assessment.** Oakbrook Terrace, IL:

Jonikas, Cook, Fudge, Hlebechuk, and Fricks (2005). Charting a Meaningful Life: Planning Ownership in Person/Family-Centered Planning. Paper presented at **SAMHSA's National Consensus Initiative on Person/Family Center Planning Meeting** on December 8, 2005, Washington, D.C.

James, W.H., Kim G.K., and Moore D.D. (1997). Examining racial and ethnic differences in Asian adolescent drug use: The contributions of culture, background and lifestyle. **Drugs Education, Prevention and Policy.** Vol. 4 (1). pp.39-51.

Jeff, M. (1994). Afrocentrism and Afro-American Male Youths. In R. Mincy (Ed). **Nurturing Young Black Males.** Washington, DC: Urban Institute Press. pp. 99-118.

Jenkins, J. (1991). Cross-cultural Studies in Depression. In J. Becker & A. Kleinman (Ed). **Psychosocial Aspects of Depression.** Hillesdale, NJ: Lawrence Erlbraum.

Johnston, L. D., O'Malley, P. M., and Bachman, J. G. (1991). **Drug Use Among American High School Seniors, College Students, and Young Adults, 1975-1990.** *Vol.* 1. DHHS Pub. No. (ADM) 91-1813.Washington, DC: U S Government Printing Office. Joint Commission on Accreditation of Healthcare Organizations. (1979).

Julien, R. (1995). **A Primer of Drug Action** (7th Ed.). W. H. Freeman and Co.

Jongsma, A. (1999). **The Adult Psychotherapy Progress Notes Planner.** New York: John Wiley and Sons.

Jongsma, A and M. Peterson. (1999). **The Comprehensive Adult Psychotherapy Treatment Planner.** New York: John Wiley and Sons.

Jensen, J.P. And A.E. Bergin. (1988). Mental Health Values of Professional Therapists: **A National Interdisciplinary Survey.** Professional Psychology Research Practice. Vol. 19. 290-297.

Jung, C (1964). **Man and His Symbols.** New York: Anchor Books.

Jung, C.G. (1963). **Memories, Dreams, Reflections.** New York: Random House.

Kaufman, J., and Zigler, E. (1993). The intergenerational transmission of violence is overstated. In: Gelles, R.J., and Loseke, D.R., eds. **Current Controversies on Family Violence** (pp. 167–196). Newbury Park, CA: Sage Publications.

Kendall, R. E. and Staton, M. C. (1966). The Fate of Untreated Alcoholics **Quart. J. Stud. Alc.,** 27:30-41

Kissin, B., Platz, A. and Su, W. H. (1970). Social and Psychological Factors in the Treatment of Chronic Alcoholics. **J. Psychiatric Res.,** 8:13-27.

Kepner, E. Application of Learning Theory to the Etiology and Treatment of Alcoholism. (1963) **Quart. J. Stud. Alc.** Vol. 25. 279-291.

Kleinke, C. (1994). **Common Principles of Psychotherapy**. California: Brooks/Cole.

Kurtz, L. F., & Fisher, M. (2003). Participation in community life By AA and NA members **Contemporary Drug Problems**, 30, 875-904.

Kail, B.L., Watson, D.D., and Ray, S. (1995). Needle using practices within the sex industry. **American Journal of Drug and Alcohol Abuse** Vol. 21. pp. 241-255.

Kanter, J. (1996). Case management with long-term patients: A comprehensive approach. In: Soreff, S., (Ed.). **Handbook for the Treatment of the Seriously Mentally Ill.** Seattle: Hogrefe and Huber. pp.171-189.

Kaplan, (1984). Philosophy of Science in Anthropology. **Annual Rev. Anthropology.** Vol. 13. pp. 25-39.

Katz, J. H. (1985). The sociopolitical nature of counseling. **The Counseling Psychologist.** Vol. 13

Kaufman, Edward. (1994). **Psychotherapy of Addictive Persons.** New York: Sculford Press Kaufman. p. 51.

Kedes, D.H, Ganem, D., Ameli, N., Bacchetti, P., and Greenblatt, M. (1997). The prevalence of serum antibody to human herpesvirus 8 (Kaposi sarcoma-associated herpesvirus) among HIV-seropositve and high-risk HIV seronegative women. **JAMA.** Vol. 277. pp. 478-481.

Kettner, R M., Daley, J. M., & Nichols, A. W. (1985). **Initiating Change in organizations and communities**, CA: Brooks/Cole.

Kirk, S. A., & Koeske, G. F. (1995). The fate of optimism: A longitudinal study, of case manager's hopefulness and subsequent morale. **Research on Social Work Practice,** 5 (1), 47-61.

Koenig, H.G. (2001a). Religion and medicine II: Religion, mental health, and related behaviors. **International Journal of Psychiatry in Medicine** 31(1):97–109.

Kotlowitz, A. (1991). **There are no children here**. New York: Doubleday.

Kurtz, P. D., Jarvis, S. V., & Kurtz, G. L. (1991). Problems of homeless youths: Empirical findings and human services issue **Social Work,** 36 (4), 109-314.

Kok, J. and A. Jongsma. (1998). **The Pastoral Counseling Treatment Planner.** New York: John Wiley and Sons.

Kuramoto, F.H. (1994). Drug abuse prevention research concerns in Asian and Pacific Islander populations. A. Cdzares and L.A. Beatty (Eds.), **Scientific method for prevention intervention and research**. NIDA Research Monograph139. Rockville, MD: U S Department of Health and Human Services. pp. 249-272.

Kleinke, Chris L. (1991). **Coping With Life Challenges.** California: Brooks/Cole p.100.

LaFromboise, T. D., and Rowe, W. (1983). Skills training for bicultural competence: Rationale and application. **Journal of Counseling Psychology.** Vol. 30. pp. 589-595.

Lamb, R., Evans, A. and White, W. (2009). **The Role of Partnership in Recovery- Oriented Systems of Care: The Philadelphia Experience.** Retrieved December 26, 2009 from: www.dbhids.org /technical- papers-on-recovery-transformation.

Lemere, F. (1953). What Happens to Alcoholics. Amer. J. Psychiat.109 674-675

Lievegoed, Bernard (1997). Phases: the spiritual rhythms of adult life. GB: Rudolf Steiner Press.

Loevinger, J. (1976). Ego Development: Conceptions and Theories. San Francisco: Jossey-Bass.

Langton, P.A., Epstein, L.G., and Olandi, M.A. (Eds). (1995). **The challenge of participatory research: Preventing alcohol- related problems in ethnic communities.** Rockville, MD: Center for Substance Abuse Prevention.

Latkin, C., Mandell, W., Vlahov, D., Oziemkowska, M., Knowlton, A., and Celentano, D. (1994). My place, your place, and no place: Behavior settings as a risk factor for HIV related injection practices of drug users in Baltimore, Maryland. **American Journal of Community Psychology.** Vol. 22 (3). pp. 415-430.

Laudet, A.B., Magura, S., Vogel, H. S., & Knight, E. (2000). Support, Mutual Aid and Recovery from Dual Diagnosis. **Community Mental Health Journal,** 36 (5), 457-476.

Lawlis, F. (1996). **Transpersonal Medicine. The New Approach to healing the Body-Mind-Spirit.** Boston: Shambhala Press.

Lawson, P. E., and Morris, C. P. (1991). The Native American Church and the new court: The Smith case and Indian religious freedoms. **American Indian Culture and Research Journal** Vol. 15 (l). pp. 79-91.

Leal, A. (1990). Hispanics and substance abuse: Implications for rehabilitation counselors. **Journal of Applied Rehabilitation Counseling.** Vol. 21. pp. 52-54.

Lehman, A.F., Herron, J.D., Schwartz, R.P., and Myers, C.P. (1993). Rehabilitation for adults with severe mental illness and substance use disorders: A clinical trial. **Journal of Nervous and Mental Disease** Vol. 181(2). pp. 86-90.

Lehman, W.E., and Bennett, J.B. (2002). Job risk and employee substance use: The influence of personal background and work environment factors. **American Journal of Drug and Alcohol Abuse** 28(2):263–286.

Leong, F. & Kim, H. (1991). Going Beyond Cultural Sensitivity on The Road to Multiculturalism. **Journal of Counseling and Development.** Vol.70. pp. 112-118.

Leong, F. T., and Kim, H. W. (1991). Going beyond cultural sensitivity on the road to multicultural ism: Using the intercultural sensitizer as a counselor-training tool. **Journal of Counseling and Development**. Vol. 70. pp.112-118.

Leshner, A. 1. (1995). **Hearing,** Department of Labor, Health and Human Services, Education. Washington, D.C.: Government Printing Office.

Lidz, V., Bux, D.A., Platt, J.J., and Iguchi, M.Y. (1992). Transitional case management: A service model for AIDS outreach projects. In: Ashery, R.S., (Ed.). **Progress and Issues in Case Management.** NIDA Research Monograph Series, Number *127*. DHHS Pub. 92-1946. Rockville, MD: National Institute on Drug Abuse. pp.112-144

Liuzzi, G., Chirianni, A., Clementi, M.; Bagnarelli, P., Valenza, A., Cataldo, P.T., and Piazza, M. (1996). Analyses of HIV-1 load in blood, semen, and saliva: Evidence for different viral compartments in a cross-sectional and longitudinal study. **AIDS.** Vol. 10 (14). F51-F56.

Long, D. D. & Holle, M. C. (1997). **Macro systems in the social environment.** Itasca, IL: F. E. Peacock.

Longres, J. F., & Torrecilha, R. S. (1992). Race and the diagnosis placement and exit status of children and youth in a mental health and disability system. **Journal of Social Science Research,** 15 (3/4), 43-63.

Lori A, W. Anthony, and M. Chris. (2008) Home is where recovery begins: Why do we assume that having a home is a reward for recovery and not part of it? **Behavioral Healthcare, May.**

Lamb, R., Evans, A. and White, W. (2009). **The Role of Partnership in Recovery-Oriented Systems of Care: The Philadelphia Experience.** Retrieved December 26, 2009 from: www.dbhmrs.org/technical-papers

Lewis D, Pincus J, Bard B et al. (1988). "Neuropsychiatric, Psych Educational and Family Characteristics of 14 Juveniles Condemned to Death in the United States." **American Journal of Psychiatry** (145:584-589).

Leong, F. T., and Kim, H. W. (1991). Going beyond cultural sensitivity on the road to multiculturalism: Using the intercultural sensitizer as a counselor-training tool. **Journal of Counseling and Development.** 70, 112-118.

Lawson, P. E., and Morris, C. P. (1991). The Native American Church and the new court: The Smith case and Indian Religious freedoms. **American Indian Culture and Research Journal** Vol. 15(l). 79-91.

Markides, K. S. (1983). Aging, religiosity, and adjustment: A longitudinal analysis **Journal of Gerontology**, 38, 621-625.

Marlatt, G. A., & Kristeller, J. L. (1999). Mindfulness and meditation. In W. R. Miller (Ed.) **Integrating spirituality into treatment** (pp. 67-84). Washington, DC: American Psychological Association.

Manson, S. M. (1986). Recent advances in American Indian mental health research: Implications for clinical research and training. In: M. R. Miranda and H. H. L. Kitano (Eds.). **Mental Health Research and Practice in Minority Communities, Development of Culturally Sensitive Training Programs.** Rockville, MD: NIMH.

May, R. (1999). **Love and Will.** New York: W.W. Norton.

McCullough, M. E., & Larson, D. B. (1999). Prayer. In W. R. Miller (Ed.). **Integrating spirituality into treatment.** Washington, DC: American Psychological Association. 85-110.

Miller, M and S. Cook-Greuter (1994). **Transcendence and Mature Thought in Adulthood.** Rowman & Littlefield Publishing.

Miller, W. R., & Hester, R. K. (1986). Matching problem drinkers with optimal treatments. In W. R. Miller & N. Heather (Eds.). **Treating addictive behaviors: Processes of change** (pp. 175-203). New York: Plenum Press.

Miller, W. R., Leckman, A. L., Delaney, H. D., & Tinkcorn, M (1992). Long-term follow-up of behavioral self-control training. **Journal of Substance Abuse Treatment,** 12 (4), 249-261.

Miller, W.R., and Rollnick, S. (2002). **Motivational Interviewing: Preparing People for Change,** 2nd ed. New York: Guilford Press.

Myers, L, S. Speight, P. Highlen, C. Cox, A. Reynolds, E. Adams, and C. Henley. (1991). Identity Development and Worldview: Toward an Optimal Conceptualization. **Journal of Counseling and Development.** 70, 54-63.

Marshall, Helen. (1937). **The Forgotten Samaritan.** Chapel Hill: University of North Carolina Press.

Moore, Q. (1994). The Whole New World of Diversity. **Journal of Intergroup Relations,** Vol. 20 (4). pp. 28-40.

Morris, Eboni. (2010). Youth Violence: Implications for Post-Traumatic Stress Disorder in Urban Youth. **An Issue Report from the National Urban League Policy Institute.**

Murray, J.E. (1975). Failure of the Community Mental Health Movement. **The American Journal of Nursing,** Vol.75, 11 (November), pp. 2034-2036.

Mead, S. & Copeland, M.E. (2000). What Recovery Means to Us: Consumers' Perspectives. **Community Mental Health Journal,** 36(3).

META Services, (2005). **Self-directed Recovery Plan: A Guide to Your Individual Service Plan.** Recovery Education Center, Phoenix, AZ. **Social Work,** 27, 244-249.

MacDougall, D.S. (1998). HIV/AIDS behind bars: Incarceration provides a valuable opportunity to implement HIV/AIDS treatment and prevention strategies in a high-risk population. **Journal of the International Association of Physicians in AIDS Care.** Vol. 4 (4). pp. 8-13.

319

MacGowani R.J., Brackbill, R.M. Rugg, D.L., Swanson, N.M., Weinstein, B.; Couchon, A., Scibak, J., Molde, S., McLaughlin, P., Barker, T., and Voigt, R. (1997*)*. Sex, drugs and HIV counseling and testing: A prospective study of behavior-change among methadone maintenance client in New England. **AIDS.** Vol. 11(2) pp. 229-235.

Manson, S. M (1986). Recent advances in American Indian mental health research: Implications for clinical research and training. In M. R. Miranda and H. H. L. Kitano (Eds.), **Mental Health Research and Practice in Minority Communities, Development of Culturally Sensitive Training Programs.** Rockville, MD: NIMH.

Markoff, L.S., and Cawley, P.A. (1996). Retaining your clients and your sanity: Using a relational model of multi system case management. **Journal of Chemical Dependency Treatment.** Vol. 6 (12). pp. 45-65.

Maslow, A. H. (1987). **Motivation and Personality** (3rd ed.). New York: Harper & Row.

Mason, J.L. (1995). **Cultural competence- assessment questionnaire: A manual for users.** Portland, OR: Portland State University Research and Training Center on Family Support/Children's Mental Health.

Marin, G., and Marin, B. V. (1991). **Research with Hispanic Populations.** Newbury Park, CA: Sage Publications.

Martin, P. Y., & O'Connor, G. G. (1989). **The social environment: Open systems applications.** New York: Longman.

Mattesisch, P. W., & Monsey, B. R. (1992). **Collaboration: what makes it work** Saint Paul MN: Amherst Wilder Research Center.

McChesney, K. Y. (1995). Urban homeless families. **Social Service Review,** 69 (3), 428-460

McCurdy, K., and Daro, D. (1994). **Current Trends in Child Abuse Reporting and Fatalities: The Results of the1993 Annual Fifty State Survey.** Chicago: National Committee to Prevent Child Abuse.

McLoyd, V. (1997). The impact of poverty and low, socioeconomic status on the socio-emotional functioning of African-American children and adolescents. In R. W. 'l'aylor & M. C. Wang (eds.), **Social and emotional adjustment and family, relations in ethnic minority families,** NJ: Lawrence Erlbaum Associates. 2-34.

Mercer, S., & Kane, R. (1979) Helplessness and hopelessness among the institutionalized aged. **Health and Social Work,** 4, 90-116.

Moore, S. T. (1990). A social work practice model of case management: The case management grid. **Social Work,** 35(5), 444-448.

Moroney, R. M. (1987). Social planning. In **Encyclopedia of social work, II** Silver Spring, MD: National Association of Social Workers, 593-602.

Mosley J. C., & Lex, A. (1990). Identification of potentially Stressful Life events experienced by a population of urban minority youth, **Journal of Multicultural Counseling and Development,** 18(3),118-125.

May, P.A (1996). Overview of alcohol abuse epidemiology for American Indian
populations. In G.D. Sandefur, R.R. Rundfass, and B. Cohen (Eds.),
**Changing numbers, changing needs: American Indian
demography and public health**. Washington, DC: National
Academy Press

Mayers, R.S., and Kail, B.L. (1993). Hispanic substance abuse: An overview. In
R.S. Mayers, B.L. Kail, and T.D. Watts (Eds.). **Hispanic Substance
Abuse**. Springfield, IL: C. Thomas.

McCusker, J., Wilfis, G., McDonald, M., Lewis, B.F., Sereti, S.M., and
Feldman, Z.T. (1994) Admission of injection drug users to drug abuse
treatment following HIV counseling and testing. **Public Health
Reports**. Vol. 109. pp.212-218.

McGoldrick, Pearce, and Giordino. (1982). **Ethnicity and Family Therapy**.
New York: The Guilford Press.

McLellan, A.T., Luborsky, L., O'Brien, C.P., Woody, G.E., and Druley, KA.
(1982). Is treatment for substance abuse effective? **Journal of the
American Medical Association**. Vol. 247.pp. 1423-1428.

McNeely, R.L., Cook, P.W., and Torres, J.B. (2001). Is domestic violence a
gender issue, or a human issue? In See, L.A.L., ed. **Violence as Seen
Through Prism of Color** (pp. 227–251). Binghamton, NY: Haworth
Social Work Practice Press.

Mejta C.L., Bokos, P. J., Mickenberg, J.H., Maslar, E.M., Hasson, A.L., Gil, V.,
O'Keefe, Z., Martin, S.S., Isenberg, H., Inciardi, J.A., Lockwood, D.,
Rapp, R.C., Siegal, H.A., Fisher, J.H., and Wagner, J.H. (1994).
Lewis, J., (Ed.). **Addictions: Concepts and Strategies for
Treatment**. Gaithersburg, MD: Aspen.

Melus, A. (1980). Culture and language in the treatment of alcoholism: The
Hispanic perspective. **Alcohol Health & Research World,** Summer

Micozzi, Marc. (ed.) (1996).**Fundamentals of Contemporary and Alternative
Medicine.** New York, Churchill Livingstone.

Miller, E. (1997). Drugs, AIDS, and human rights. **Peace work**. 275:7-9. Mirin.

Miller, W.R., Andrews N.R., Wilbourne, P., and Bennett, M.E. (1998). A wealth
alternatives: Effective treatments for alcohol problems. In: Miller,
W.R., and Heather, N., eds. **Treating Addictive Behaviors:
Processes of Change,** 2nd ed. (pp. 203-216). New York: Plenum
Press.

Moffic, H.S., and Kinzie, D.J. (1996). The history and future of cross-cultural
psychiatric services. **Community Mental Health Journal**. Vol. 32.
pp. 581-592.

Mokuau, N. (1997*).* Pacific Islanders. In J. Philleo, F.L. Brisbane,
And L.G. Epstein (Eds.). **Cultural competence in substance abuse
prevention**. Washington D.C.: NASW Press. pp.127-152.

Moore, Q. (1994). The Whole New World of Diversity. **Journal of Intergroup
Relations,** Vol. 20 (4). pp. 28-40.

Moos, R.H., Finney, J.W., and Cronkite, R.C. (1990). **Alcoholism Treatment: Context, Process, and Outcome.** New York Oxford University Press. pp.220-248.

Morales, T., Gomez, C.A., and Marin B.V. (1995). Freedom and HIV prevention: Challenges facing Latino inmates leaving prison. Paper presented at the **103rd American Psychological Association Convention,** New York.

Moran, J.R., and May, P.A. (1997). American Indians. In J. Philleo, F.L. Brisbane, and L.G. Epstein (Eds.), **Cultural competence in substance abuse prevention** Washington D.C.: National Association of Social Workers Press. pp.1-31.

Morrison, James. (1995). **DSM IV Made Easy: The Clinician's Guide to Diagnosis**. New York: Guilford Press.

Morrison, James (1995a). **The First Interview**. New York; Guilford.

Mumola, C.J. (1999). Substance Abuse and Treatment, State and Federal Prisoners 1997. **Bureau of Justice Statistics**. Pub. No. NCJ-172871. Washington, DC: U.S. Department of Justice, Office of Justice Programs.

Murry, M. and Pizzorno, J. (1991). **Encyclopedia of Natural Medicine.** California: Prima Publications. National Association of Alcoholism and Drug Abuse Counselors.

National Association of Social Workers. (1997). Ethical Issues, HIV/AIDS, and Social Work Practice. Workshop sponsored by the **HIV/AIDS Spectrum: Mental Health Training and Education of Social Workers Project.**

National Association of Social Workers. (1992). Case management's cost, benefits eyed. **National Association of Social Workers News** Washington, DC: NASW Press. 12.

National Clearinghouse for Alcohol and Drug Information. (1997). **Prevention primer: Hispanic Latino Americans**. Rockville, MD:

National Center for Health Statistics (NCHS). (1997). **Health, United States, 1996-97 and Injury Chart book**. Hyattsville, MD: United States DHHS.

National Commission on AIDS. (1992) **The Challenge of HIV/AID in Communities of Color.** Washington, DC: National Commission on AIDS.

National Council of La Raza (1992). **State of Hispanic America 1991: An Overview** Washington, DC: National Council of La Raza.

National Association of Social Workers. (1996). **Code of Ethics,** Washington, D.C.

Netting, F., Kettner, P., & McMurtry S. (1993). **Social work macro practice,** New York: Longman.

Nord, M., & Luloff, A. E. (1995). Homeless children and their families in New Hampshire: A rural perspective. **Social Service Review**, 69 (3), 461-478.

National Farm Workers Association. (1992). Personal communication Ramos-Sayre with Center for Substance Abuse Treatment. Washington, DC.

National Institute on Alcohol Abuse and Alcoholism. (1994). **Alcohol Alert** 23:1-3. Nieto, S. (1992). **Affirming Diversity: The Sociopolitical Context of Multicultural Education**. New York: Longman.

National Institute of Allergy and Infectious Diseases. (1999). HIV and Adolescents. **NIAID Fact Sheet**. Washington, DC: National Institutes of Health. February.

Nobles, W. (1972). African philosophy: Foundations for Black psychology. In: Jones, R. H., (Ed.), **Black Psychology**. New York: Harper & Row. pp.103-104.

North, C.S., and Smith, E.M. (1993). A systematic study of mental health services utilization by homeless men and women. **Social Psychiatry and Psychiatric Epidemiology**. Vol. 28. pp.77-83.

Novins, D.K., Beals, J., Shore, J.H., Manson, S.M. (1996) Substance abuse treatment of American Indian adolescents: Comorbid symptomatology, gender differences and treatment pattern. **Journal of the American Academy of Child and Adolescent Psychiatry.** Vol. 35 (12). pp.1593-1601.

National Association of Social Workers (1996). **Code of Ethics**.

National Association of Social Workers (2005). http://www.socialworkers. org/practice/behavioral health/0206snapshot.asp

Nelson, G., Ochocka, J., Griffin, K., and Lord, J. (1998). Nothing about Me, Without Me: Participatory Action Research with Self-Help/Mutual Aid Organizations for Psychiatric Consumer/Survivors. **American Journal of Community Psychology** 26(6), 881-912.

Nerney, T. (2005) **Quality issues in consumer/family direction**. Downloaded http://www.mentalhealth.samhsa.gov/publications/allpubs/NMH05-0194/default.asp [July 13, 2005].

NSDUH 2017 Report. SAMHSA. gov. 2017.

Null, Gary, (1998). **Secrets of The Sacred White Buffalo: Native American Healing Remedies, Rites & Rituals**, Paramus, N.J.: Prentice Hall.

Olandi, M. (1992). Defining Cultural Competence: An organizing Framework. In: M. Olandi (Ed) **Cultural Competence for Evaluators: A guide for alcohol and other drug abuse prevention practitioners working with ethnic/racial communities.** Rockville, MD: U.S. Department of HHS.

O'Brien J. & O'Brien, C. (Eds.). (2002) **Implementing person-centered planning: The voices of experience.** Toronto: Inclusion Press.

O'Farrell, T.J., Fals-Stewart, W., Murphy, C.M., Stephan, S.H., and Murphy, M. Partner violence before and after couples-based alcoholism treatment for male alcoholic patients: The role of treatment involvement and abstinence. **Journal of Consulting and Clinical Psychology** 72(2):202–217, 2004.

Osher, T. W., & Osher, D. (2001). The Paradigm Shift to True Collaboration with Families. **Journal of Child and Family Studies, 11:1, 47-60.**

Ogborne, A.C., and Rush, B.R. (1983). The coordination of treatment services for Problem drinkers: Problems and Prospects. **British Journal of Addiction.** Vol. 78. pp. 131-138.

Olandi, M. (1992). Defining Cultural Competence: An organizing framework. In: M. Olandi (Ed) **Cultural Competence for Evaluators: A guide for alcohol and other drug abuse prevention practitioners working with ethnic/racial communities.** Rockville, MD: U.S. Department of HHS.

Oppenheimer, E., Sheehan, M., and Taylor, C. (1988). Letting the Client speak: Drug misusers and the process of help seeking. **British Journal of Addiction.** Vol. 83. pp.635-647.

O'Hara, M. (1998). Gestalt therapy as an emancipatory psychology for transmodem world. **Gestalt Review,** *2,* 154-168

Pablo, C. J. (1992). Reactions by, Native American parents to child protection agencies: Cultural and community factors. **Child Welfare,** 71 (4), 329-342

Pargament, K. I. (1997). **The psychology of religion and coping.** New York: Gulford Press.

Pargament, K. I., Kennell, J., Hathaway, W., Grevengoed, N., Newman, J & Jones, W. (1998) Religion and the problem-solving process: Three styles of coping. **Journal for the Scientific Study of Religion,** 27 90-104.

Pargament, K. I., Smith, B. W., Koenig, H. G., & Perez, L. (1998). Patterns of positive and negative religious coping with major life stressors. **Journal for the Scientific Study of Religion,** *37,* 711-725.

Peck, M.S. **Further Along the Road Less Traveled.** (1993). New York: Simon and Shuster.

Pedersen, P. B. (991). Multiculturalism as a generic approach to counseling. **Journal of Counseling and Development.** Vol.70. 6-12.

Peele, S. (1992). Alcoholism, politics, and bureaucracy: The consensus against controlled-drinking therapy in America. **Addictive Behaviors,** 17, 49-62.

Perry, M. (1996). Relationship of social class and mental illness. **Journal of Primary Prevention.** 17(1), 17-30.

Platt, J.J. (1995). Vocational rehabilitation of drug abusers. **Psychological Bulletin** 117(3):416–433.

Poloma, M. M. & Gallup, G. H., Jr. (1991). **Varieties of prayer,** Philadelphia: Trinity Press International.

Poor Thunder, C. (1991**). People in Prison Entering Sobriety (P.I.P.E.S.)** Program Manual. Minneapolis MN: Heart of the Earth Survival School.

Prochaska, J.O. and DiClemente, C. C. (1986). Toward a Comprehensive model of Change. In: Miller, W. and Heather, N. (Eds.). **Treating Addictive Behaviors:** Processes of Change. New York: Plenum Press. 3-27.

Prochaska, J.O. and DiClemente, C. C. (1984) **The Transtheoretical Approach: Crossing the Traditional Boundaries of Therapy.** IL Dorsey/Dow Jones-Irwin

Propst, L. R., Ostrom, R., Watkins, P., Dean, T., & Mashburn, D. (1992). Comparative efficacy of religious and nonreligious cognitive-behavioral therapy for the treatment of depression in religious individuals. **Journal of Consulting and Clinical Psychology**, 60, 94-103.

Padilla, A. M., Cervantes, R. C., Maldonado, M., and Garcia, R. E. (1988). Coping responses to psychological stressors among Mexican and Central American Immigrants. **Journal of Consulting Psychology.** Vol. 16. pp. 418-427.

Padilla, A. M., Ruiz, R. A., and Alvarez, R. (1975). Community mental health services for the Spanish speaking surnamed population. **American Psychologist.** Vol.30. pp. 892-904.

Parsons, R. J., Jorgensen, J. D., &- Hernandez, S. H. (1988), Integrative practice approach: A framework for protein solving. **Social Work**, 35 (5), 417-421.

Parsons, R. J., Jorgensen, J. D., &- Hernandez, S. H. (1994). **The Integration of social work practice**, CA: Brooks/Cole.

Patterson, D. A., & Lee, M. (1998). Intensive case management and rehospitalization: A survival analysis. **Research on Social Work Practice**, 8 (2), 152-171.

Piliavin, I., Wright, R. W., Mare, R. D., & Westerfelt, A. H. (I 996). Exits from and returns to homelessness. **Social Service Review**, 70 (1), 33-57.

Paul, J.P., Stall, R.D., and Bloomfield, K. (1991b). Gay alcoholics: Epidemiological and clinical issues. **Alcohol Health and Research World.** Vol. 15. pp.151-160.

Paul, J.P., Stall, R.D., Crosby, G.M., Barrett, D.C., and Midanik, L.T. (1994). Correlates of sexual risk taking among gay male substance abusers. **Addiction.** Vol. 89. pp. 971-983.

Paul, J.P., Stall, R.D., and Davis, F. (1993). Sexual risk for HIV transmission among gay/bisexual men in substance-abuse treatment. **Journal of AIDS Education and Prevention.** Vol. 5. pp.11-24.

Peck, S. (1993). **Further Along the Road Less Traveled.** New York: Simon & Schuster.

Pedersen, P. B. (1988). **A Handbook for Developing Multicultural Awareness.** Alexandria, VA: America Association for Counseling and Development.

Pedersen, P. B. (1991). Multiculturalism as a generic approach to counseling. **Journal of Counseling and Development.** Vol.70. pp. 6-12.

325

Pena, J., and Koss-Chioino, J. (1992). Cultural sensitivity in drug treatment research with African American male In J. Pena and J. Koss-Chioino (Eds.), **Ethnic and multicultural drug abuse** Binghamton NY: The Haworth Press. pp.157-179.

Perkinson, R. and A. Jongsma. (1998). **The Chemical Dependency Treatment Planner.** New York: John Wiley and Sons **Physicians' Reference** (2000). New Jersey. Medical Economics.

Pizzorno, J. (1996). Naturopathic Medicine **in: Fundamentals of Contemporary and Alternative Medicine.** M. S. Mecozzi (Ed.). New York: Churchill Livingstone.

Polednak, A.P. (1997). Gender and acculturation in relation to alcohol use among Hispanic (Latino) adults in two areas of the northeastern United States. **Substance Use and Misuse.** pp.1513-1524.

Ponterotto, J. (1988). Racial consciousness development among white counselor trainees: A stage model. **Journal of Multicultural Counseling and Development.** Vol. 16.

Ponterotto, J., and Casas, J. M. (1991). **Handbook of Racial Ethnic Minority Counseling Research.** Springfield, IL: Charles C. Thomas Publisher.

Poor Thunder, C. (1991). **People in Prison Entering Sobriety (P.I.P.E.S.) Program Manual.** Minneapolis MN: Heart of the Earth Survival School. Practice Guideline for the Treatment of Patients with Major Depressive Disorder (Revision). (2000)

Practice Guideline for the Treatment of Patients with Schizophrenia (1997). American Psychiatric Association. **Am J Psych.** Vol. 157:4. Supplement, April.

Practice Guideline for the Treatment of Patients with Bipolar Disorder. (1994). American Psychiatric Association. **Am J Psych.** Vol. 151:12 Supplement, December.

Peck, M. S. (1993). **Further along the road less traveled.** New York: Simon & Schuster.

Pew Center on the States: Corrections and Public Safety (2008). www.pewcenteronthestates.org

Philadelphia Department of Behavioral Health and Mental Retardation Services (2010). http://www.phila-bhs.org

PRO-ACT: Pennsylvania Recovery Organization Achieving Community. **www.proact.org**

Randall, David, E. (1989). **Strategies for Working with Culturally Diverse Communities and Clients.** Bethesda, MD: The Association for Care of Children's Health.

Rank, M.R., & Hirschl, T. A. (1999). The likelihood of poverty across the American adult life span. **Social Work,** 44 (3), 201-208.

Reitan, T. (1998). Theories of inter-organizational relations in the human services. **Social Service Review,** 72 (31), 285-309.

Rice, A. H. (1998). Focusing on strengths: Focus group research on the impact of welfare reform. A paper presented for the **XX Symposium Association for the Advancement of Social Work with Groups,** October 1998, Miami, Florida.

Roberts-DeGennaro, M. (1987). **Developing case.** New York: Columbia University Press.

Robertson, J.E. (2003). Rape among incarcerated men: Sex, coercion and STDs. **AIDS Patient Care and STDs** 17(8):423–430,

Rodgers, A. Y., & Potocky, M. (1997). Evaluating culturally, sensitive practice through single system design: Methodological issues and strategies. **Research on Social Work Practice,** 7(3), 391-401.

Rooney, G. D. (2000). Examining the values and ethics reflected in policy decisions. In K. Strom-Gottfried (ed.), **Social Work Practice: Cases, activities and exercises,** Thousand Oaks, CA: Pine Forge Press. 50-54.

Rooney, G. D., Neathery, K., &, Suzek, M. (1997). **Defining child neglect: A community perspective**: MN: Minneapolis Human Services Network Research Report.

Rose, S. M. (Ed.). (1992). **Case management and social work practice.** White Plains, NY: Longman.

Rothman, J. (1991). A model of case management: Toward Empirically based practice. **Social Work,** 36 (6), 521-528.

Rothman, J. (194). **Case management with highly vulnerable clients: Case management and community-based service,** NJ: Prentice Hall.

Rothman, J. (1995). Approaches to community intervention. In J. Rothman, J. Erlich, & J. E. Tropman (eds.), **Strategies of community intervention,** (5th ed.). Itasca, IL: F. E. Peacock.26-63.

Rapp, C.A. (1996). The Active Ingredients of Effective Case Management. In: L.J. Giesler (Ed.) **Case Management for Behavioral Managed Care.** Cincinnati: NACM.

Rapp, C.A..Siegal, H.A., and Fisher, J.H. (1992). A strength-based model of case management/advocacy: Adapting a mental health model to practice work with persons who have substance abuse problems. In: Ashery, R.S., (Ed.) **Progress and Issues in Case Management.** NIDA Research Monograph Series, Number 127. DHHS Pub. No. (ADM) *92-1946.* Rockville, MD: National Institute on Drug Abuse. pp.79-91.

Red Horse, J. (1982). Clinical strategies for American Indian families in crisis. **The Urban and Social Change Review.** Vol. 15(2). pp. 17-19.

Reed, D.F., and Reed, E.L. *(1997).* Children of incarcerated parents. **Social Justice.** Vol. 24 (3). pp.152-169.

Regier, D.A., Farmer, M.E., Rae, D.S., Locke, B.Z., Keith, S.J., Judd, L.L., and Goodwin, F.K. (1990). Comorbidity of mental disorders with alcohol and other drug abuse: Results from the epidemiologic catchment area (ECA) study. **Journal of the American Medical Association.** Vol. 264 (19). pp. 2511-2518.

Reid, W. and Wise, M. (1995). **DSM-IV Training Guide**. New York: U.S. Department of Health and Human Services.

Robin, R.W., Chester, B., Rasmussen, J.K., and Jarason, J.M. (1997). Factors influencing utilization of mental health and substance abuse services by American Indian men and women. **Psychiatric Services.** Vol.48 (6). pp.826-832.

Romero, J.T. (1996). Operationalizing cultural competency in managed care environment. **Focal Point**. Vol. 10. pp.26-28.

Ross, M.W., and Darke, S. (1992). Mad, bad, and dangerous to know: Dimensions and measurements of attitudes toward injecting drug users. **Drug and Alcohol Dependence.** Vol. 30. (l).pp.71-74.

Royce, R.A., Sena, A., Cates, W., and Cohen, M.S. (1997). Sexual transmission of HIV. **New England Journal of Medicine.** Vol. 336 (15). pp.1072-1078.

Rush, B., and Ekdahl, A. (1990). Recent trends in the development of alcohol and drug treatment services in Ontario. **Journal of Studies on Alcohol**. Vol. 51(6). pp. 514-522.

Ralph, R.O. & Recovery Advisory Group (1999). The Recovery Advisory Group recovery model. Paper presented at the **Joint National Conference on Mental Health Systems Block Grant and Mental Health Statistics,** Washington, DC.

Rapp, C.A. (1993). Theory, principles, and methods of the strengths model of case management. In M. Harris, (Ed) & H. C. Bergman, (Ed) (Eds.), **Case management for mentally ill patients: Theory and practice.** (pp. 143-164): Harwood Academic Publishers/Gordon & Breach Science Publishers, Langhorne, PA, US.

Reidy, D. (1992). Shattering illusions of difference. **Resources**, 4(2), 3-6

Repper, J. & Perkins, R. (2006) **Social Inclusion and Recovery: A Model for Mental Health Practice**. Bailliere Tindall, UK.

Reid, W. and Wise, M. (1995). **DSM-IV Training Guide**. New York: U.S. Depart. of Health and Human Services.

Rothbaum, R., Weisz, J., & Snyder, S. (1982). Changing the world And changing the self: A two process model perceived control. **Journal of Personality and Social Psychology**, 42, 5-37.

Scarlett, W. G., & Periello, L. (1991). The development of prayer in adolescence. **New Directions for Child Development,** 52, 63-76.

Salzer, M.S. (ed.). (2006). **Psychiatric Rehabilitation Skills in Practice: A Preparation and Skills Workbook**. Columbia, MD.: United States Psychiatric Rehabilitation Association.

Storr, A. (1983). (Ed.). Archetypes: Shadow; Anima; Animus; The Persona; The Wise Old Man. **The Essential Jung**. Part 4. pp.87- 127.

Storr, A. (1983). Jung's Involvement with Freud and His Divergence from Freud's Theories. **The Essential Jung**. **Part 2**. pp.45- 64.

Substance Abuse and Mental Health Services Administration (2012). **Results from the 2012 National Survey on Drug Use and Health: Summary of National Findings,** NSDUH Series H-46 HHS Publication No.(SMA) 13-4795. Rockville, MD: Substance Abuse and Mental Health Services Administration, 2013, p. 1.

Schrimsher, G.W., Parker, J.D., and Burke, R.S. (2007). Relation between cognitive testing performance and pattern of substance use in males at treatment entry. **Clinical Neuropsychologist** 21(3):498–510.

Schumacher, J.A., Fals-Stewart, W., and Leonard, K.E. (2003). Domestic violence treatment referrals formen seeking alcohol treatment. **Journal of Substance Abuse Treatment** 24(3):279–283.

Scoles, P. (2002). **Jung, Addiction and Recovery.** MA: Erudition Books.

Scoles, P. (2016). **Faith and Spirituality in Behavioral Health Counseling.** Cengage Learning.

Siegel, J. (1986). The Multidimensional Angry Inventory. **Journal of Personality and Social Psychology**. Vol. 51, 191-200.

Singer, J. (1994). **Boundaries of the Soul.** New York: Doubleday Publishing.

Snow, M. G., Prochaska, J. O., & Rossi, J. S. (1994). Processes of change in Alcoholics Anonymous: Maintenance factors in long-term sobriety. **Journal of Studies on Alcohol,** *55,* 362-371.

Saleeby, D. (1997). **The Strengths Perspective in Social Work.** (2ⁿᵈ ed.). Boston: Allyn & Bacon.

Singer, Audrey & Wilson, Jill. (2006). From 'There to Here': Refugee Resettlement in Metropolitan America. **Brookings Institute Living Cities Census Series.** http://www.brookings.edu.

Saleeby, D. (2001). The diagnostics strengths manual. **Social Work,** 46,

Samuels, A. (1991). **Psychopathology: Contemporary Jungian Perspective.** New York: Gilford Press.

Sandfort, J. (1999). The structural impediments to human services collaboration: Examining welfare reform at the front lines. **Social Service Review**, 73 (3), 314-339.

Schein, E. H. (1985). **Organizational culture and leadership**. San Francisco: Jossey-Bass.

Smith, C., & Carlson, B. E. (1997). Stress, coping, and resilience in children and youth. **Social Service Review,** 71(2), 231-256.

Solomon, P. (2004). Peer support/peer provided services underlying processes, benefits, and critical ingredients. **Psychiatric Rehabilitation Journal,** 27(4), 392-401.

Solomon, P., & Draine, J. (1996). Service delivery, differences between consumer and non-consumer case managers in mental health. **Research on Social Work Practice,** 6 (2), 193-207.

Sosin, M. (1979). Social work advocacy and the implementation of legal mandates. **Social Casework**, 60, 265-273.

Sosin, M. (1983). Advocacy: A conceptualization foe social work practice. **Social Work,** 281, 12-17.

Specht, H., & Courtney, M. E. (1994). **Unfaithful angels: How social work abandoned its mission.** Toronto: Maxwell Macmillan Canada.

Sterling, R.C., Gottheil, E., Glassman, S.D., Weinstein, S.P., Serota, R.D., and Lundy, A. (2001). Correlates of employment: A cohort study. **American Journal of Drug and Alcohol Abuse** 27(1):137–146.

Strom-ottfried, K., Morrissey, M. (2000). The organizational Diversity audits. In K. Strom-Gottfried (ed.), **Social work practice: Cases activities, and exercises,** Thousand Oaks, CA: Pine Forge Press.168-172.

Stuart, P. H. (1999). Linking clients and policy: Social workers distinctive contribution. **Social Work,** 44 (4), 335-347.

Stuart, G.L. (2005). Improving violence intervention outcomes by integrating alcohol treatment. **Journal of Interpersonal Violence.** 20(4): 388–393.

Schoenbaum, E. E., et al. (1986). Risk factors for human immunodeficiency virus infection in intravenous drug users. **New England Journal of Medicine.** Vol. 321. pp.874-879.

Seale, J.P., and Muramoto, M.L. (1993). Substance abuse among Minority populations. **Primary Care.** Vol. 20. pp. 167-180.

Sherman, D.W., and Ouellette, S. (1999). Moving beyond fear: Lessons learned through a longitudinal review of the literature regarding health care providers and the care of people with HIV/AIDS. **Nursing Clinics of North America.** Vol. 34 (1). pp.1-48.

Shilony, E, Lacey, D., O'Hagan, P., and Curto, M. (1993). All in one neighborhood: A community-based rehabilitation treatment program for homeless adults with mental illness and alcohol/ substance abuse disorders. **Psychosocial Rehabilitation Journal.** Vol.16(4).103-116.

Siegal, H.A., Fisher, J.A., Rapp, R.C., Kelleher, C.W., Wagner, J. H., O'Brien, W.F. and Cole, A P. (1996). Enhancing Substance. 13(2). pp.93-98.

Siegal, H.A., Rapp, R.C., Kelleher, C.W., Fisher, J.H., Wagner, J.H. and Cole, P.A. (1995). The strengths perspective of case management: A promising inpatient substance abuse treatment enhancement. **Journal of Psychoactive Drugs.** Vol. 27(1). pp. 67-72.

Simon, F., Mauciere, P., Roques, P.; Loussert-Ajaka, I., Mufler-Trutwin, M. C., Saragosti, S., Georges-Courbot, M.C., Barre-Sinoussi, F., and Brun-Vezinet, F. (1998). Identification of a new human immunodeficiency virus type I distinct from group M and group 0. **Nature Medicine.** Vol. 4 (9). pp.1032-1037.

Singer, M. (1991). Confronting the AIDS epidemic among IV drug users: Does ethnic culture matter? **AIDS Education and Prevention.** Vol. 3. pp. 258-283.

Singer, J. (1991). **Seeing through the visible world: Jung, Gnosis, and Chaos.** New York: Harper-Collins.

Singer, J. (1994). **Boundaries of the Soul.** New York: Doubleday Publishing.

Stein, L., and Test, M. (1980). Alternatives to mental hospital treatment. Conceptual model, treatment program, and clinical evaluation. **Archives of General Psychiatry.** Vol. 37. pp.392-397.

330

St. Lawrence, J.S., and Brasfield, T.L. (1995). HIV risk behavior among homeless adults. **AIDS Education and Prevention.** Vol. 7. pp. 22-31.

Storms, D. (1994). Healing the hurt: A conference on homophobia. Paper presented at **the Parents, Families, and Friends of Lesbians and Gays (PFLAG) Conference,** Houston.

Stout, C. and Arthur E. (1999). **The Continuum of Care Treatment Planner.** New York: John Wiley and Sons.

Straus, M.A. (1999). The controversy over domestic violence by women: A methodological, theoretical, and sociology of science analysis. In: Arriaga, X.B., and Oskamp, S., eds. **Violence in Intimate Relationships** (pp. 17–44). Thousand Oaks, CA: Sage.

Stryker, J. (1993). Correctional Systems. In: Jonsen, A.R., and Stryker, J., (Eds) **The Social Impact of AIDS in the United States.** Washington, DC: National Academy Press. pp. 176-200.

Stubben, J. (1992). Substance abuse treatment policy: A Failure For American Indians. Paper delivered at **Midwest Political Science Association Meeting,** Chicago, April.

Sue, S. (1976). Patients' demographic and therapeutic treatment: Differences that make a difference. **Journal of Consulting and Clinical Psychology.** Vol. 44. pp. 864.

Sue, S. (1977). Community mental health services to minority groups. **American Psychologist.** Vol.32. pp.616-624.

Sue, S., and McKinney, H. (*1975*). Asian Americans in the community mental health care system. **American Journal of Orthopsychiatry.** Vol. 45. pp.111-118.

Susser, E., Valencia, E., and Conover, S. (1993) Prevalence of HIV infection among psychiatric patients in a New York City men's shelter. **American Journal of Public Health.** Vol. 83. pp. 568-570.

Sy, F.S., Cling, C.L., Choi, S.T., and Ong, F.Y. (1998). Epidemiology of HIV and AIDS among Asian and Pacific Islander Americans. **AIDS Education and Prevention.** Vol. 10.

Teague, G.B., Schwab, B., and Drake, R.E. (1990). **Evaluation of Services for Young Adults with Severe Mental Illness and Substance Use Disorders.** Alexandria, VA: National Association of State Mental Health Program Directors.

Test, M.A. (1981). Effective community treatment of chronically mentally ill: What is necessary? **Journal of Social Issues.** Vol. 37 (3). pp. 71-86.

Tolan, P. H., & Gorman-Smith D. (1997). Families and the development of urban children. In H. J. Wallberg, 0. Reyes, & R. P Weissberg (eds.), **Children and youth: Interdisciplinary perspectives,** Thousand Oaks, CA: Sage. 67-91.

Tracy, E. M., & Whittaker, J. K. (1990). **Social Treatments an introduction to interpersonal helping in social work practice,** New York: Aldine de Gruyter.

Torgerson, S. (1979). The Nature and Origin of Common Phobic Fears. **British Journal of Psychiatry.** Vol.134. pp. 343-351.

Trepper, T.S., Nelson, T.S., McCollum, E.E., and McAvoy, P. (1997). Improving substance abuse service delivery to Hispanic women through increased cultural competencies: A qualitative study **Journal of Substance Abuse Treatment.** Vol. 14. pp.225-234.

Trimble, J. E., Bryan, J., and Padilla, A. M. (1985). Drug abuse prevention research priorities for ethnic minority populations. Paper prepared for the **National Institute on Drug Abuse, Division of Clinical Research.**

Trotter, R.T. (*1982*). Ethnic and sexual patterns of alcohol use: Anglo and Mexican American college students. **Adolescence.** Vol. 17. (66). pp. 305-325.

Turner, J., and TenHoor, W. (1978). The NIMH community support program: Pilot approach to a needed social reform. **Schizophrenia Bulletin.** Vol. 4 (3). pp. 319-348.

Tondora, J. & Davidson, L. (2006). **Practice guidelines for Recovery oriented behavioral healthcare.** Hartford, CT: Connecticut Department of Mental Health and Addiction Services.

Tondora, J., Sangster, S., Miller, R., Piczko, M. (2005). **Preparing for Your Person Centered Recovery Planning Meeting: What You Need to Know.** New Haven, CT: Yale Program for Recovery and Community Health.

Trattner, Walter I. (1999). **From Poor Law to Welfare State: A History of Social Welfare in America.** New York: Free Press.

The Bill W. - Carl Jung Letters (1963). **A.A. Grapevine** Princeton N.J.: Princeton University Press.

Tonigan, J. S., & Hiller-Sturmhofel, S. (1994). Alcoholics Anonymous: Who benefits? **Alcohol, Health, & Research World.** 18 (4), 308-310.

Tonigan, J. S., Connors, G. J., & Miller, W. R. (2003). Participation and involvement in Alcoholics Anonymous. In T. F. Babor & F. K Del Boca (Eds.), **Treatment matching in alcoholism.** Cambridge, England: Cambridge University Press. pp. 184- 204.

Twerski, A. (1993). Spirituality, Prayer, the Twelve Steps and Judaism. **JACS Journal** Vol. 3, No-l.

Uba, L. (1994). **Asian Americans: Personality Patterns, Identity, and Mental Health.** New York: Guilford Press. U.S. Bureau of the Census. (1997). **Income, poverty, and health insurance.** Washington, DC: U.S. Government Printing Office.

U.S. Bureau of the Census. (1998). **Resident population of the United States: Estimates by sex, race, and Hispanic Origin, with median age.** Washington, DC: US Government Printing Office.

U.S. Bureau of the Census. (1997). **Current Population Survey.** Washington, DC: U.S. Government Printing Office.

U.S. Bureau of the Census. (1998). **Resident population of the United States: Estimates by sex, race, and Hispanic origin, with median age.** Washington, D.C.: U.S. Bureau of the Census.

U.S. Department of Health and Human Services. (1998). **Prevalence of substance abuse among racial and ethnic subgroups in the United States, 1991-1993.** Rockville, MD: Substance Abuse and Mental Health Services Administration.

U.S. Department of Health and Human Services (1998). **Prevalence of substance abuse among racial and ethnic subgroups in the United States, 1991-1993.** Rockville, MD: Substance Abuse and Mental Health Services Administration.

U.S. Department of Health and Human Services (1985). **Report of the Secretary's Task Force on Black and Minority Health.** Washington, DC: US Government Printing Office.

U.S. Department of Health and Human Services. (1997). **Healthy People 2000 Progress Review/Hispanic Americans).** Rockville, MD: Alcohol, Drug Abuse, and Mental Health Administration.

U.S. General Accounting Office. (1998). **Drug Abuse: Research Shows Treatment Is Effective, But Benefits May Be Overstated.** GAO/HEHS-9872. Washington, DC: U.S. Government Printing Office.

U.S. Government Office of Technology Assessment. (1994). **Technologies for understanding and preventing substance abuse addiction.** Washington, DC: US Printing Office.

U.S. Government Office of Technology Assessment. (1994). **Technologies for understanding and preventing substance abuse and addiction.** Washington, D.C.: U.S. Printing Office.

U.S. Government Office of Technology Assessment. (1994). **Technologies for understanding and preventing substance abuse and addiction.** Union Pacific Railway Co. v. Botsford, 141

U.S. 250 (1891) **Union Pacific Railway Company v. Botsford No. 1375** Submitted January 6, 1891. Decided May 25, 1891.

US Dept of Health and Human Services and SAMHSA Center for Mental Health Services (2004) **National Consensus Statement on Mental Health Recovery.**

Van der Kolk, B. (1989). The Compulsion to Repeat the Trauma: Re-enactment, Revictimization, and Masochism. **Psychiatric Clinics of North America,** (Volume 12, Number 2, p.389-411, June).

Vail, A. (*1978*). Factors influencing lower-class Black patients' remaining in treatment. **Journal of Consulting and Clinical Psychology.** Vol. 46. pp.3-41.

Varma S.C., and Siris S.G. (1996). Alcohol abuse in Asian Americans: Epidemiological and treatment issues. **American Journal of Addictions.** Vol. 5. pp. 136-143.

Vosler, N. R. (1990). Assessing family, access to basic resources: An essential component of social work practices. **Social Work,** 35 (5), 434-441.

Vurzman, I., Rounsaville, B., Kleber, H. D. (1982). Cultural Values of Puerto Rican Opiate Addicts: An Exploratory Study. **American Journal of Alcohol Abuse.** Vol. 9. pp.141-153.

Walker, L. (1989). A Longitudinal Study of Moral Reasoning. **Child Development.** Vol. 60, pp.157-166.

Walsh, J. (2000). **Critical case management with persons having mental illness: A relationship-based approach.** Pacific Grove, CA: Brooks/Cole.

Withorn, A. (1998). No win...facing the ethical perils of welfare reform. **Families in Society,** 79 (3), 177-287.

Wolf, K. T. (1991). The diagnostic and statistical manual and The misdiagnosis of African-Americans: An historical perspective **Social Work,** 10 (1), 33-38.

Ward, J.W., and Duchin, J.S. (1998). The epidemiology of HIV and AIDS in the United States. **AIDS Clinical Review 1997-98.** pp. 1-45.

Weinsheimer, R.L., Schermer, C.R., Malcoe, L.H., Balduf, L.M., and Bloomfield, L.A. (2005). Severe intimate partner violence and alcohol use among female trauma patients. **Journal of Trauma** 58(1):22–29.

Westermeyer, J. (1989). Cross-cultural studies on alcoholism. In: Goedde, W., and Agarwal, D.P., (Eds). **Alcoholism: Biomedical and Genetic Aspects.** Elmsford, NY: Pergamon Press. pp. 305-311.

White, W. L. (2001). **The rhetoric of recovery advocacy: An essay on the power of language.** Bloomington, IL: Chestnut Health Systems.

White, W. (1998). **Slaying the Dragon: The History of Addiction Treatment and Recovery in America.** Bloomington, IL: Chestnut Health Systems.

White, W. (2008). **Recovery management and recovery-oriented systems of care: Scientific rationale and promising practices.** Pittsburgh, PA: Northeast Addiction Technology Transfer, Great Lakes Addiction Technology Transfer Center, Philadelphia Department of Behavioral Health and Intellectual disAbility Services.

White, W. and E. Kurtz. (2006**). Linking Addiction Treatment & Communities of Recovery: A Primer for Addiction Counselors and Recovery Coaches.** This report was supported through funding from the Clark Hagen Trust PNC. grant and the Northeast Technology Transfer Center (NeATTC) under a cooperative agreement from the Substance Abuse and Mental Health Services Administration's (SAMHSA) Center for Substance Abuse Treatment (CSAT).

White, W and S. Ali. (2010). **Lapse and Relapse: Is it time for a new language?** Retrieved May 20, 2010 from dbhmrs.org/technical-papers-on-recovery-transformation.

White, W. (1998). Slaying the Dragon: **The History of Addiction Treatment and Recovery in America.** Bloomington, IL: Chestnut Health Systems.

White, W. and E. Kurtz. (2006**). Linking Addiction Treatment & Communities of Recovery: A Primer for Addiction Counselors and Recovery Coaches.** This report was supported through funding from the Clark Hagen Trust PNC. grant and the Northeast Technology Transfer Center (NeATTC) under a cooperative agreement from the Substance Abuse and Mental Health Services Administration's (SAMHSA).

White, W., A. Evans, Jr., S. Ali, I. Achara-Abrahams, & J. King (2009) **The Recovery Revolution: Will it include children, adolescent and transition age youth?** DBHIDS.

White, F., Hayes, B., & Livesey, D. (2005). **Developmental Psychology: From Infancy to Adulthood.**

Wiger, D. (1999). **The Clinical Documentation Sourcebook.** New York: John Wiley and Co.

Wilber, K. (1995). **Sex, Ecology, Spirituality: The Spirit of Evolution.** Boston: Shambhala.

Wilber, K. (1996). **A Brief History of Everything**. Boston: Shambhala.

Wilber, K. (1977). **An Integral Theory of Consciousness.** Boston: Shambhala.

Wilber, K. (1999). **One taste: the journals of Ken Wilber.** Boston: Shambhala.

Wilber, K. (2000). **Integral Psychology: Consciousness,** Spirit, Psychology, Therapy. Boston: Shambhala.

Wilber, K. (2001). **A Theory of Everything**. Boston: Shambhala.

Wilber, K. (2006). **Integral Spirituality. A startling New Role for Religion in the Modern and Postmodern World.** Boston: Integral Books.

Willenbring, M. L., Whelan, J.A., Dahlquist, J.S., and O'Neal, M.E. (1990). Community treatment of the chronic public inebriate: Implementation. **Alcoholism Treatment Quarterly**. Vol. 7. (2). pp. 79-97.

Wing, D.M., Crow, S.S., and Thompson, T. (1995). An ethno nursing study of Muskogee (Creek) Indians and effective health care practices for treating alcohol abuse. **Family and Community Health**. Vol. 18. pp. 52-64.

Withum, D.J. (1993). High HIV prevalence among female and male entrants to U.S. correctional facilities (1989-1992): Implications for prevention and treatment strategies. Paper presented at the **121**[st] **Annual Meeting of the American Public Health Association.** San Francisco, CA, Oct. 24-28.

Woll, C. (1996). What difference does culture make? Providing treatment to women different from you. **Journal of Chemical Dependency Treatment.** Vol. 6. pp. 67-85.

Woods, W.J., Avins, A., Lindan, C., Hudes, E., Boscarino, J., and Clark W. (1996). Predictors of HIV- related risk behaviors among heterosexual's in alcoholism treatment. **Journal of Studies on Alcohol.** Vol. 57. pp. 486-493.

Wu, L, and Windle, C. (*1980).* Ethnic specificity in the relative minority use and staffing of community mental health centers. **Community Mental Health Journal.** Vol. 16. pp.156-168.

Woodside, Marianne & McClann, Tricia. (2009). **An Introduction to Human Services.** (6th ed.). Belmont, CA.: Thompson Higher Education.

www.hinduism.iscon.com

www.dbhids.org/transformation-tools-2/

www.dbhids.org/technical-papers-on-recovery

www.dbhids.org/conceptual-framewor

www.buddhist12steps.com

www.cnsproductions.com/pdf/12step

www.en.wikipedia.org/wiki/karma

www.en.wikipedia.org/wiki/Ihsan

www.12steps.com/faithrecovery/islam

www.friendsofrecoveryvt.org/articles/rhetoric.pdf

Zoya, L. (1989). **Drugs, Addiction and Initiation***:* **The Modern Search for Ritual.** Boston: Sigo Press.

Made in the USA
Middletown, DE
01 December 2020